New Directions in Architectural and Engineering Practice

Other McGraw-Hill Books of Interest

New Directions in Architectural and Engineering Practice

Howard G. Birnberg Editor

Birnberg & Associates
Chicago, Illinois

McGraw-Hill, Inc.
New York   St. Louis   San Francisco   Auckland   Bogotá
Caracas   Lisbon   London   Madrid   Mexico   Milan
Montreal   New Delhi   Paris   San Juan   São Paulo
Singapore   Sydney   Tokyo   Toronto

Library of Congress Cataloging-in-Publication Data

New directions in architectural and engineering practice / Howard G.
   Birnberg, editor.
          p.   cm.
      Includes bibliographical references and index.
      ISBN 0-07-005399-5
      1. Architectural firms—United States—Management.   2. Engineering
   firms—United States—Management.   I. Birnberg, Howard G.
   NA1996.N48   1992   92-5931
   720'.88—dc20   CIP

1 2 3 4 5 6 7 8 9 0   HAL/HAL   9 8 7 6 5 4 3 2

ISBN   0-07-005399-5

The sponsoring editor for this book was Joel Stein, the editing supervisor
was David E. Fogarty, and the production supervisor was Donald Schmidt.
This book was set in Garamond by North Market Street Graphics.

Printed and bound by Arcata Graphics/Halliday.

Contents

20 Construction Cost Control   267

Contributors

Thomas W. Berg is the Quality Control Manager for the architectural firm of Bassetti Norton Metler Rekevics in Seattle, Washington. He has over 25 years of experience in commercial, institutional, recreational, residential, and industrial architecture as both leading technical architect and project manager. He has worked with both public and private clients under conditions of design-build and fast-track construction. He is a past chairperson of the Winslow Planning Agency where he served two terms; was on the Winslow Traffic Advisory Committee; and served as curriculum advisor to the North Kitsap School Board of Education. He is on the Board of Directors of the Housing Resources Board in Bainbridge Island, Washington, and The Board of Directors of the Association for Project Managers in the Design Professions (APM). His education is in engineering from St. Norbert College in DePere, Wisconsin, and he has been a licensed architect in the state of Washington since 1985. *(Chapter 18)*

Howard G. Birnberg is president of Birnberg & Associates, a Chicago-based firm providing publishing, consulting and educational services to design firms. He is an architect by training, having received his bachelor's degree in architecture from the Ohio State University and his master's of business administration from Washington University (St. Louis). Mr. Birnberg is also executive director of the Association for Project Managers, an organization of project managers in the design professions. He is active in the American Institute of Architects and is the author of eight manuals on design practice. He is also the author of *Project Management For Small Design Firms*, to be published by McGraw-Hill. *(Chapters 5, 13, and 17)*

Brian Bowen is an executive vice-president of Hanscomb Associates Inc., the U.S. company of the Hanscomb International Group. He was trained as a quantity surveyor in the United Kingdom, is a fellow of the Royal Institution of Chartered Surveyors, a certified cost engineer (American Association of Cost Engineers), and a certified value specialist (Society of American Value Engineers). Within Hanscomb he is responsible for research and development activities within the construction industry, value engineering, and computer applications. He acts as a liaison officer with Hanscomb offices in Europe and Asia. Throughout his career, Mr. Bowen has been active in writing for publications, delivering papers, and training seminars in a wide range of construction subjects related to building economics. He was the Hanscomb project manager in the development of the MASTERCOST system for the American Institute of Architects and UNIFORMAT for the General Services Administration. He has consulted to the American Institute of Architects in developing new educational programs for project cost control for the architectural profession. He is co-chairman of an ASTM subcommittee task group which is developing a standard for elemental cost estimating for design. *(Chapter 20)*

Steven A. Etkin is an executive with a major association representing architects. He has served in that capacity since 1985 and is responsible for the products offered and sold to the design and construction industry. Prior to 1985, Mr. Etkin served with a major trade association in the energy industry and a multinational management consulting practice. *(Chapter 10)*

Kenneth Gibble is president of Besier Gibble Norden Consulting Engineers Inc. of Old Saybrook, Connecticut. He joined Milo Ketchum and Partners in 1964. In 1972, he entered a partnership with Rudolph Besier, Consulting Engineers. He was visiting professional on the Yale University School of Architecture faculty from 1978–1987 and has served on the ASCE Professional Activities Committee and as chairman of several ASCE committees including the Executive Committee of the Engineering Management Division. Mr. Gibble is past president of Connecticut Engineers in Private Practice, the combined ACEC and NSPE/PEPP state organization. He is also co-founder of the Structural Engineers Coalition of Connecticut. *(Chapter 14)*

Susan Greenwald, AIA, CSI, CCS, is the owner of ArchiText, a firm specializing in specifications consulting, technical publishing, and information management. Ms. Greenwald is a graduate of Oberlin College and received the Master of Architecture degree from MIT. She worked with Booth, Nagle, and Hartray Assoc. Ltd. in Chicago, and with Harry Weese & Assoc. in Washington, D.C., before starting her firm. Ms. Greenwald is a member of the AIA Library and Archives Committee and MasterSpec Architectural Review Committee, and was a member of CSI's Ad Hoc MASTERFORMAT Committee. She is currently vice president, president-elect, of the Chicago Chapter CSI. *(Chapter 6)*

Bryce Hastings, AIA, is founder, president and general manager of Hastings & Chivetta Architects. In this capacity he has designed and directed over 300 of the firms major projects representing a full range of educational, recreational, retail, justice, health care, housing, and office projects. Much of this work has been renovations and additions to existing facilities. Active in the American Institute of Architects, Mr. Hastings is chairman of the Architectural Practice/Research Committee of the St. Louis Chapter. Together with representatives from the Professional Services Management Association, the committee sponsors seminars for the area's design professionals. Mr. Hastings has been involved with the Missouri Parks and Recreation Association, the National Employee Services and Recreation Association, and attends the annual Recreation Facility Design and Management School in Colorado. He is also a member of the Society for College and University Planning and the Missouri Council of Architects. Mr. Hastings has served on the American Institute of Architects National Committee on Criminal Justice; the Washington University Alumni Board of Governors; the Washington University Century Club (President); American Institute of Architects (President of the St. Louis Chapter); Building Officials Conference of America; Home Builders Association (Associate Member); and the City of Kirkwood Planning and Zoning Commission (Chairman). Mr. Hastings received his Bachelor of Architecture from Washington University. He is a registered architect (with NCARB Certification) in 16 states. *(Chapter 15)*

David Haviland earned his degree in architecture and building sciences at Rensselaer Polytechnic Institute. He joined Rensselaer's faculty in 1965 and was promoted to Professor in 1979. He has served as Director of the Center for Architectural Research (1969–1977), Associate Dean (1972–1980), and Dean of Architecture (1980–1990). At present he holds a concurrent appointment as Visiting Professor, Construction Management and Engineering, at the University of Reading in the United Kingdom. Professor Haviland's research and teaching interests lie in the building procurement, design and construction process, including its management and economics. He is author of over 70 books, monographs, articles, and other publications in this field. During the past fifteen years he has developed a number of practice publications for The American Institute of Architects, including the *Life Cycle Cost Analysis* and *Managing Architectural Projects* series, *You and Your Architect,* and the most recent edition of *The Architect's Handbook of Professional Practice.* In 1989 he received an AIA Institute Honor for sustained contribution to the field of practice management and education. *(Chapter 12)*

William D. Hooper, Jr., AIA, is an architect with Daniel, Mann, Johnson & Mendenhall (DMJM) in Washington, D.C., where he is presently managing the $800 million renovation of Washington National Airport. Mr. Hooper was formerly Director of Practice Programs for the American Institute of Architects, during which time he worked closely with the Architect's Liability Committee, and conducted the initial surveys of the professional liability insurance market. Mr. Hooper practices architecture in Washington, D.C., Maryland, Virginia, and North Carolina. *(Chapter 3)*

Paul M. Lurie received his B.A. and Juris Doctor from the University of Michigan. He is a Partner in the Chicago law firm of Schiff Hardin & Waite, and heads the Construction Practice. He is a Fellow of the American College of Construction Lawyers. Mr. Lurie's publications include *Managing Ownership Transition in Design Firms* (Birnberg & Associates). He has written numerous articles concerning the impact of computerization on the construction industry for *Progressive Architecture, Architectural Record, The Software Law Journal, Professional Services Management Journal,* and the *Journal of Professional Issues in Engineering.* Mr. Lurie is a member of the Editorial Board of the American Society of Civil Engineers' *Journal of Performance of Constructed Facilities.* In addition, he is advisor to the American Society of Civil Engineers on the *Manual for Quality in the Constructed Project. (Chapter 1)*

Thom McKay is an associate principal with RTKL, the architecture and planning practice responsible for marketing the firm's services throughout Europe. Having joined RTKL in 1985, he has been responsible for managing the firm's headquarters marketing activities, writing proposals and overseeing RTKL's award-winning direct mail program and in-house communications. Mr. McKay received his degree from Georgetown University, Washington, D.C., and attended the University of London. He currently lives in London with his wife and son. *(Chapter 8)*

Lou Marines is president of the Advanced Management Institute for Architecture and Engineering, the San Francisco-based graduate business and leadership school for architects, engineers, and related design professionals. He also consults on matters of strategic planning, management transition, and staff development. Mr. Marines is former CEO of the American Institute of Architects and General Manager of HLW, Architects and Engineers, New York City. *(Chapter 4)*

Gene L. Montgomery directs all computer applications for architectural design at Jack Train Associates. He manages the operations of the firm's in-house Intergraph and Autocad computer-aided design systems. He has also developed several software applications for cost estimating, building area calculation, and design evaluation and optimization. Currently Gene Montgomery is responsible for computer graphics for the Merchandise Mart redevelopment in Chicago, and is coordinating production for Mulberry Place luxury condominiums which are under construction in Highland Park, Illinois. Mr. Montgomery was formerly president of Arcturus Consultants, Inc., an architectural firm specializing in computer graphics applications and consulting. *(Chapter 17)*

Robert E. Olden, AIA/CPM, founded OLDEN/ASSOCIATES to provide business consulting services to professional design practices. He has authored numerous publications and articles on the "Business of the Practice" and has lectured extensively, conducting business seminars for the design professions. His writings have been published in such professional journals as SARA's *Practicing Architect;* the Financial Managers Group's *Journal;* PSMA's *ASCENT* and *AE Business Review* Newsletters; *Progressive Architecture, Suncoast Architect/Builder,* the *Florida Architect,* and *A&E Systems* magazines; *THE PRINCIPALS REPORT;* and the *Architects' Clearinghouse.* Mr. Olden is a past chapter president of the American Institute of Architects (AIA), has served on AIA National Committees; was a charter chapter member of the Construction Specifications Institute (CSI); maintains registration as an architect in fourteen states, D.C., and the National Council of Registration Boards (NCARB); and is a member of the Professional Services Management Association (PSMA). He has additionally been designated as a Certified Professional Services Manager (CPM) by the Professional Services Management Institute (PSMI). *(Chapter 19)*

Rebecca M. Renfro is with K. Lentz MMA Inc., a Houston-based marketing consulting firm serving the design industry. She has been involved in marketing A/E services since 1978, gaining experience from CRSS, Morris Aubry Architects, 3D/International, and Rolf Jensen & Associates. Ms. Renfro is a member of the Society for Marketing Professional Services (SMPS), Texas Society of Architects, and Houston Chapter AIA. She has conducted numerous marketing seminars and authored *The Marketing Coordinator,* an SMPS Marketing Information Report. Honors include Second Place, Direct Mail Category, SMPS National Awards Competition, and Member of the Year for the Houston Chapter SMPS. She holds a B.S. degree in education from Stephen F. Austin State University. *(Chapter 7)*

Patricia M. Rosenzweig is principal of Rosenzweig Professional Services Market in Chicago. Established in 1984, the firm provides marketing, market research, public relations and graphic design services for architectural, engineering, interior design and general contracting firms. She received her Bachelor of Arts degree in Social Sciences from the University of Chicago. She is on the Board of Directors of the American Institute of Architects Chicago Chapter, chairs its Office Practice Committee, and is a member of its Strategic Planning and Programming Committees. Previously she was on the Board and Education Chair for the Chicago Chapter, Society for Marketing Professional Services. *(Chapter 9)*

Steven S. Ross is a consulting editor to *Architectural Record* magazine and is a member of the graduate faculty in Journalism at Columbia University. In 1969 Mr. Ross earned his bachelor's degree in physics from Rensselaer Polytechnic Institute, and a master's degree in journalism in 1970 from Columbia University. He has published numerous articles on CADD and other technology issues, as well as having published several books, including *SPREADSTAT: How to Build Statistics into Your Lotus 1-2-3 Spreadsheets* (McGraw-Hill). Mr.

Ross is a fellow of the Council on Economic Priorities, and past president of New Jersey's Environmental Education Fund. *(Chapter 16)*

Ralph J. Russell, P.E., is a graduate of Iowa State University with a degree in Civil Engineering. He is a licensed engineer in Iowa, Wisconsin, Minnesota, and Nebraska. Mr. Russell is president of Howard R. Green Company, a multidisciplined consulting engineering firm with a staff of 120, headquartered in Cedar Rapids, Iowa. He is also president of the Consulting Engineers Council of Iowa and is active in several technical societies. *(Chapter 5)*

Kerry T. Smith is an associate in the law firm of Schiff Hardin & Waite. He obtained his B.S. from the University of Illinois, Urbana-Champaign in 1983 and his J.D. from Loyola University of Chicago, School of Law, in 1989. He is also a certified public accountant and practiced with one of the "Big Six" public accounting firms before attending law school. Mr. Smith currently practices corporate law. *(Chapter 1)*

Steven G.M. Stein received his Juris Doctor degree from the University of Chicago and his Bachelor of Arts degree from the University of Wisconsin. He is an adjunct professor at IIT Chicago-Kent College of Law, where he has taught construction law since 1982. Mr. Stein is editor in chief of *Construction Law* (1986) and has constributed articles on construction law to the *St. Louis University Law Review* and the *Chicago-Kent Law Review*. Mr. Stein is director of the IIT Chicago-Kent Construction Law Institute and is a member of the Chicago Bar Association, having served on the Executive Committee for the Civil Practice section, the Panel of Construction Arbitrators for the American Arbitration Association, the American Bar Association's Section of Litigation, Committee on Construction Contracts, the American Bar Association's Forum Committee on the Construction Industry. He is also a member of the Board of Governors of the American College of Construction Lawyers, the Chicago Building Congress, the Builders Association of Greater Chicago, the American College of Real Estate Lawyers, and Construction Specifications Institute. *(Chapter 2)*

Bill Truby is a member of the leadership and staff development faculty of the Advanced Management Institute for Architecture and Engineering. He is also a psychology-trained management consultant and trainer who deals with interpersonal skills, team-building, conflict resolution, leadership training, and conducts workshops for the major national professional societies. *(Chapter 4)*

Steve L. Wintner, AIA, is the Director of Operations for Brooks/Collier, a Houston-based architectural firm specializing in healthcare and institutional facilities for a national client base. Mr. Wintner has more than 35 years of practical experience, the last 15 years of which have been focused on management of architectural firm operations. This encompasses financial, project and office administration management. Previous senior management positions were held with CRSS-Houston, Gensler & Associates in San Francisco and Houston and as the founder and President of Management Consulting Services. Mr. Wintner has been active at all levels of the AIA for more than 20 years and was the 1989 Chair of the National Practice Committee. *(Chapter 11)*

Preface

In 1976 the AIA Press and Architectural Record Books jointly published *Current Techniques in Architectural Practice*, edited by Robert Class and Robert Koehler. This excellent text far exceeded any similar survey book on the design professions. Over the past sixteen years, some of the material has become quite dated.

Many changes have occurred since 1976. For example, the personal computer did not even exist at that time. Tax laws, accounting practices, ownership transition concepts, marketing needs and ideas, the economy, to name a few, have all changed drastically in recent years. CADD systems are now available to the mass of firms, not simply a few giants.

Clearly, it is time for a new overview of design practice. Most architects and engineers lack the time to identify, obtain, and read a myriad of books on the subjects covered in this text. *New Directions in Architectural and Engineering Practice* offers the expertise of a score of experts who have performed this task for you. This book offers a state-of-the-art look at design practice and provides insight into the changes to come in the remainder of the decade and beyond.

I would like to thank the many individuals who have made the preparation of this book possible. Each contributing author has given their time and expertise for the benefit of the design professions. Bob Class and Bob Koehler deserve high praise for their trailblazing efforts in their 1976 book. In my office, I must thank Sara Mason, Northwestern University, Medill School of Journalism, Class of 1991, who spent endless hours editing contributors' manuscripts, and Bonnie Pendlebury who assembled the final text and exhibits.

HOWARD G. BIRNBERG

1

General Firm and Legal Organization

Paul M. Lurie and Kerry T. Smith

Architects, engineers, and other design professionals often focus on their clients' needs and forget the needs of their own businesses. To survive, however, design professionals cannot ignore their own business needs. This chapter is an overview of some of the pros and cons of doing business in various legal forms and should shed some light on certain points that professionals may not have previously considered.

Since design professions such as architecture and engineering directly affect the health, safety, and welfare of society, all states and territories exercise regulatory authority over them. The regulatory laws differ significantly from jurisdiction to jurisdiction. Even when two states have virtually identical laws, other state laws regarding insurance, contract law, taxes, tort law, and other areas can differ enough to affect organizational decisions made by design professionals.

The selection of a form of business will have an important effect not only on the operation of a professional design firm but also on personal income tax planning, retirement planning, estate planning, and personal liability of employees and owners. While relatively few forms of business are available to choose from, the process of finding the form best suited for a design firm may take considerable analysis. In analyzing which form is best, you should ask three basic questions:

1. What do you want to practice?

2. Where do you want to practice?

3. What size do you want your firm to be?

What Do You Want to Practice?

What a design professional can practice is dictated largely by a jurisdiction's licensing requirements. Almost all jurisdictions require that individuals who are responsible for design activities in architecture and engineering be registered in that jurisdiction and may require one or more other professionals in the firm to be licensed as well. The licensing reciprocity provisions, however, may permit an individual who is registered in one jurisdiction to practice in another jurisdiction.

Where Do You Want to Practice?

Many factors influence this decision. For instance, it may be cheaper to operate a design practice in some locations than in others. As of this writing, Connecticut, South Dakota, New Mexico, Nevada, Hawaii, and New York City have enacted taxes on design services, and many other states and cities are considering similar taxes. The zoning ordinances, building codes, and other restrictions that exist in a given area also may impact your practice. Also, licensing requirements may vary. A few areas, such as Puerto Rico and the District of Columbia, will not allow certain incorporated design professionals to practice in that form in their jurisdiction.

What Size Do You Want the Organization to Be?

Many of the factors that influence this decision are contingent largely upon the personal preferences of the owners. Some professionals are satisfied with the sizes of their businesses, while others wish to expand. Larger design firms with numerous owners may be precluded from making certain tax elections or find it extremely difficult to manage and operate their practices in some business forms.

An important consideration for firms that wish to expand is whether or not key employees should receive ownership interests in the firm. Such decisions are not easy to make, since many professionals want to keep as much control over the business as they can. However, many design professionals are realizing that good ownership transition plans can greatly enhance their design practice. A transition plan can give younger professionals an incentive to work harder and stay with the design firm. It also provides a useful means by which older design professionals can liquidate their investment in the design firm. Certain forms of organization facilitate such ownership transition plans.

Design businesses operate in three basic legal forms: sole proprietorships, partnerships, and corporations.

Sole Proprietorship

This is the easiest type of business for a beginning practitioner. A design professional who simply hangs out a shingle and starts practicing without doing more is a sole proprietor. A sole proprietor needs to comply with very few state requirements other than obtaining business permits and licenses and complying with professional registration requirements. The sole proprietor who plans on conducting business in a fictitious name will be required to register that name in the state where the business operates.

Partnership

Like a sole proprietorship, a partnership is easy to form and organizational fees are generally not required. A partnership is the most basic form in which two or more owners conduct business. Very few legal formalities other than professional registration requirements must be followed for design professionals to do business as a partnership.

The rules that govern a partnership are largely contractual. The oral or written agreement between the partners controls the operation of the firm and the allocation of profits and losses. Where a partnership agreement does not address an issue or problem, state law will decide. If no written partnership agreement exists, state law may produce results that differ significantly from what the partners may expect.

Since a partnership is easy to form, many design professionals mistakenly believe that it is cheaper to form a partnership than to incorporate. Unfortunately, a properly drafted partnership agreement can easily cost a design professional as much (if not significantly more) in attorney's fees as it would to incorporate. A well-drafted partnership agreement, however, will address difficult issues at the forefront of the relationship and thereby later save attorney's fees and hard feelings if problems develop.

Example Assume A and B are both architects who decide to form a partnership and share profits equally. A invests $100,000 in the partnership and B, who has a lot of talent but no money, promises to do a majority of the work instead of making a monetary investment. Both A and B are anxious to start the practice and decide "to worry about everything else later" and never execute a partnership agreement. B works day and night trying to turn a profit. After a few months, however, the partnership loses the $100,000 that A contributed. A, who did very little work for the partnership, decides that he does not want to invest any more money in the partnership and the partnership is dissolved. Most people would logically believe that A and B would part company owing each other nothing. However, all states, with the exception of Louisiana, have adopted some form of the Uniform Partnership Act. Under the Uniform Partnership Act, B would owe A $50,000, or one-half of the losses incurred by the partnership even though B performed most of the work. In addition, B would not be entitled to compensation for all his work. Had these issues been addressed at the outset in a written partnership agreement, B could have avoided this liability.

Corporation

A corporation is the most complex of the three business forms in which design firms operate. The four basic attributes of a corporation are limited liability, free transferability of ownership interests, unlimited life, and centralized management. Contrary to popular belief, there is generally no advantage for design firms to be incorporated in Delaware. In fact, purely local enterprises usually have no reason to incorporate outside the state in which they are doing business. If a corporation is going to do business outside of the state of its incorporation, the corporation must make sure that it is qualified to do business in that jurisdiction. Unlike sole proprietorships and partnerships, fees must be paid to the state of incorporation in addition to any state in which the corporation is doing business.

As corporations are a creation of state law, many state regulations and licensing requirements apply to corporations. To incorporate, a certificate of incorporation must first be filed with the secretary of state in which business is incorporated. The certificate contains information about the corporation, such as the number of directors, the corporate purpose, the name, the duration, and the registered office of the corporation. In addition, the certificate sets the terms of the various classes of share and the number of authorized shares in each class of stock. After filing for the certificate, the corporation can have organizational meetings to elect directors and officers, adopt bylaws, and structure the financing of the firm.

In states that allow design firms to practice as a corporation, design professionals will often have the following types to choose from: a general business corporation, a close corporation, or a professional corporation. Virtually any kind of business may incorporate as a general business corporation in many states. For the most part general business corporations do not have statutory restrictions on who may own stock or who may be a director. Close corporations and professional corporations, however, do have statutory provisions that affect stock ownership and director positions. Professional corporations restrict stock ownership and directorships to licensed professionals of the design firm. Close corporation acts streamline some of the corporate formalities to ease some of the administrative burdens that would otherwise be placed upon closely held businesses by the general business corporation statutes. Close corporation acts allow substantial restrictions on the transferability of the closely held business stock to discourage the transfer of stock without the approval of the other owners.

Some states charge incorporation fees based on the number of authorized shares. Thus, the fees can be quite high if there is a large number of authorized shares. Therefore, in those states it may make sense, when organizing a corporation in which you expect to have a small number of shareholders, to have a small number of shares authorized. The certificate of incorporation may later be amended if more shares are needed. In addition, some states impose annual franchise taxes on the businesses incorporated or doing business within the state (i.e., a tax on the privilege of being incorporated in that state or a tax on the privilege of doing business in the corporate form in that state). Most states also impose a corporate income tax on corporations doing business within the state.

Sole Proprietorship

A sole proprietor has total control of the firm and makes all management decisions. Since only one person makes decisions, it can be run much more efficiently than a partnership. Although it is highly recommended for tax reporting purposes, there is no requirement that a sole proprietor keep other business books and records separate from personal books and records.

Having a sole proprietor in total control involves risk. Since total control of the proprietorship is vested in one person, the practice can suffer greatly if that person becomes disabled. Although a sole proprietor's control can be highly efficient, efficiency does not ensure that the best decisions are made. As design practices become increasingly complex, certain decisions need consultation. Sole practitioners may not have the time (or want to take the time) to focus on the pros and cons of various opportunities or to spot emerging problems.

Partnership

Partnerships are somewhat easier to administer than corporations. Partnerships, however, have less flexibility than a sole proprietorship because more than one person is involved in the management decisions. The partnership agreement generally determines the voting power of each individual partner and, therefore, who controls the partnership. If the agreement, however, is silent on voting, or if there is no partnership agreement, each partner has an equal vote. This result can be upsetting to a partner who put up 100 percent of the capital and is expecting to have total control of the business.

Unlike a sole proprietor who does not have to account to anyone other than the state and federal government, partners must account to each other for the partnership's activities. Generally, any partner has the right to inspect the partnership books and records at any time. All states provide rules that govern the fiduciary accountability of partners, which usually goes far beyond financial disclosure. Thus, a partnership should keep its books and records current and all its partners well informed regarding partnership affairs.

In addition, no person can become a member of a partnership without the consent of all the partners. Although in most states a partner can assign a partnership interest to a third party, that assignment only entitles the third party to the profits that the assigning partner would have received. Such an assignment does not entitle the third party to make any management decisions in the partnership. Therefore, it can be difficult for a partner to sell a partnership interest without the consent of the other partners because a buyer will not have a voice in the management of the business.

Corporation

A corporation has somewhat less flexibility than either a sole proprietorship or a partnership with respect to control and operation. State law, the articles of incorporation, and the bylaws of the corporation provide the structure for the operation and control of the corporation. The majority shareholder generally has ultimate control of the corporation. Many states, however, permit the articles of incorporation to be drafted to require unanimity for certain corporate action, thereby giving even small shareholders a veto power over majority shareholders.

Shareholders may arrange to govern certain aspects of the corporation through the use of voting or pooling agreements. For instance, shareholders may agree to vote for each other as directors. These voting and pooling agreements are generally valid so long as they are not used to the detriment of shareholders who are not a party to the agreement and enforcement of the agreement would not be contrary to public policy.

The board of directors is responsible for the business affairs of the corporation. It elects the officers who are responsible for the day-to-day operations of the firm and who carry out the policies formulated by the board. Normally, the principals of the business are both directors and officers.

Being a director involves no formal training requirements. Directors do not have to be stock owners and do not have to be compensated. They do not even have to be design professionals so long as there are enough licensed design professionals on the board to satisfy state law requirements. In fact, it is common to have one or more nondesign professionals who have expertise in other business areas sit on the board. Although outside directors can provide useful input in the operation and management of a design practice, it is not always wise to have the firm's lawyer or accountant sitting on the board. If tough decisions have to be made regarding the practice, the accountant or lawyer may be hesitant to give a candid opinion in fear of alienating a client. When tough decisions have to be made, outside directors who are otherwise unaffiliated with the design firm are more likely to provide input that they believe to be most beneficial to the practice.

Contrary to popular belief, corporations are not much more burdensome to run than partnerships. It is true that corporations must follow certain procedures that do not have to be followed by partnerships or sole proprietorships. For instance, corporations must file annual reports with their state of incorporation and in the states where they do business. Also, corporations must give formal notices of meetings, document the election of board members, and document salaries for last year's board members and certain officers. For most incorporated design firms, however, these take only a few minutes to prepare. Some design professionals believe that the legal formalities of director meetings and shareholder meetings are annoyingly burdensome. However, unless otherwise restricted by the certificate of incorporation or bylaws, any action required or permitted to be taken at any meeting of the board may be accomplished, instead, by the written consent of the directors. Thus, a formal meeting is not required.

There are advantages, however, to having formal board of directors meetings. Such meetings force directors to discuss and analyze a firm's opportunities and problems. It is also easier for directors to raise issues and ideas in formal meetings.

Sole Proprietorship

A sole proprietor is personally liable for all debts incurred in the business. Some states provide limited relief by protecting assets held jointly in the names of both husband and wife from the business creditors of either. Bankruptcy laws also exempt certain properties from creditors.

As a result of a sole proprietor's virtually unlimited liability, his or her design firm's credit rating and his or her personal credit rating are one and the same. A sole proprietor who has had credit problems in the past may find it difficult to receive credit in the current business.

Partnership

General partners, like a sole proprietor, are jointly and severally liable for all debts and liabilities of the partnership regardless of their percentage of ownership. Therefore, creditors can look to all the personal assets of any of the partners to satisfy their claims. Another disadvantage of doing business as a partnership is that a partner may be held liable for the acts of the other partners or agents of the partnership whether or not those actions were authorized. Thus, professionals must pick their partners and agents very carefully.

Corporation

Unlike a sole proprietor or partnership, shareholders of a corporation are not liable for all debts of the corporation. The corporate form generally insulates the personal assets of shareholders from corporate trade creditors. This corporate attribute, known as limited liability, is often cited as the greatest benefit to doing business as a corporation. Limited liability gives corporations an advantage in raising capital because investors know that their amount at risk is limited to their investment.

The protection of corporate limited liability is by no means absolute. Design professionals still can become personally liable for corporate actions and debts in a number of ways. Because the work performed by design professionals directly affects the health, safety, and welfare of society, design professionals generally will be held liable for the work they personally perform and supervise. Bankers, landlords, and other creditors are aware of corporate limited liability and will often ask for personal guarantees for some, if not all, of the shareholders before they extend credit. Shareholders also may be liable for other federal and state corporate taxes that are not properly disclosed and paid by the corporation. Shareholders that become personally liable for federal and state corporate taxes generally cannot discharge these debts in bankruptcy.

In certain other circumstances a court will ignore the corporate form and hold its shareholders accountable for all obligations of the corporation. As a general matter, this occurs where the corporation has been used to perpetrate a fraud, where shareholders have failed to differentiate between their personal activities and those of the corporation, or where an insolvent corporation is found to have been undercapitalized when formed. Recently, many courts have expanded individual stockholder's liability where an employer fails to make contributions to a welfare or pension plan.

Taxation

Sole Proprietorship

Since a sole proprietor's business is not considered a separate entity, the tax consequences of forming and operating a sole proprietorship are very straightforward. The sole proprietor's business activities are taxed only once at the sole proprietor's personal tax rate and are reported on Schedule C of his or her personal income tax return. A sole proprietor may use appreciated property in the business and not incur a tax on the appreciation. Most of the property that the sole proprietor contributes to the business may be depreciated and thereby generate deductions from his or her personal income.

The termination or sale of a sole proprietorship also has very standard tax consequences. Since the sole proprietor personally owns all assets of the business, he or she only needs to cease operations to terminate the business. If the sole proprietor sells his or her practice, then for tax purposes, the sale will be treated as if the sole proprietor sold each asset separately. The sale price will be allocated among the assets, based on each asset's fair market value. Gain or loss will then be computed asset by asset.

Partnership

Unlike a sole proprietorship, the tax consequences of running a partnership are anything but straightforward. The tax provisions that apply to partnerships are some of the most complex provisions in the Internal Revenue Code. The taxation of partnership income is structured so that partnerships do not pay federal income tax. Instead, each year every partner is allocated his or her distributive share of partnership income, gain, loss, deduction, or credit, which is then reported on each partner's individual tax return. How a partner's distributive share is determined is largely a function of the allocations set forth in the partnership agreement. The Internal Revenue Service (IRS) generally recognizes the partnership agreement's allocations so long as their allocations have substantial economic effect.

The items included in a partner's distributive share retain their tax character when reported by the partners. Thus, generally, any operating losses allocated to a partner are deductible as trade or business losses and qualify for net operating loss carryback and carryover. Similarly, capital losses allocated to a partner are subject to the capital loss carryover provisions that apply to that partner.

No gain or loss generally is recorded by the partnership or its partners when a partner contributes property to it in exchange for an interest. Similarly, partnership distributions are nontaxable to the extent of the partner's tax basis in the partnership. Any distributions in excess of a partner's tax basis are treated as a capital gain.

Corporation

Corporations are generally separate taxpaying entities. Corporate income generated by a regular or C corporation can be subject to two levels of tax. Any income is first taxed at the corporate level at a maximum corporate income tax rate of 34 percent. The same income is then taxed again when distributed out as dividends to individual shareholders. Assuming the corporation has earnings and profits, individual shareholders will pay another income tax at a maximum rate of 31 percent upon receipt of the dividend.

Corporate earnings also can be subjected to a third different type of tax if the corporation unreasonably accumulates its income in the corporation, rather than pay out the income as dividends. This tax applies, however, only if the corporation accumulates income beyond its reasonable business needs.

Shareholder employees who plan for taxes properly can take some earnings out of their corporation without paying a corporate level tax. The shareholder employees can take earnings out of a corporation by taking *reasonable* salaries. This has the effect of lowering taxable corporate income and subjecting those salary payments to only one tax at the shareholder employee's tax rates. Similarly, a shareholder employee may also rent property to the corporation that the corporation uses in its business and avoid the corporate level tax on the earnings paid out as rental income.

The IRS often contests salaries and rental income paid to shareholder employees if they believe that the amounts paid are excessive. In addition, there are other tax consequences to such arrangements that will affect shareholder employees' personal tax liability.

A corporate level tax may be avoided by having the corporation and all the shareholders elect to become an S corporation. S corporations, like partnerships, generally pay no federal income tax as long as the S election remains in effect. The profits and losses of an S corporation pass through to the shareholders in a manner similar (but not identical) to the pass-through from a partnership to partners.

Certain corporations are prohibited from becoming S corporations even if they otherwise meet all the eligibility requirements. A corporation's status as an S corporation can be involuntarily terminated upon the occurrence of certain events, and additional limitations are imposed in S corporations.

An S corporation must continuously meet all of the following requirements:

1. The corporation can have no more than 35 shareholders.

2. All shareholders must be either individuals or certain types of trusts.

3. The corporation cannot have nonresident aliens as shareholders.

4. The corporation cannot have more than one class of stock. For purposes of this requirement, a corporation shall not be treated as having more than one class of stock if the classes differ only with respect to voting.

An advantage to making an S election is that the shareholders still enjoy the limited liability of the corporate form while avoiding the corporate level tax. Corporations and shareholders often make S corporation elections in the early years when losses are expected so that the shareholders can deduct corporate losses from their tax returns.

Key Employees

Sole Proprietorship

Conducting business in this form may make it difficult to keep valued employees where they see little or no chance of obtaining any ownership in the business. In fact, these employees are often lured away by other design firms with the promise of future ownership after the sole proprietor has spent a considerable amount of time training them.

Partnership

Partnerships are more flexible than sole proprietorships. Since partnerships tend to be larger than sole proprietorships, the training of key employees can be split among a number of professionals. In addition, partnership agreements can also provide for the admission of key employees as partners and thereby give key employees an incentive to work harder. Because of the complex nature of partnership taxation, both the key employee and the partnership generally will require tax and accounting advice if a partnership decides to extend an ownership interest to a key employee.

Corporation

A corporation has an advantage over partnerships and sole proprietorships when it comes to key employees. If the shareholders of the corporation want to offer a key employee an ownership interest to give an employee more incentive to stay with their practice, corporate stock is much easier to transfer than either a proprietorship or a partnership interest. Key employees may simply purchase stock or receive stock or stock options as part of their compensation. Extensive accounting, tax advice, or corporate formalities may be needed to transfer stock or stock options as compensation.

Death and Disability

Sole Proprietorship

A sole proprietorship, by definition, cannot survive the death of its owner. Estate planning is essential to properly wind down the affairs of a sole proprietor's business and to ensure that the beneficiaries of a sole proprietor's estate receive the property they are entitled to without unreasonable delay. Numerous legal expenses and delays can result if proper estate planning is not done.

Several estate planning techniques commonly are used. As part of their estate plan, some sole proprietors make extensive use of trusts. These sole proprietors put all their business assets into a revocable trust while they are alive, naming themselves as trustee. By using a revocable trust, sole proprietors have the same control over the business assets as they would if they owned them outright and have very few administrative burdens placed on them as trustee. The revocable trust agreement disposes of all the business assets upon death and, therefore, the sole proprietor's business assets need not go through the expense and delay of a probate proceeding after the owner's death. Also, since probate proceedings are a matter of public record, many professionals prefer the use of a revocable trust because their business affairs will remain confidential.

A sole proprietor also may have an agreement with another design professional, such as an employee or another sole proprietor, to help each other in case of death or disability. This is a useful method and may be used in combination with a revocable trust. If for no other reason, such arrangements can give some peace of mind to sole proprietors who are worried about losing clients if they are disabled for a period of time.

Partnership

It is important that the partnership address what will happen in case a partner withdraws because of death or disability. Waiting until someone dies or is seriously disabled before considering death and disability can have serious consequences for the business.

It is easier to plan for death and disability when everyone is healthy because professionals can then objectively consider what should be done when these events take place. A partnership can take many steps to lessen the effects of the death or disability of one of its partners. For instance, the partnership agreement may provide for a buy-out arrangement in the event of death or disability or may allow the partner or the partner's estate to sell the interest to a designated party. Life and disability insurance are key ingredients in every plan. These give the partnership the ability to purchase a deceased or disabled partner's interest in addition to replacing some of the income stream lost by a partner's death or disability. If no planning is done, state law will automatically dissolve the partnership upon a partner's departure.

Corporation

Since a corporation is considered to have a life of its own, corporations are theoretically unaffected by the death of an employee shareholder. Nonetheless, planning is essential to provide for the continuation and management of a design firm in case of the death or disability of an employee shareholder and to effectively transfer ownership to a deceased or disabled shareholder's successors. This can be accomplished through a variety of planning devices.

One way is by having a buy-sell agreement among the shareholders of the corporation. The buy-sell agreement can be drafted in a number of ways to accommodate the needs of the parties. Shareholders in these situations normally have life or disability buy-out insurance on each other's lives and use the proceeds to buy the deceased or disabled shareholder's shares. Also, a shareholder can have a stock repurchase agreement with the corporation. In these agreements, corporations usually have insurance on the shareholder's life and use the insurance proceeds to buy back stock from a disabled or deceased shareholder. In choosing between having the remaining shareholders or the corporation buy the disabled or deceased shareholder's shares, a basic consideration is the ability of the purchaser to buy the interest. Since funds for this purpose often come from after-tax dollars, the financial burden must be shared by those best able to afford it.

Employee Benefits

Many firms establish qualified retirement plans because contributions to the plan can be deducted in the year paid, while the participants in the plan are able to defer tax until funds are distributed out of the plan. Before 1983, qualified corporate retirement plans provided much greater benefits to the participants than the benefits available to participants in a sole proprietorship's or partnership's H.R. 10 plan. Now, with certain limited exceptions, qualified corporate retirement plans have no advantage over qualified unincorporated retirement plans.

For some benefit plans other than qualified retirement plans, corporations still have significant advantages over benefit plans available to unincorporated entities. For instance, benefit plans, such as incentive stock option plans, stock bonus plans, and employee stock ownership plans, by their very nature can be offered only by corporate entities. While all entities may provide certain benefit plans, such as accident and health plans, cafeteria plans, and group term life insurance plans, only corporations receive favorable tax treatment for operating these plans.

Corporate benefit plans are not always as beneficial as they may first appear. Many of these plans, such as employee stock ownership plans, may be cumbersome and expensive to administer. Also, to take advantage of some of the tax benefits some plans provide, other tax benefits may have to be forgone.

The tax laws regarding employee benefits change constantly. What may make sense to do in one year may not make sense to do in the next. You must seek current advice from your tax counsel before implementing any benefit plans.

Capitalization

Sole Proprietorship and Partnership

A sole proprietorship and partnership are limited by the financial resources of the owners. It would be difficult for a sole proprietorship or partnership to raise capital if the owners have had previous credit problems.

Corporation

A corporation's ability to raise capital is not limited to the financial resources of its owners. A corporation has a number of ways of raising capital that are not available to sole proprietorships or partnerships. For instance, a C corporation may accumulate its earnings rather than pay them out as dividends. As discussed previously, a corporation may accumulate its earnings without incurring any additional taxes so long as the accumulation does not exceed its reasonable business needs. Another corporate financing device is the pledging of stock as collateral for loans. In this event, however, the creditor knows that if there is a default, it will own a portion of the corporation and thereby will be able to influence, if not control, the corporation's actions. The corporate form also makes it easier to facilitate mergers with or acquire another design practice through the use of stock and thereby increase its capital base.

Additional Considerations for Multiple Owners

Design professionals who jointly own their practice with others must document their relationship in either a partnership agreement or a shareholders' agreement. This ownership agreement should detail specifically how the firm is to be managed. There is no one correct way to manage a firm: some firms require all owners agree before certain actions are taken, while other firms may require only a simple majority.

Design professionals that invest with others generally expect to have some input in the operation of the firm. The ownership agreement should give the design professional some idea as to the extent that they will be heard on firm matters and, in most cases, be drafted in a way that precludes one owner from controlling the entire firm. Minority owners generally should make sure that they will not be in a position where they are frozen out of the decision-making process while they have a substantial monetary investment in the design firm.

Joint owners of design firms do not like new owners thrust upon them. This could happen, for example, where a disgruntled stockholder of a general business corporation sells stock to an unknown third party. In this example, absent an agreement to the contrary, the third party is entitled to the same rights and interests as the disgruntled shareholder. Such a sale could have adverse tax consequences to the corporation and remaining shareholders if the stock were sold to an entity that would bar the corporation from making an S election. To prevent this from happening, joint owners should make sure that they have a shareholders' agreement that restricts the transfer of stock.

Joint owners also should note that nothing is stopping someone from owning part of one design firm and working for another. Joint owners can restrict this by agreement if they so choose.

Another issue that joint owners should consider is the effect of the divorce of one of its owners upon the firm. Divorced spouses may be entitled to certain firm assets or be able to force the dissolution of the firm to satisfy a divorce settlement. As the laws that govern divorce differ substantially between states, an attorney in your area should be contacted to discuss this issue.

There may be times when your organization does not have the resources or the contacts to obtain a particular project. However, by joining with other firms, the combined organization may overcome the weaknesses of individual member firms.

The combined firm could take the form of a prime-consultant team or a joint venture. In a prime-consultant arrangement, only the prime firm has a contract with the owner. Therefore, if the consultant wants to be assured of proper publicity, payment, and job controls, these items have to be spelled out in the agreements between the parties.

A joint venture is subject to the earlier comments on a partnership. The advantage over a consultant arrangement is that the parties have equivalent status vis-à-vis the owner, modified only by the parties' express contractual arrangements. A major disadvantage of this form is that all the joint venturers are responsible jointly and severally for acts, errors, omissions, and debts of the venture. This is true regardless of their individual interests in the profits and losses of the venture. This potential liability demands that parties contemplating such a venture be comfortable with the capabilities and morality of each other.

Most professional liability carriers will not insure a joint venture on the practice policy of any member of the venture. Securing proper endorsements and even special policies should be discussed with a competent insurance adviser.

Bibliography

Bittker, B., and J. Eustice, *Federal Income Taxation of Corporations and Shareholders* (6th ed. 1987), Warren, Gorham and Larnert, Boston.

The Business Corporation Act of 1983, Ill. Rev. Stat. Ch. 32 §1.01 et seq. (1990).

Cary, W., and M. Eisenberg, *Cases and Materials on Corporations* (5th ed. 1980), Foundation Press, Mineola, N.Y.

Delaware Corporation Law, 8 Del. Laws §101 et seq. (1990).

Getz, L., and P. Lurie, *Managing Ownership Transition in Design Firms* (1989), Birnberg & Associates, Chicago.

Hall, M., *Ownership Distribution and the Expense of Leadership in a Closely Held A/E Firm: Part TWO*, PSMA Assent, May/June 1990 at 2.

Illinois Architecture Practice Act of 1989, Ill. Rev. Stat. Ch. 111 §1301 et seq. (1990).

Internal Revenue Code, 26 U.S.C. §1 et seq. (1986).

Korman, R., *States in Financial Straits Target Sales of Professional Services,* ENR NEWS, March 15, 1990 at 8.

Margolies, E., *The Expanding Personal Liability of Corporate Managers and Gambino,* 78 Ill. B. J. 46 (1990).

Price, J., *Contemporary Estate Planning* (1983).

Professional Engineers Practice Act of 1989, Ill. Rev. Stat. Ch. 111 §5202 et seq. (1990).

Revenue Reconciliation Act of 1989, Pub. L. 101-239 (1989).

Revenue Reconciliation Act of 1990, Pub. L. 101-501 (1990).

Structural Engineers Licensing Act of 1989, Ill. Rev. Stat. Ch. 111 §6602 et seq. (1990).

Uniform Partnership Act, 6 U.L.A. 1 et seq. (1990).

Wolfman, B., *Federal Income Taxation of Business Enterprise* (2d ed. 1982).

2

Legal Issues in Design Practice

Steven G. M. Stein

Designers and clients often view contracts as an impediment to a good working relationship and the successful completion of a project. But there is more to contract negotiation than protecting yourself from liability and preserving your right to compensation. A clear understanding of legal issues and a well-designed path for resolving conflicts can help your marketing effort. A thought-out, concise, well-negotiated, and thoroughly explained contract often is the first step toward creating or improving a relationship. A sloppily handled, poorly thought-out, and imprecise contract can lead to an adverse impression of your firm. This chapter focuses on resolving legal issues and how that can result in a positive outcome for both designer and client.

What to Consider When Entering into a Contract with Your Client

Investigating a Client's Creditworthiness

The thrill of a marketing success can cloud even the most clear-thinking design professional's judgment. Many design professionals fail to thoroughly review the prospective client's creditworthiness. It is not enough to analyze your ability to design a project—although that is essential to avoid undue liability exposure. It is also necessary to determine a client's ability to pay and history of paying designers.

There are three impediments to obtaining information about a prospective client's creditworthiness. First, many professionals do not know how to make such a determination and therefore avoid the task. Second, it is a common assumption that clients will be affronted by the necessary questioning to determine creditworthiness. Third, some believe that the project itself is adequate security for payment since design professionals usually have mechanics lien rights.

Determining a client's creditworthiness is not difficult. All but the smallest projects are financed. The owner of such a project will be required by its lender to provide detailed information concerning the financial viability of the project and of the project owner. This includes financial statements and funds source descriptions. The design professional needs only to ask to get the information and review it.

Some design professionals argue that such a request will be an affront to the client. Often, those clients that are offended are precisely the ones who do not have the financial strength to support the project. A well-funded client should have no difficulty sharing information about the source of funds and ordinary financial statements with its architect or engineer. Therefore, the refusal by the client to provide this information should be your first warning that something may be wrong with their credit. Furthermore, most clients today expect their design professionals to be business-wise and to perform services in light of business and economic realities. They expect projects to be completed on time and they expect the design professionals to prepare drawings and specifications that will yield the maximum benefit for the least cost. That kind of hardheaded realism should be reflected in all of the design professional's dealings. Most good clients will respect a design professional's need for financial information and his or her wisdom in seeking it in advance of performing work.

Mechanics liens are not a panacea. Some states do not grant design professionals a lien. In other states design services that never result in construction may not be "lienable." Similarly, a design professional's services may enjoy no priority over prior lenders' rights. Other lien claimants may have an equal right to share project equity with the design professional. Simply, there is no assurance that lien rights will secure an unpaid design professional. When in doubt, get an initial payment that should cover the services rendered until invoices can be sent and credit can be established.

Fully Negotiate Up Front

Common sense would indicate that before performing substantial professional services a written contract specifying compensation and terms of service must be established. Such a commonsense approach is at odds with the way some design professionals negotiate agreements. Many start services with no written agreement whatsoever, only an oral arrangement to commence services. Even those who carefully work out compensation arrangements before beginning work frequently do not establish terms of service as a condition for commencing work. In extreme cases, projects are finished with written agreements still being negotiated.

Establishing terms of compensation and commencing work before negotiating an agreement creates an artificial distinction between compensation issues and the other economic risks covered by a written contract. Compensation not only should be based on the scope of services, but it also should reflect the type of risks that the owner seeks to shift to the design professional. Often, what would seem to be reasonable compensation for basic services may very well be unreasonable in light of later negotiated terms that shift risks and impose liabilities upon the design professional.

Compensation is a product of both the scope of work and risk. A client must be made aware that the contract negotiations involve dollar issues and that it is not free to push upon the design professional all concerns and risks. This process also allows a design professional further flexibility. What might be deemed inappropriate risks given a previously established compensation agreement may very well be appropriate if compensation remains flexible.

Types of Agreement

When design professionals perform services, they must do so under an agreement. That agreement is either oral or written—but the absence of a written document does not mean that no agreement exists. The law implies reasonable terms to the parties if they have not otherwise put them in writing. Obviously, with an oral agreement there is the risk that a court will impose different parameters to the design professional's services than the design professional had intended. Furthermore, when errors or omissions are alleged, or work deviates from the contract documents, the court will have to presume the scope and level of services the architect or engineer was to perform and the degree of skill and care the designer was to take to the project in making an evaluation of liability. Similarly, if third parties, such as injured workers or facility users, should bring a claim against a design professional, the court would have to consider the nature of the design professional's duties to those individuals in a vacuum. This could lead to very adverse results. For this reason, designers should use neither oral agreements nor short-form letter agreements, which describe only compensation.

It is sometimes suggested, however, that a letter agreement or oral agreement is superior to many written agreements. This could, in some instances, be true. After all, an owner-imposed agreement may have terms and conditions that far exceed what any court would imply. However, the logic does not hold up when third-party claims are taken into consideration. Most design professionals' contracts will protect them against claims made by facility users or injured workers. The absence of a contract will preclude most of the best defenses to an action brought by such injured individuals. Notwithstanding these considerations, it may, in fact, be better to complete a project under a letter agreement setting forth full compensatory information, including identification of additional services, than to sign an overwhelmingly adverse agreement.

Using standard form agreements is preferred, but not without some risks. Standard forms of agreement have been prepared by the

American Institute of Architects (AIA), the Engineers Joint Contracts Documents Committee (EJCDC), and other organizations. They are well drafted and easily understood, and generally fully describe and allocate the risks of design and the requirements for compensation. Their main benefits are their ease of use and the fact that they have become accepted as customary in many segments of the design and construction industry. Deviations from the standard form documents can be viewed as deviations from customs and practices entitling the design professional to protest the change or to ask additional compensation in light of the change. The agreements are generally more superior to any letter agreement and serve to protect design professionals from claims by third parties.

The use of standard form agreements is not without problems, however. Standard form agreements by their very nature are drafted for "typical" projects and contain language and provisions purposefully vague so that virtually any project can be documented with them. For instance, in the American Institute of Architects' agreements the site observation clause requires the architect to make "periodic" inspections as the project may require instead of specifying a fixed number of site visits. Obviously fixing a number for the site visits is impossible for a standard form agreement. However, the architect might be better served by having a fixed number specified because it is easier to comply with objectively described requirements. Similarly, the standard form documents sometimes fail to address important issues for a specific project—for instance, those encountered for a renovation or to be performed in the presence of known hazardous or special wastes. These concerns require that the standard form agreements be modified for more complicated projects. When a form is changed, however, it loses the "magic" quality of immutability that the design professional may very well want its client to presume. Once changes have been made, owners will feel even freer to make changes of their own.

Why and How to Negotiate a Professional Services Agreement

Most design professionals treat as axiomatic that going "bare" (without a written agreement) is risky. Many economic risks are shifted in an agreement: the risk of untimely (delayed) completion, the risk of code compliance, the risks of hazardous substances on the site, the risks of shop drawing errors, etc. But, the least appreciated economic risk not dealt with by oral agreements is what is frequently called the "expectation" risk.

Many clients are not familiar with the design or construction industry. Their expectations about what a design professional will provide are often based on little prior experience or some loose sales talk preceding the project. Such clients expect drawings that are perfect, error-free construction under the continued watchful eye of the design professional, and full budgetary compliance. While it is not the purpose of the design professional to dash these expectations, its purpose should be to put them into perspective. Negotiating a contract achieves that result. It permits the design professional to discuss the necessary design steps, the need for owner approvals at various stages, the cost the owner will incur by making later changes, the need for owner input and decision making, the cost and benefit of more detailed drawings and design time, how the design professional relates to contractors, to what extent the design professional may be responsible for contractors' failure to execute the work, and many, many more issues. At the end of a detailed contract negotiation, even an unsophisticated client should be aware of how the owner will affect the ultimate success of the project and have a better idea of the nature of the design professional's role. Realistic expectations then hopefully will be met during the project delivery, with the end result being a satisfied client. A client whose expectations have not been put in perspective may be disappointed.

Detailed negotiations of the scope of services may result in increased compensation to the design professional. As project requirements are thoroughly reviewed, many owners will decide to purchase additional services from the design professional to enhance the probability of an outstanding outcome.

Finally, negotiations do not just resolve legal issues; they reveal the true nature of the parties' relationship and set the tone for their future dealings with one another. After all, the responsiveness of the client to the negotiation process probably will mirror the responsiveness of the client during design and construction. The client who has no time to negotiate or is not focused on details is most certainly going to be equally distant from the project and important points of decision. The design professional should allow for this type of client both in the organization of the project and in fee considerations. Equally, a client who is extremely detailed can be expected to bring that detail to the remainder of the project. Again, such a personality will have an impact on how the services are delivered and their costs.

Negotiating an agreement also will reveal to the design professional the flexibility of the client. Some, while negotiating in good faith, will nevertheless leave little room for movement or change in their position. The design professional should expect an equally unyielding attitude as the inevitable problems in any design and construction project arise. A fee adjustment may be necessary to compensate for anticipated problems of dealing with this kind of owner. On the other hand, a flexible owner will probably remain flexible throughout the project, allowing for a different and perhaps less formal processing of information without undue risk.

This is not to say that contract negotiations do not have apparent "adverse" results. It is possible that although both parties believed they were of the same mind about the project, when the detailed discussion of contract terms and compensation is had, the apparent agreement dissolves. This is not an adverse result from negotiation. It is a positive result. After all, the breakdown between the parties was bound to occur. If it occurs during the project, the result may be a lawsuit.

The following are some negotiating techniques that you should ordinarily follow. This list is not all-inclusive but generally outlines sound negotiating techniques and postures.

Avoid Piecemeal Negotiations Piecemeal negotiations, where new demands are made after negotiations have begun, are essentially unfair and will result in one side's feeling the other is taking advantage. Avoiding this is simple. Both sides should be required to identify every term or change they wish to negotiate at one time before the negotiations commence. Concessions then can be made in light of the total package of concerns presented, and each side can understand how the agreement is maturing into a format that each can justify. A design professional should not make last-minute demands because it impeaches its credibility. Last-minute demands by the owner should be flatly refused on the ground that the deal has not been cut and that any new demand opens *all* issues.

Make No Concessions Until All the Comments Are Discussed A negotiation should start with a discussion of each point raised by the parties with the understanding that neither side will make a concession initially. Often, concessions made early in the process later turn out to be unjustified in light of the entire package of owner requests. Refusing to make early concessions before understanding all of the objectives of the owner will not impugn a design professional's "good faith," provided the owner is initially informed that the negotiations will be following such a format.

Meet Face to Face Early in the negotiations much can be accomplished merely by trading papers. Each side can be apprised of the other's position through lists of provisions and through the identification of language which suits them. However, a face-to-face meeting between principals, with or without counselors in attendance, is necessary for two reasons. First, there is an importance and dignity to the negotiation of a contract which should not be ignored. By relegating the contract negotiations to advisers only or to negotiations through the mail belittles the importance of the process and does not allow the design professional to achieve the marketing objectives that negotiating a contract can create.

Face-to-face negotiations result in agreements being made more quickly. If the principals to the contract are not involved, they may fail to understand the needs and objectives of the party with whom they are seeking to contract. As a result, they may fail to understand the concessions that may be required or to identify alternatives to positions they have previously taken.

Put a Time Limit on the Negotiation Wrapping up the negotiations of the design professional's contract in a timely fashion is a major objective. Negotiations that drag on will inevitably result in the owner's feeling ill at ease and will interfere with the constructive building of the relationship. Time limits cause principals and their counselors to focus and to move from negotiations to the first stage of the project.

There is another reason to set time limits for negotiations. A design professional's greatest leverage exists before the project is well under way and substantial sums are due from the owner in compensation. Establishing time limits for negotiations ensures that the negotiations of the contract will be completed during the time that the design professional enjoys this greater leverage.

Do Not Treat the Negotiations as a "Trading Session" Negotiations do not necessarily mean trading concession for concession. A well-thought-out negotiating position sets forth the objectives of the design professional and does not assume those objectives will necessarily have to be traded for objectives of the owner. This does not mean that the owner will not require, and that the design professional will not accede to, changes in proposed language. But such changes should be reasoned of themselves and not in exchange for an unrelated concession by the owner. A negotiation is not a street barter.

Do Not Request Contract Terms You Know the Other Party Cannot Agree to In contract negotiations, it is important to establish stature. Proposing language or terms that the other party cannot and will not agree to and are immediately conceded merely reduces the stature of the proposer. Soon none of the provisions that such a party proposes will be credibly dealt with. Treating the negotiation seriously from both parties' points of view and seeking only a fair allocation of risk leads to the opposite result. This does not mean that the design professional should not consider requesting terms that may under certain circumstances be conceded. They must be well within the parameters of what is reasonable.

Do Not Treat Negotiations as a Game Professional services negotiations are not a game with winners and losers. Approaching them as such does not promote a long-term professional relationship. Negotiations are supposed to be and should be treated as long-term discussions designed to reach agreement on how the risks that the project entails are to be allocated. No matter how much or how little of a bargaining advantage one side may have, the negotiations should be treated as reasoned discussions toward reasonable objectives. Figure 2.1 is a list of important issues which a design professional should consider in negotiating a contract.

How the Owner-Contractor Agreement Affects Your Legal Duties

There is a substantial amount of confusion about how the contractor's agreement legally affects the rights and duties of a design professional. This confusion results, in part, from the integrated sets of documents prepared by the AIA and the EJCDC. These documents include owner-contractor agreements and owner–design professional agreements that mirror one another and which cause many design professionals to presume that the duties set forth in the contractor agreement impact their contracts.

In part, these design professionals are correct. For instance, the American Institute of Architects Standard Form of Agreement

ISSUES WHICH A DESIGN PROFESSIONAL SHOULD CONSIDER IN NEGOTIATING A CONTRACT

1. *Standard of Care.* A design professional should agree to exercise that degree of care generally exercised by other design professionals under similar circumstances. The design professional should be careful not to make any express or implied warranties of its services.

2. *Compliance with Laws.* An owner frequently requires the design professional to agree that its design shall comply with all applicable laws, statutes, ordinances, rules, and regulations. This requirement creates a problem because interpretation of such laws and ordinances may differ within the governmental authority administering the laws and ordinances. Therefore, it is suggested that if a design professional agrees that its design will comply with applicable laws, such agreement should be limited to compliance with such laws as interpreted for the design professional during the design phase of the project by the appropriate governmental authorities. In addition, because of the particularly complex nature of laws concerning asbestos and other hazardous materials, pollution control, and environmental regulation, it is suggested that the design professional try to exclude its compliance with such laws.

3. *Adjustments to Schedule or Budget.* If the owner or the general contractor makes changes to the work schedule or the budget for a project, they will often require the design professional to perform additional services in connection with such changes. The design professional should take steps to see that it receives additional compensation for such additional services. A suggested approach is to clearly provide that any services performed by the design professional to accommodate any schedule or budget adjustment shall entitle the design professional to additional compensation, unless and to the extent that such schedule or budget adjustment is required as a result of acts of the design professional.

4. *Duty to Make Observations of the Work.* The scope of a design professional's duty to observe the work is sometimes vague, which may support a future claim that the design professional should have detected all errors in the contractors' work. Consider limiting the duty to observe the work to an objectively verifiable and specific number of hours or visits. The design professional should require that any additional observation of the work shall entitle the design professional to additional compensation.

5. *Limitation of Liability for Damages Resulting from Defective Design.* A design professional may take steps to limit its potential liability. A suggested approach is to limit the design professional's liability to owner for any damages suffered by owner on account of any negligent act or omission on the part of the design professional to the amount of insurance proceeds available from the design professional's professional liability policy at the time judgment is entered against the design professional. The design professional should attempt to avoid personal liability for any such damages.

6. *Liability for Acts or Omissions of Others.* An owner often requires the design professional to coordinate the transmittal of documents and information among the various contractors and owner's consultants on a project. This role exposes the design professional to potential liability for the acts and omissions of others. The design professional should take steps to avoid such liability. A suggested approach is to contractually provide that the design professional is not liable for any damages arising from the acts of any other person, unless and to the extent such damages arise from the negligence of the design professional. Furthermore, consider requesting that the owner

Figure 2.1

indemnify the design professional from any damages arising from the conduct of any other person. This indemnity should include reimbursement of attorneys' fees.

7. *Scope of Certifications.* The design professional typically is required to provide a number of certifications. Because these certifications can be a source of liability for the design professional, the scope of these certifications should be limited. Issue certifications only in connection with matters within the scope of services. Furthermore, all certifications should be "to the best knowledge and belief" of the design professional and only with respect to matters of which the design professional has direct knowledge through the performance of its services.

8. *Duty of Design Professional to Review Information Provided by Owner's Consultants.* An owner frequently requires the design professional to analyze or review information provided by owner's consultants. By analyzing or reviewing such information the design professional exposes itself to potential liability arising from errors or omissions contained in such information. The design professional should take steps to limit its exposure to such liability. A suggested approach is that the design professional agree to analyze or review information provided by owner's consultants only if such information is necessary for the performance of the design professional's own services. Furthermore, the design professional should have no liability for any error or omission contained in such information unless the design professional has actual knowledge of such error or omission.

9. *Owner's Failure of Payment.* In order for the design professional to have the leverage it needs to get paid for its services, the agreement between owner and the design professional should state that the failure of owner to pay the design professional for services rendered within a fixed number of days after such services are invoiced is a material default entitling the design professional to cease performance under the agreement. Furthermore, the agreement should state that the acceptance by the design professional of late or partial payment on a particular occasion will not waive any default.

10. *Assignment of Design Professional's Agreement.* It is advisable for the design professional to require, as a condition to any assignment by owner to a lender of the design professional's agreement with owner, that the lender agree to pay to the design professional all sums owing for services previously rendered under the agreement at the time of such assignment and all sums to become due under the agreement for services to be rendered after such assignment.

Figure 2.1 *(Continued)*

Between Owner and Architect AIA Document B141 (1987 edition) provides that the architect "shall provide administration of the Contract for Construction as set forth below and in the current edition AIA Document A201 General Conditions of the Contract for Construction" (paragraph 2.6.2). The obligation to perform the construction administration in accordance with both the architect's agreement and the general conditions could result in a conflict to the extent that the general conditions and architect's contract are not carefully integrated. The AIA General Conditions provide at paragraph 9.2 that "terms in this Agreement shall have the same meaning as those in AIA Document A201 General Conditions of the Contract for Construction." This provision need not overly concern the design professional since the source for term definition is not usually consequential. However, in some respects definitions may affect the scope of the architect's responsibility. In the 1987 edition of the AIA Document A201 the term "Work" is defined to include not only materials and equipment incorporated into the project but also "all other labor, materials, equipment and services provided or to be provided by the Contractor to fulfill the Contractor's obligations." This conceivably includes temporary shorings, scaffolding, hoists, and other facilities and activities. Since the architect is responsible under Article 4 to observe the "Work," it could be improperly argued that the architect's responsibilities include observing temporary shoring, scaffolding, and the like.

The nature and extent of the contractor's duty to perform certain tasks, when they are to be performed, and in what fashion certain information is provided to the designer may be critical to the design professional's ability to properly perform its services. In that sense, the construction contract affects the economics of the architect's or engineer's services.

The contractor's duties also may impact the design professional's liabilities as well. For example, to the extent the contractor is not required to fully review and approve shop drawings, a higher burden is placed on the design professional from both a practical and, perhaps, liability perspective. The situation gets further complicated when, for example, performance specifications are used. The duties of the contractor to perform design work have to be mirrored carefully by a provision relieving the design professional from the duty to review the designs upon submittal review. Otherwise, the shop drawing process may cause the design professional to take responsibility for the designs prepared by the contractor despite the fact that the design professional believed that the contractor was made fully responsible for design under a performance specification.

Fortunately, design professionals are often charged with drafting supplementary general conditions, if not the contractor's agreement itself. They may wish to make alterations and corrections to conform the contractor's agreement to the understanding the architect or engineer may have about its construction administration duties. This is not contrary to the owner's best interests. A frequent problem owners may have is the fact that architect's duties during the construction effort and the contractor's duties do not mirror one another. As a result, a gap is created where responsibilities may not be assumed by either party. Overlapping duties resulting in questions about liability also may result. Figure 2.2 is a list of possible changes to consider to the AIA General Conditions of the Contract for Construction, Document A201 designed to insulate architects from liability. Similar changes would be appropriate for the EJCDC Documents. All contract changes should be reviewed with your advisers.

Why Consulting Agreements Are Necessary

Consulting agreements cannot be justified or negotiated in the same light as agreements with owners. It is not usually necessary to establish expectations and understandings through the negotiation of a

ARCHITECT-ORIENTED AMENDMENTS TO THE AIA GENERAL CONDITIONS, AIA DOCUMENT A201, 1987 EDITION

Steven G. M. Stein[1]

The Architect's agreement is with the Owner, and the architect is not a party to the construction contract between the Owner and the Contractor. However, because the Architect is the administrator of the construction contract and is prominently mentioned in it, the terms of that contract (especially the General Conditions contained therein) can affect the Architect's services and liability.

The most common form of General Conditions is Document A201, published by the American Institute of Architects, most recently in 1987. The printed form is often changed unilaterally by the Owner, or by the Owner and contractor in the course of their negotiations. Indeed, it is likely that owners will make more changes in the 1987 edition of A201 in order to protect their interest than they made in prior editions of this document. Architects also have concerns which are directly related to the two issues mentioned above: the Architect's services and liability. In general, the Architect's concerns are not inconsistent with the Owner's interest, although the Architect's priorities may be different from the Owner's.

Following is a summary of the changes which Architects may wish to make in the 1987 edition of AIA Document A201 in order to protect their own interest:

1.1.3   The term "Work" is now defined to include not only materials and equipment incorporated into the Project, but also "all other labor, materials, equipment and services provided or to be provided by the Contractor to fulfill the Contractor's obligations." This includes temporary shoring, scaffolding, hoists, and other facilities and activities. The architect's duties and obligations, under Article 4 and elsewhere, relate to the "Work." The Architect has never before had any responsibility of any kind relating to temporary facilities and activities. Either the definition of "Work" could be replaced by that contained in the 1976 edition of A201, or something like the following should be added to 1.1.3:

> Nothing in these General Conditions shall be interpreted as imposing upon the owner, the architect, or their agents, consultants, or employees any duties, obligations, or authority with respect to components incorporated into the project, such as shoring, scaffolding, hoists, weatherproofing, or other temporary facilities or activities, it being understood that such temporary facilities and activities are the sole responsibility of the contractor.

2.2.7   Provision of information through the Architect may result in claims by the Contractor against the architect that the information was misleading, incomplete, or erroneous. The same claims may be made against the Owner. To disclaim liability the following new provision may be added:

> Surveys, soil borings, geotechnical information, data, or plans generally describing the unimproved land or existing structures at the site may be provided to the contractor by the owner directly or through the architect. Such information is not warranted by the owner or architect to be accurate. The contractor shall not be entitled to rely on it. When such information is provided by the owner through the architect and it appears on contract documents prepared by the architect, the contractor acknowledges that the architect has neither obtained such information nor verified that obtained by others. Site plans prepared by the architect are based on surveys performed by the owner through its consultants which have not been verified by the architect. Site plans do not constitute any representation by architect to the contractor of site boundaries or characteristics.

---

[1]A portion of these materials was prepared by Christopher Noble of Hill & Barlow, One International Place, Boston, Massachusetts (617) 439-3555, who has generously permitted their modification and reuse for the purpose of this publication.

Figure 2.2

2.4.1 The second to last sentence requires the Architect to approve the Owner's decision to take action to correct deficiencies in the work. Although consultation between Owner and Architect is useful in this regard, neither should want the Architect's consent to be a precondition to Owner action. Revise the second to last sentence of 2.4.1 to read, "If the Owner and the Contractor cannot agree upon the amount of such deduction, it shall be determined by the Architect."

3.3.1 Architects have long received protection against liability to injured workers by the exclusion of means, methods, sequences, and techniques from their responsibilities. This blanket exclusion is stated in 4.2.3 but is subject to an unnecessary and potentially dangerous qualification in 3.3.1. The last ten words of 3.3.1 should be deleted.

3.12.5 It is important to keep track of when shop drawing submittals have been made and to reiterate that the Contractor has the full responsibility to review and approve submittals. Accordingly, add the following sentence at the end of Subparagraph 3.12.5:

> For record keeping purposes, on all submittals the Contractor shall indicate the date the Contractor received or created each submittal and the date it was transmitted to the Architect. The Architect shall not be required to take any action or any submittal not showing such dates. Any transmittal of any submittal by the Contractor to the Architect constitutes a representation that the Contractor has reviewed and approved the submittal whether or not such dating procedures are followed.

3.18.1 Since the Architect is covered by the Contractor's indemnity, the Architect is as concerned as the Owner about the scope of such indemnity. The words "but only to the extent" should be deleted from the tenth line of 3.18.1.

4.1.2 In order to negate any implication that the Architect's obligations run to the Contractor, the word "Contractor" should be deleted from 4.1.2. The last sentence of this subparagraph should also be deleted.

4.1.3 Similarly, the following words should be deleted from this subparagraph: "against whom the Contractor makes no reasonable objection and."

4.1.4 Delete the subparagraph, consistent with the changes in 4.1.2 and 4.1.3.

4.2 The Architect should review this paragraph carefully to assure that it has not been changed in any manner which is inconsistent with the Owner/ Architect agreement. Particular attention should be given to site visits and the standard of care in observing work (4.2.2), the allocation of responsibility between the Architect and the Contractor (4.2.3), communications (4.2.4), rejection of work (4.2.6), and submittal review (4.2.7).

4.2.4 The printed text of this subparagraph does not provide for clear channels of communication, to the detriment of both the Owner and the Architect. Either (a) all Owner-Contractor communications should be directed through the Architect, or (b) the Owner and the Contractor should communicate directly, with copies of all written communications and notes of all oral communications being provided to the Architect.

4.2.7 An important cross reference should be added to the end of the second sentence:

> , taking into account the time periods set forth in the latest submittal schedule prepared by the contractor and approved by the architect pursuant to Subparagraph 3.10.2.

Also, consistent with the change in 3.3.1, revise the fifth sentence of 4.2.7 to read as follows:

Figure 2.2 *(Continued)*

The Architect's review shall not constitute approval of safety precautions or of any construction means, methods, techniques, sequences, or procedures.

When the Contractor prepares designs from the performance specifications, the Contractor will submit them in the form of shop drawings to the Architect for the Architect's review. If the Architect approves the shop drawings or makes suggestions for changes to the shop drawings, the design liability which the Architect shifted to the Contractor through the use of performance specifications will rebound back to the Architect. Accordingly, a disclaimer of liability for the receipt and comment upon Contractor's shop drawings prepared from performance specifications is necessary. The following language may be added at the end of Subparagraph 4.2.7:

> The Architect may advise the Contractor of alternatives relating to equipment or systems designed by the Contractor for the sole purpose of providing to the Contractor additional information the Contractor may choose to utilize in the Contractor's design. The Contractor shall advise the Owner of the alternatives, evaluate the alternatives in terms of its original design, and assess whether to incorporate any of them, the design of such systems or equipment remaining the exclusive responsibility of the Contractor. Any subsequent action taken on submittals or any certification made by the Architect shall not constitute an approval of or representation by the Architect of the appropriateness of the systems or equipment designed by the Contractor or the Contractor's decision whether to utilize alternatives of which the Contractor was advised by the Architect.

4.3, 4.4, 4.5   The dispute resolution provisions have been made extremely complex in the 1987 edition of A201. This additional complexity benefits neither the Owner nor the Contractor, and it places a large administrative burden upon the Architect. Simplification can be achieved through the following changes:

4.3.2   Revise to read as follows:

> Claims arising prior to final payment shall be referred initially to the Architect for action as provided in Paragraph 4.4.

4.3.3   Revise the last sentence to read as follows:

> Any change or addition to a previously made claim shall be made by timely written notice in accordance with this Subparagraph 4.4.3.

4.4.1 through 4.4.4   Delete, and replace with the following:

> Upon receipt of notice of a claim, the Architect shall request the Owner and the Contractor to furnish such information relating thereto as the Architect deems necessary. Within a reasonable time following such receipt, the Architect shall render a written decision with respect to the claim, or shall notify the parties in writing that such written decision will not be rendered. The Architect may decline to render a written decision for any reason deemed appropriate, including but not limited to (1) the fact that the claim involves allegations of negligence or default on the part of the Architect, or (2) the fact that the claim involves matters outside of the Architect's professional expertise.

4.5.1   Delete everything in this subparagraph following the words "relating to aesthetic effect."

4.5.4   Revise to read as follows:

> Demand for arbitration of any claim may not be made before the earlier of (1) the date on which the Architect has rendered a final written decision on the claim or has notified the parties in writing that such written decision will not be rendered, or (2) the expiration of forty-five days following the submission of the claim in writing to the Architect and the other party.

4.5.4.2   Change "Subparagraphs 4.5.1 and 4.5.4" to "Subparagraph 4.5.4."

9.4.2   To assure that the appropriate professional standard applies to the

Figure 2.2 *(Continued)*

Architect's Certificates for Payment, change the first sentence of 9.4.2 to read as follows:

> The issuance of a certificate for payment will constitute a representation by the Architect to the Owner, based on the Architect's observations at the site and the data included in the application for payment, that to the best of the Architect's knowledge, information and belief the work has progressed to the point indicated, the quality of the work is in accordance with the contract documents, and the Contractor is entitled to the amount certified.

Delete the third sentence of 9.4.2.

9.6.3, 9.6.4, 9.6.5   Delete these subparagraphs. It is not in the interest of either the Owner or the Architect to have the Architect involved in payments to subcontractors.

9.8.2   In the 1987 edition of A201, a procedure has been added whereby the correction of punchlist items *precedes* the issuance of a Certificate of Substantial Completion. This is not appropriate. The fifth and sixth sentences of 9.8.2 should be deleted.

10.1.2   Because the Architect has no responsibility under its contract with the Owner for asbestos or hazardous materials, the last sentence of 10.1.2 should be revised by deleting all the words following "or when it has been rendered harmless."

11.1.4   It is important that the Architect be named as an additional insured on the Contractors commercial general liability policy. This will protect the Architect from, among other claims, those arising out of the Illinois Structural Work Act. These objectives may be accomplished by adding the following new paragraph as Subparagraph 11.1.4:

> The Contractor shall cause the Architect and Owner to be named as an additional insured on the Contractor's Commercial General Liability that the coverage afforded the additional insureds shall be primary insurance for the additional insureds with respect to claims arising out of operations performed by or on behalf of the Contractor, that if the additional insureds have other insurance which is applicable to a loss, such other insurance shall be on an excess or contingent basis and that the amount of the company's liability under this insurance policy shall not be reduced by the existence of such other insurance.

11.3.1.5   The standard AIA documents are set up so that the Architect and consultants, on the one hand, and the Owner and Contractor, on the other hand, waive claims against each other to the extent that those claims are covered by builder's risk or other property insurance (AIA A201, par. 11.3.7, 1987 ed.; AIA B141, par. 9.4, 1987 ed.). The standard AIA documents do not require that the Architect-engineer be named on the builder's risk or other property insurance (AIA A201, par. 11.3.1, 1987 ed.). The enforceability of the AIA's waivers in favor of Architects, however, may be questionable, especially if the Architect is required under the contract documents to maintain professional liability coverage. *See St. Paul Fire & Marine Insurance Co. v. Freeman-White Associates, Inc.,* 322 N.C. 77, 366 S.E.2d 480 (1988). To accomplish this result add as new paragraph 11.3.1.5 the following:

> Owner shall cause the Architect to be named as an additional insured on property insurance obtained for the project.

14.2.2   The Owner's decision to terminate the construction contract should be made in consultation with the Architect and with legal counsel, but the following words should be removed from the first sentence of 14.2.2: "upon certification by the Architect that sufficient cause exists to justify such action."

Figure 2.2 *(Continued)*

consultant's agreement with another qualified professional. Both the prime design firm and its consultants are well aware of the nature of the design business and the risks and concerns that arise from it. Nevertheless, there are reasons to have and to negotiate a consulting agreement. First, it is essential that the prime design professional establish a consultant's scope of services. The failure to identify scope properly may yield both an economic loss and potential liability to the owner for errors or omissions in the design documents. Other issues that must be dealt with in a consultant's agreement as well simply cannot be dealt with by letter agreements for compensation or oral agreements. For instance, any consulting agreement must contain a "flow down" provision. Flow down provisions make the consultant responsible to the prime design professional to the same extent as the prime design professional is responsible to the owner. This same principle is used universally by contractors when contracting with subcontractors. A proper flow down clause eliminates the risk that the prime design professional will be responsible to the owner for something that the consultant should have been legally required to do but was not required to perform.

Another provision that should appear in any consultant's agreement is an indemnity provision. The indemnity should provide that the consultant indemnify the prime design professional for results of errors or omissions that the consultant makes. Typically an indemnity would include the duty to pay the prime design professional's attorneys fees resulting from suits brought by others arising from the consultant's negligence. Additionally, an indemnity clause may impose upon the consultant the duty to pay fines, penalties, or other costs and expenses incurred by the prime design professional that have not resulted from a suit being brought against it.

Additional services and correction of work are other subjects that should be addressed in a consultant's agreement. A consultant should be required to provide additional services under the same conditions as the design professional. Particularly important is the requirement that the consultant provide additional services at no cost if the prime design professional's agreement requires the prime design professional to do so under certain circumstances. That the consultant be required to correct its work if improperly performed should be unquestioned. A provision to this effect should be included in the consultant's agreement. The duty to correct work may arise from the prime professional's rejection of the work under a clause that requires the consultant's work be "satisfactory to" the design professional or may be required only when the consultant's work has been rejected by the owner.

Arbitration should be provided for, but only in the event that the owner's agreement with the prime design professional requires arbitration. Otherwise, the prime design professional could find itself in one forum dealing with the owner's claims and in another forum litigating the resultant loss with its consultant. The arbitration clause should provide that the arbitration between the consultant and prime design professional can be consolidated into the owner's arbitration with the prime design professional.

The prime design professional should be entitled to "back charge" the consultant by withholding payment in the event the prime design professional is exposed to loss or damage as a result of the consultant's activities. Obviously, a "pay when paid" clause—enforceable in many states—should be considered. It may be financially impossible for the prime design professional to pay the consultant until it is itself paid by the owner.

Finally, insurance requirements need to be thoroughly described in the consultant's agreement. Not only should professional liability insurance be required, but the limits, deductibles, and time during which it will remain in force should all be specified. Other insurance also should be listed and described.

Liability Management

Claims Trends

In order to address liability management, it must be recognized that the majority of claims are made by clients of design professionals. In recent years, more than one-half of claims made against both architects and engineers have been made by the project owner. Nonworker injuries accounted for less than 20 percent of such claims and worker injuries less than 10 percent. Of all the claims made, over 75 percent were property damage claims. Although it is disheartening to know that a design professional's greatest exposure lies with the persons with whom they contract, this statistic means that design professionals have some control over whether or not they are subject to claims. After all, the project owner is someone the design professional knows and contracts with, whereas the fortuity of a worker or nonworker being injured on the site is well beyond the design professional's control.

Preventing Disputes

Disputes can be prevented by delivering quality products and by maintaining communication with clients. Quality assurance for services is easily described but not so easily employed. The chief impediment to quality assurance programs is the belief that the economics of the profession do not allow spending additional time and energy on projects for quality assurance. Furthermore, most design professionals do not suffer claims frequently and when they do, their sole exposure is the deductible under their professional liability policy. Yet quality assurance may not be as cost-ineffective as it initially appears. Many design professionals are faced regularly with the time and expense of redrawing construction documents and paying for all or a part of omitted items during construction projects. These costs are not subject to an artificial "deductible" threshold. Furthermore, there is the "cost" of failing to maintain a reputation. Sometimes quality assurance ensures the next project with its prospective profit, itself a reward from a quality assurance program.

Client relations, starting with client selection and contract negotiation, contractor selection, and maintaining contact throughout the project are important keys to preventing disputes. This chapter previously addressed the importance of identifying creditworthy clients for the purposes of getting paid. Creditworthy clients make fewer claims. Claims often arise in response to the design professional's suit for fees. When a client is able to pay a design professional promptly, it is less likely that *any* suits will arise.

Contract negotiations clearly also improve client relations, set reasonable expectations, and lay the groundwork for good future client relations. To the extent the design professional is successful in identifying project risks and allocating them to others in the negotiations, claims are muted or avoided.

The quality of the contractor frequently determines whether or not a project owner will make a claim. A good contractor will identify the problems in advance, solve them, and push a project on to completion in a manner satisfactory to the client. The overall positive impact of a good contractor's performance benefits the entire design and construction team and results in projects where few suits arise. Unfortunately, the reverse is also true. Poor contracting skills lead to claims against design professionals. When a project is not completed on time or is shoddy workmanship, the owner inevitably looks to all parties involved in the project for compensation and may not be able to distinguish the quality of the design professional's services from the lack of quality of the contractor's.

Because of the importance of a contractor to the claims exposure of design professionals, they should be involved in contractor selection. In fact, the standard form AIA documents contemplate some involvement by the architect in evaluating contractors' bids or proposals. However, substantial involvement in the selection of the contractor may cross an important line subjecting the design professional to more liability exposure. If the design professional actually selects the contractor or induces the client to select a certain contractor, a later claim could be made against the design professional if the contractor's work is inadequate or if the contractor financially fails during the project. Although such claims are often viewed by courts as frivolous, under the right circumstances and given a certain set of facts, such a claim could yield disastrous results. These claims are not ordinarily covered by professional liability policies.

To resolve this dilemma, prequalification of contractors is the best solution. Without selecting a specific contractor, the design professional can present a list to the owner or can review an owner's prospective list and identify several contractors who have reputations for excellent work on the type of project contemplated. Care should be taken not to address the contractor's financial situation, however. First, design professionals are rarely in a position of accurately knowing a contractor's financial position. Second, the design professional should not be responsible if the contractor is financially unable to complete the project.

What to Do When Confronted with a Claim

When confronted with a claim, three simple rules should be followed. First, refer the claim immediately to your counsel and to your professional liability insurance broker for reporting to your insurance carrier.

Second, do and say nothing, especially to the claimant, until securing advice of your insurance and legal counsel. Frequently, the most damaging statements in litigation arise in the short period of time after the claim first becomes known. It is then when the design professional feels a sense of guilt, which is often completely unjustified, and the need to resolve the problem before it worsens. Claims are serious business and attorneys are trained to manage them for design professionals who will take all the right steps to preserve the best posture for immediate settlement or long-term litigation. Informing consultants and employees not to discuss the claim with anyone is necessary also.

Third, gather the facts. The best and most factual investigation occurs early in any claim, and the best strategies and techniques come from a thorough understanding of the surrounding factual context. No design professional can rely on professional counselors, insurance brokers, and attorneys to solve problems without full and adequate disclosure of the necessary underlying facts.

This is not to say that claims cannot and should not be immediately resolved without resort to litigation. No assumption should be made that by bringing in insurance and legal counsel litigation will result. Counselors familiar with the design industry know how to help resolve disputes quickly and without litigation.

Selecting Arbitration, Mediation, or Other Alternative Dispute-Resolution Techniques

Dispute-resolution techniques have continually evolved. Courts of law existed in biblical times even though trial by combat or with champions was common until the nineteenth century. Dispute resolution in the twentieth century largely has meant litigation with a judge or jury as the fact finders. Statutory and common law devices enabling the system to achieve the fairest results have been perfected. In perfecting justice, however, the system has also run into problems. A system that provides free discovery of all facts prior to trial, enlists the aid of highly trained advocates and a sophisticated court system, and ensures one or two levels of appeal costs a substantial amount of money to run and a great deal of time to implement. Often, even this system fails to achieve the substantial justice that its costs could justify. As a result, alternatives to traditional dispute-resolution process have been the subject of increasing scrutiny in the last 20 years. Each advertises itself as having advantages of economy and speed not common to the judicial system. But, as with any other lower-cost and speedier system of resolving disputes, alternative dispute-resolution techniques cannot ensure the same level of justice. This can most clearly be seen by comparing the arbitration system with court litigation.

In arbitration, the parties dispense with detailed pleadings of their case—describing the facts and circumstances that give rise to their claim and the legal theories behind them—removing the possibility of procedural and substantive attacks prior to resolution of disputes. Therefore, although in court a party may test the other's legal claim before it needs to be tried, no similar process separates wheat from chaff in the arbitration system. All claims go through the arbitration process unless otherwise settled. Thus, the litigation system allows greater preliminary legal scrutiny at the consequent higher cost.

Similarly, the court system permits each side "discovery" of the facts surrounding their dispute. Pretrial statements of witnesses are taken in depositions and documents are required to be traded between the parties and are available from nonparties through a subpoena process. The cost of obtaining the information and categorizing and understanding it is very great, but it does reduce the chance that one side will be caught by surprise during trial.

In arbitration no discovery is usually allowed. Although the parties may voluntarily exchange documents, depositions are a rarity. This is often a problem in cases where expert testimony is involved. It is very difficult to cross-examine an expert witness with whom the design professional and its counsel have no familiarity. Nevertheless, the deletion of this process frequently causes a substantial cost savings.

The proceedings themselves are substantially different. In court the parties generally are entitled to a jury trial with rules of evidence developed over the centuries for the purposes of ensuring a fair proceeding. Those same rules cause the proceedings to be cumbersome and technical. In arbitration, the rules of evidence are relaxed greatly, allowing for freer testimony albeit with the risk that the testimony will become infected with truly unfair facts or evidence that should never have been disclosed to the arbitrators. Again, there is often a substantial difference in cost because of the more related proceeding. However, arbitrators are constrained to listen to "*all* evidence," which may result in longer proceedings. A judge exercises great control over the type of evidence submitted.

Furthermore, arbitration does not suffer the same long wait for resolution frequently encountered in urban areas of the United States for trial. There is no backlog to interfere with the parties' quick resolution of the dispute. What does interfere with the quick resolution of the dispute is the unavailability of the arbitrators and the parties. It is not uncommon to have arbitrations of only a few days continue over several months. Again though, on balance, an arbitration will be completed before trial will be completed.

Another savings arising from the arbitration process arises from the lack of appeal. Appeals of arbitration awards are extremely difficult to win and are justified by statute only in extreme cases that include arbitrator bias. On the other hand, after litigants complete a suit in court, they are entitled to appeal on the grounds that the decision is contrary to law, contrary to the manifest facts, or was procured through inadmissible evidence.

The above described differences between arbitration and litigation and their attendant cost effects reveal something about the relative merits of the two processes. Many attorneys would agree that arbitration is economical and advantageous for disputes that do not involve large sums of money. After all, the quality of the justice may be reduced, but so is the cost. For extremely large sums that jeopardize a company's or person's financial condition, arbitration may not be suitable. The costs of proceeding in court, while greater, do ensure a higher degree of justice, a justice that may be worth paying for under those circumstances.

Arbitration can take place only by the consensual agreement of the disputing parties. Usually arbitration clauses are made part of design professional agreements. It is much less frequent that the parties can agree to arbitration after a dispute occurs. Because arbitration rules are made by consent of the parties, an arbitration clause may provide simply for arbitration in accordance with American Arbitration Association rules, or other rules, or may detail procedures that the parties prefer regarding scheduling, discovery, submission of evidence, timing of hearings, and the like. In other words, arbitration can be tailor-made to affect the parties' own beliefs as to the value of certain processes and procedures and to protect them from costs or procedures they think are unjustified.

Numerous other alternative dispute-resolution devices are available today. Chief among them is mediation. Mediation uses the skills and insights of a trained mediator as an intermediary to resolve a dispute. Although the parties themselves resolve the dispute through agreement and the mediator has no power to bind them, the mediator's skill in identifying the strengths and weaknesses of the respective parties' cases, insight into the true nature of the dispute, and ability to help identify common grounds between disputants often is the key to a resulting voluntary agreement. Mediation can be made a contractually required precondition in either court litigation or arbitration.

Other alternative dispute-resolution techniques are shortcuts in the litigation process or arbitration process but are subsumed within them. These techniques have been developed principally by lawyers interested in avoiding the lengthy and costly litigation process. Although it is not necessary to describe them in detail here, a design professional who is subject to litigation should ask counsel whether alternative dispute-resolution techniques have been considered, and why they have been selected or rejected.

Bibliography

Acret, James. *Architects and Engineers*. Colorado Springs, Colo.: Shepard's, 1977.

Office of Professional Liability Research, ed. *Guidelines for Improving Practice—Architects and Engineering Professional Liability*. Chevy Chase, Md.: Victor O. Schinnerer & Co., 1987–current.

Office of Professional Liability Research, ed. *Legal Newsletter*. Washington, D.C.: Victor O. Schinnerer & Co., 1987–current.

Professional Engineers in Private Practice, ed. *Guidelines for Development of Architect/Engineer Quality Control Manual*. National Society of Professional Engineers, 1977.

Stein, Steven G. M., ed. *Construction Law*, vols. 1–4. Albany, N.Y.: Matthew Bender, 1986 (suppl. 1991).

Stein, Steven G. M., and Howard G. Birnberg. *Professional Liability Management for Design Firms*. Chicago, Ill.: Birnberg, 1987.

Sweet, Justin. *Legal Aspects of Architecture Engineering and the Construction Process*, 3d ed. St. Paul, Minn.: West, 1985.

3

New Directions in Insurance Management for the Design Firm

William D. Hooper, Jr., AIA

Design firms have long attempted to reconcile the need for insurance against cost, which can be prohibitively expensive for many smaller firms. Whether for health care, professional liability, automobiles, or premises and contents coverage, all firms have had to equally balance value versus cost. An emerging trend is for design firms to more aggressively manage their coverages, avoiding onerous endorsements that might limit the protection offered under each policy and generally looking to better control risks. This risk management is regularly displayed by designers with professional liability insurance, or errors and omissions coverage by their selection of coverages, deductibles, etc.

The concept of insurance management for architects and engineers assumes that designers have the capacity to control their risks and the costs of coverage. The controlling of risks is desirable and to a certain extent achievable. But, the final ability of firms to control costs is largely out of the hands of most architects and engineers and is likely to remain that way in the years ahead.

Historical Trends, Future Indicators

In the near future, architectural and engineering firms will most likely see trends similar to those that occurred in the mid- to late 1970s and early 1980s: a declining availability of insurance and increased costs for coverage. The insurance market will see an increase in claims filed against architectural and engineering firms for work designed since 1985 and a greater demand for protection for the beleagured small firm by the design community.

Most design firms can protect themselves to an extent against clients who bring suit or claim as a result of work done under design contract. Growing commitment to tighter contracts between client and designer and better business practices within firms has resulted in a steady reduction in this type of claim, a trend that should continue. However, this may result in only modest changes in costs of insurance. The larger concern is that while the firm improves its practices, its basic insurance may become unavailable, limited by a worldwide insurance market that will control what insurance will be available and where it will be offered.

In recent years, the greatest increase in claims against architectural and engineering firms has been from third party claims. These are brought against the designer by users of the building. They involve the "slip and fall" claims that have, for the past twenty years, been one of the largest areas of litigation against designers. This category is likely to decrease in the future, given recent court decisions granting summary judgment to architectural and engineering firms. This has provided some protection against broad claims, where the designer is simply brought in as one of multiple defendants.

The Effect of the Economy

The potential for cyclical economic downturns or recession will continue. Whether this takes the form of a steep decline or a more modest slowdown of the economy in specific markets, most architectural and engineering firm clients have a propensity to tighten their construction and design budgets. The result is reduced construction contingencies and reduced margins to make the project financially feasible. Unforeseen site conditions, a contractor's fabrication error, and an uncoordinated detail are all more likely to deteriorate into a claim as the owner's profit margins decrease. Claims often arise after a building has been completed but may not be adequately maintained by an owner, an instance that occurs more often during economically difficult times.

During a recession, firms are more vulnerable to claims. The reason is that architects and engineers are more likely to reduce insurance coverage in less prosperous times. Because of the unique nature of professional liability insurance, they may be shortsightedly leaving themselves open to claims as the frequency and severity of claims increase. Professional liability insurance is sold on a claims-made basis. For coverage to be in force, the architectural and engineering firm must have had coverage when the design work was done, as well as when the claim was filed. Professional liability insurance requires a long-term commitment. Firms that buy insurance coverage in good times and discontinue coverage in lean times would be better advised to self-insure. This is the setting aside of pretax income against the potential of a future claim. This is a trend that will increase significantly in the future.

Self-insurance

Self-insurance will become a very clear choice for many firms. Many will benefit from an ability to manage funds that were set aside, i.e., money that would have been earmarked for the insurance premium and the deductibles that would occur with each claim.

With the instability in many financial institutions and a likely economic conservatism resulting in harder-to-get loans from the managers of those companies, credit for smaller architectural engineering firms is becoming more costly or unavailable. As a result, these self-insuring set-aside assets can be used as collateral for establishing lines of credit to enable the design firm to minimize cash flow variances.

An increasing number of smaller design firms are choosing to practice without professional liability insurance coverage. Other trends from the 1980s will continue. Design firms are continuing to gravitate into either very large or very small firm structures. Four times as many large firms, i.e., 100 persons or more, existed when the 1980s ended as when the decade started. These large firms are likely to keep their conventional insurance coverage. Some of the most sophisticated firms, however, have chosen to pool their insurance procurement with other large firms, creating a large, ready, and attractive market for insurers. This will continue as a trend in the years ahead. Many large firms can negotiate the most favorable long-term rates with a short list of preselected insurers. In effect, those insured will pool their risk, much as their insurers pool theirs.

Retroactive Coverage

Large firms have available retroactive coverage (Fig. 3.1) for catastrophic situations, such as the collapse of a building, an opportunity more driven by tax advantages than by coverage. When a major claim occurs, some insurers will offer coverage based on the final anticipated claim settlement. As an example, if claims are likely to be brought for $30 million and the settlement is anticipated to be $5 million or less, the insured buys retroactive coverage, and can write off the $5 million coverage cost as a business expense versus a $5 million loss that is not covered.

For the small firm, going without coverage will remain a purely business decision, and should not affect the relationship with a client unless the client demands certain coverage levels. A major change in the future is that individual client markets will dictate the insurance needs of the small firm. Residential market clients are rarely concerned with the designer's coverage; institutional clients seem most concerned and make specific requirements of the designer, establishing limits of coverage and naming themselves as coinsureds. This trickle-down requirement also leads from prime designer to subcon-

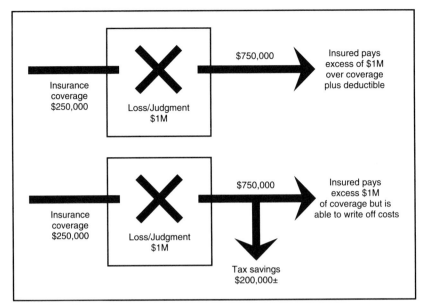

Figure 3.1   Retroactive coverage.

sultants, each looking to hand off risks commensurate with the level of work done. Recently, design firms have been warned that limitations of liability required by some insurers may create problems between prime designer and subconsultants. If the subconsultant limits its liability to the prime designer and the prime designer has not followed suit with the client, then the prime designer may have assumed any gap in coverage between the limit of insurance and any claimed amounts. More contractual stipulation of insurance levels will result as part of the agreement between prime consultants and subconsultants, not less.

Regardless of the client market, most designers continue to gravitate toward higher deductibles. In a sense they are acting to self-insure for the initial levels of risk. It is likely that insurers will offer an ever broader range of deductibles, especially in the higher ranges, if the insured has the necessary liquid capital to cover the initial claim cost. Simply, the designer will be self-insured for most projects but will be reinsured by a conventional insurer for the potential devastating claim that could someday arise.

The Reinsurance Market and the Designer

Reinsurance markets are also changing. This will have a direct impact on design professionals. While most architects and engineers have been under the impression that they were insured by Company A, Company A passed on a risk above certain limits to international reinsurance cartels. Until the early 1980s, the reinsurers were most likely to follow the lead of the local professional liability insurer, who ostensibly knew the market. Some reinsurers took large losses in the pair of financial downturns that occurred in the early and mid 1980s and are unlikely to play such a benign role in the future. This is especially true given the likely occurrence of periods of poor investment returns. Design firms likely will see the reinsurers more actively writing the exclusions and limitations directly into the insurance contracts, rather than allowing the insurance terms solely established by the primary insurance underwriters. Reinsurers are already starting to set demands on the types and levels of architectural engineering risks that they will be willing to cover, and occasionally have overruled the local professional liability insurer in what coverages will be made available and where they will be sold. The clear implications are that insurance may not be available nationwide and the level of competitiveness, with insurers offering multiple choices in each state, may be a thing of the past.

In the future, architects and engineers will need to take the fight to the state legislatures in order to maintain existing coverages. In the 1980s, some states created consumer protection language for insurers that became so onerous that it caused some companies to decline to offer coverage in those states. In some architectural engineering markets, coverage may be totally unavailable.

When an architectural engineering firm chooses to change insurers, the firm must negotiate the residual risk into its new agreement. Architects wishing to jump to Company B after having been insured by Company A, for example, must be protected for claims that may result from the time when they were insured with Company A, even if the claims occur years from now.

In addition, if Company A chooses to no longer offer coverage in a particular state it is likely that the design firm will have no warning before termination. Firms will have weaker negotiating positions with other companies who may consider insuring them in the future. It is likely that the 1990s will see some contraction in the insurance market, which may find firms suddenly left unprotected. Even a careful review of the financial strength of any insurance company may not offer any indication that the insurer may choose to stop writing coverage in a given state.

Small design firms should always be aware of who is writing coverage in their market and continually reprice their existing coverage, if only to be familiar with the insurance market. Large firms, when negotiating their special coverages, should seek legal recourse and language to protect them for any runoff risk in the possibility that the insurer may choose to leave the market.

Wrap-Up Insurance: Owner Buys Architectural Engineering Coverage

More institutional clients are turning to wrap-up insurance coverage as a method of containing costs. Both the providers of design services and the general contractors will be included in this coverage. Rather than pay multiple insurance premiums and deductibles for the many parties involved in a large project with multiple subprojects, this approach allows owner and clients to be able to consolidate coverage and avoid separate coverage negotiations for each project. It also enables the client to avoid the gaps in insurance coverage between multiple insurance packages. Last, the client can effectively reduce the overhead of the design and construction contractors by absorbing their insurance costs.

Wrap-up insurance coverage also acts as a bridge between traditional design and construction claims, so that the likelihood of time- and money-consuming cross claims is minimized. Wrap-up insurance can also be tailored to include asbestos abatement coverage, a form of coverage not widely available to designers and very costly to contractors.

Policy exclusions, such as asbestos abatement, are likely to undergo changes in the near future. It is possible that by the year 2000, coverage for design services involving asbestos removal will be handled as options available by endorsement to the basic policy. Design-build services are another area where policy exclusions now present are likely to change. With more designers performing a range of services, there will be greater pressure to provide some limited form of protection for those architects and engineers with an equity position in a project that they have designed. This is currently not covered by most policies.

The Insurance Market for the Near Future

The existing marketplace (1991) has 12 insurers that offer coverage for designers. That number, a sign of a strong design market and burgeoning design fees, is likely to decrease in number. In harder economic times, the number of available insurers will decrease to perhaps 7 companies that will have the financial wherewithal to stay in the market and deal with the likely increase in claims.

Most specialized underwriters have been active in this market for at least 12 years, some for more than 30 years. Therefore, the absolute evaporation of insurance availability that occurred in the 1950s is unlikely to recur.

In planning and managing insurance coverage for the 1990s and beyond, most design firms should begin to institute quality assurance and control programs within the office as part of every project. While larger design firms have formally and informally incorporated a review, smaller firms are starting to take the time to reexamine their contract documents before the final contract is awarded. No one is naive enough to believe that hard deadlines will not make quality assurance difficult, but a detailed review is still valuable during the bid process. Many insurers are actively rewarding those firms who instigate design reviews, with significant cost savings on their premium. Smaller firms will more actively pursue peer group reviews in the next 10 years as a way of reinforcing the concept of quality in the architectural engineering practice network.

The severity of claims (Fig. 3.2) continues to rise at a rate comparable with inflation. Assuming this trend continues, increases in the costs of coverage should remain more constant than that experienced in the volatile 1970s and 1980s.

Frequency of claims, the other component of insurance costs, has

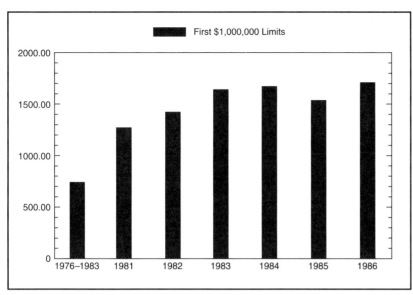

Figure 3.2   Average paid claim value—claims with indemnity payments (above insureds' deductible obligations).

been steadily declining since the peak year of 1983 (Fig. 3.3). While the decline from 44 claims per 100 insureds to 30.3 claims (1989) is heartening, it is unlikely to continue. A rise, although modest, can be expected in the near future 1990s due to a number of factors.

Much new technology was introduced in the 1980s and was quickly accepted and incorporated into building design. New glass, exterior cladding systems, stone veneers, polychrome color for metals, and many other breakthroughs have changed the way architects and engineers design. Much of this new technology can never be fully tested in the laboratory before it is offered on the market or used in full-scale construction application. As a result, claims will rise from some building materials that will fail to perform outside the warranty period. The most notable cases from the recent past are asbestos, the use of two-ply roofing systems, and fire-retardant treated plywood for roofing. In all those cases, millions of dollars are still being paid by insurers to repair the best-intentioned efforts of designers who used

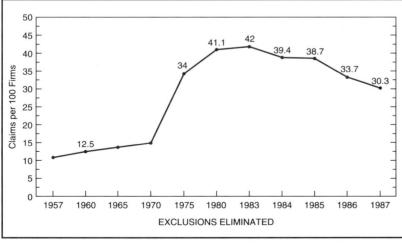

Figure 3.3

materials later found to be unacceptable in their performance. The future will most likely see significant claims resulting from untested technologies.

While most architects and engineers carry some insurance coverage against loss, most do not protect their "valuable papers." Insurers offered coverage to firms, business- as well as design-oriented, who could not survive without their historical records (or in the designer's case, drawings). More insurers will start to offer broader protection against data loss in catastrophic situations such as fire. Look for valuable papers coverage to include computer data and become more affordable for small firms.

The years ahead are likely to involve more megaprojects, whether improvements to infrastructure, large-scale residential projects, major rural and suburban developments, or large-scale transportation projects. In any case, the size of the project may well require the need for coverage far in excess of that normally available. With these projects comes a unique form of term insurance, originally offered in the early 1980s and certain to become increasingly available to more firms. Since architectural and engineering firms usually form teams on these projects, some insurers are willing to insure the venture from the beginning to the end of the project, with some residual coverage that can be renewed at various option times. Insurance companies will be under pressure to create new coverages. The demand for professional liability term insurance on smaller projects is creating possibilities of coverage that are decidedly different from conventional claims-made coverage.

Another problem is that the limits of coverage are not increasing with inflation. The $15 million ceiling for insurance coverage commonly available is not likely to be increased by the insurers in the near future. For the largest firms this may present a future problem in possibly being underinsured.

When architects and engineers are asked the most distasteful aspect of their professional life, there is surprising unanimity: professional liability insurance. It manages to hit common chords because it implies negligence, costs significant money, requires time to investigate, does not generate new work, and is perceived as boring. Unfortunately, little will soon change. However, the insurance market, availability, cost, and ways to minimize the risks of practice may well change significantly.

The Aging Designer

In the next twenty years, many practitioners will start to retire and the architects and engineers who were educated in the 1970s and 1980s will look to protect their investments in their firms while they practice less, sell their firms outright, or emerge from an ownership transition. Paralleling this will be their desire to protect themselves from liability for long-completed projects. In any case, reduced insurance levels for emeritus practitioners is needed and will be a surprisingly strong market for insurers.

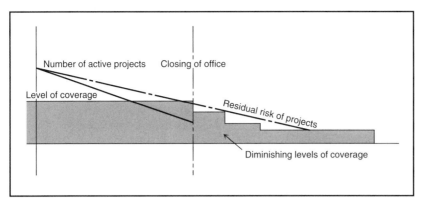

Figure 3.4 Aging architect insurance coverage.

The insurance company offering this coverage is inheriting no new risk and will probably offer multiyear policies, enabling the practitioner to carry coverage for 5 years. If no problems arise during that period, they will be able to renew for preagreed option periods until the risk of claims becomes negligible. Costs will be low given the steadily declining risks (Fig. 3.4).

In conclusion, the insurance market of the 1990s will appear to offer more diverse protection options, but at the same time there will be increased risk that some portions of the country may have limited or no coverage available for some periods.

Resources

Books, Manuals, Pamphlets, and Reports

ACEC Annual Professional Liability Survey, American Consulting Engineers Council, Washington, D.C., latest edition (report).

AIA Firm Survey Report, The American Institute of Architects, Washington, D.C., latest edition (report).

Cushman, Robert F., and Thomas Bottum, *Architect and Engineer Liability: Claims Against Design Professionals,* John Wiley & Sons, New York, 1987.

Best Insurance Report, A.M. Best, Inc., Oldwick, N.J., latest edition.

Financial Performance Survey for Design Firms, Birnberg & Associates, Chicago, Ill., latest edition (report).

A Guide to Establishing Quality Control Policies and Procedures in Geotechnical Engineering Practice, Association of Soil and Foundation Engineers, Silver Spring, Md. 1989 (pamphlet).

Guidelines for Development of Architect/Engineer Quality Control Manual, National Society of Professional Engineers/Professional Engineers in Private Practice, Alexandria, Va., 1980 (manual).

Howell, Edward B., and Richard P. Howell, *Untangling the Web of Professional Liability,* Risk Analysis & Research Corp., Monterey, Calif., 1980.

In-House Loss Prevention Programs, Association of Soil and Foundation Engineers, Silver Spring, Md., 1983 (manual).

Managing the Issues of Professional Liability, DPIC Companies, Monterey, Calif., 1986 (pamphlet).

Manual of Professional Practice for Quality in the Constructed Project, American Society of Civil Engineers, New York, 1987 (manual).

Setting Insurance Rates for Design Professionals, DPIC Companies, Monterey, Calif., 1986 (pamphlet).

Stein, Steven G. M., and Howard Birnberg, *Professional Liability Management for Design Firms,* Birnberg & Associates, Chicago, Ill., 1987.

Streeter, Harrison, *Professional Liability of Architects and Engineers,* John Wiley & Sons, New York, 1989.

Understanding and Purchasing Professional Liability Insurance, American Consulting Engineers Council, Washington, D.C., 1991 (manual).

Walker, Nathan, and Theodor Rohdenburg, *Legal Pitfalls in Architecture Engineering and Building Construction,* McGraw-Hill, 1978 (book).

Newsletters

Communique, DPIC Companies, P.O. Box DPIC, Monterey, Calif. 93942.

The Errors and Omissions Bulletin, Guidelines Publications, P.O. Box 456, Orinda, Calif. 94563.

Guidelines for Improving Practice, Office of Professional Liability Research of Victor O. Schinnerer & Co., Inc., Washington, D.C. 20016.

The Profit Center, Birnberg & Associates, 1227 West Wrightwood Avenue, Chicago, Ill., 60614.

Also various issues of newsletters published by AIA, NSPE-PEPP, and ACEC.

Additional Information

The American Institute of Architects (AIA), the American Consulting Engineer's Council (ACEC), The National Society of Professional Engineers (NSPE-PEPP), and the American Society of Civil Engineers (ASCE) sponsor peer review programs for their members. AIA may be reached at (202) 626-7300, ACEC at (202) 347-7474, NSPE at (703) 684-2862, and ASCE at (212) 644-7505.

4

Personnel Management

Lou Marines and Bill Truby

The business environment for the last decade of this century is being shaped by several factors that will profoundly affect personnel issues in architectural and engineering firms. A turbulent economy, changing patterns of loyalties among employees, increasing government interventions, a threatening legal atmosphere, an older trained work force, an increasingly diverse new work force, and intensified client demands are a few factors requiring fresh approaches. It is this bewildering diversity of challenges descending upon design firms that makes human resources management critical.

In small firms, human resources management is usually one of several responsibilities carried by a principal. In larger firms, one or more persons are designated to work full time to manage personnel issues. These issues include recruiting, employment policies, compensation, benefits, office procedures, training, communications, termination, and retirement. Whether these tasks are the principal's or the internal specialist's, the trend for the coming decade is clear: people-related issues will require more precision, greater professional training, larger allocations of time and resources, and more creativity than at any previous time.

Personnel Demands

Business issues in the design professions are seldom resolved by adopting new technology or by a marketing breakthrough. They translate into more pronounced requirements on personnel, more sharply focused human expectations, and more precise matching between client needs and staff capabilities.

In the future, every category of the traditional client base for engineers and architects—developers, private owners, government entities—will be under intense financial restraints. Clients face mounting regulatory restrictions, prompted in part by concerns for their project's impact on the natural and social environment. Costly financing makes rapid completion schedules absolutely critical to a successful project. Designers will be viewed either as a prized ally or as an annoying threat.

Principals in design firms must find, train, and retain personnel who are not only technically skilled but who can go beyond basic solutions to client problems. Staff must sense client needs that are not fully articulated. They must move with precision and urgency toward creative solutions. Your staff must have an astute understanding of deeper human and societal issues, and must be able to make efficient judgments about what really needs to be done; they must be value-driven, bright, and able to prioritize.

Power in design firms is becoming decentralized. It is shifting from a few people at the top and is spreading widely among teams and production individuals in the entire organization. Design firm staff must be adept at focused, self-confident communication, consensus building, and aggressive listening. They must be familiar with making decisions, with taking initiative, and with interacting effectively with clients and senior management, as well as with their own peers.

The sobering consensus is, however, that such multiskilled people are rare. And, they are difficult to retain. While many recent graduates are technically skilled, they have seldom been trained in the necessary people skills. As a result, few entry-level employees are able to make an immediate useful contribution to the firm. This makes lengthy in-house training a necessity.

Furthermore, middle management personnel, who have learned enough to become valuable leaders in a firm, also have learned that their abilities can offer strong income potential in parallel career paths. Many are electing to move into real estate development, consulting, investment management, and similar careers. This represents the design professions' most serious challenge: to both find and retain qualified personnel at all levels.

New Directions for Personnel

Successful personnel management requires recognition of two broad concepts. These will drive many of the policies or programs that senior management must implement.

Employees Hold a Higher Loyalty to Their Individual Careers

The notion of company loyalty stirs little passion today, as it carries with it images of subservient devotion to an impersonal corporation, whose management will be loyal to them only when it is expedient.

A more fitting description of employee attachment is "committed." This implies a carefully selected investment of energy into a specific work situation that holds the potential to enhance their own careers.

Mobility is an attitude in which people are bound by fewer of the values and traditions that held previous generations in the same career groove. The work force prizes individual fulfillment more than it values economic security. Its young men and women seek a more ideal work environment.

The obvious strategy for management is to team up with its employees in the pursuit of that ideal and to demonstrate that *this* firm sets employees free to set their own goals. Managers must encourage staff to take on as much responsibility as they believe they can handle and to be self-critical of their ability to complete the tasks. Some firms award grants (both monetary and release time) for well-planned self-development in areas only incidentally related to a job description.

Properly understood, the notion of career individuality does not conflict with the necessity for team building and joint endeavor. We are at our personal best in relationship with significant others. For many, quality living is defined in terms of enjoying a network of colleagues with whom we hold a significant bond. The design firm's team-based production methodology can promise just such an experience; it's the personnel manager's responsibility to create conditions that maximize that promise.

The Need for Purpose and Challenge

Most engineers and architects spend the majority of their waking hours at work. If that work is expressive of and supportive to their quest for meaningful involvement with their world and if it nudges them toward growth, then their employment experience will be surrounded with positive emotions. Employee loyalty, we should note, is only partly a logical or cognitive issue; it has huge emotional and affective dimensions as well.

This grounding of one's labor within a framework of meaning can best be experienced within architectural and engineering firms that are guided by clearly defined purposes. The purpose-driven organization enjoys a sense of cohesion at its core. Its people both measure and enjoy their successes based on substantive criteria rather than on fleeting moments of glory. When the distinctive values of the corporate culture are advocated and owned throughout the work force, work becomes energized and focused. One architectural firm, for example, identifies "complete client satisfaction" as its chief driving value. Yet it defines its clients as encompassing more than just the financiers of a specific project, but also as the people who will live or work within its completed life space and the neighbors and commuters who will view the project as a permanent part of their environment. The design team, then, enjoys a clear sense of making a lasting and appealing contribution to the life of the community. Meaning is rooted within a broad base of commonly shared human values. It falls within the task of the personnel specialist in any firm to articulate in a very convincing way the core values that move it.

Entry-level employment is frequently viewed as a necessary evil both by recent graduates ("The pay is too low!") as well as by employers ("The schools today just don't prepare students!"). For firms to continue to be successful, graduates and employers must court each other. Managers must shift from short-range, tactical decisions to clear, future-oriented plans. They must take personnel risks, which may be many years in paying off. This makes screening of potential recruits even more critical.

The talent search in the years ahead cannot ignore the mastery of specific technical skills. But, it will place more emphasis on finding individuals who can continually reinvent the best way to do their job. Agility of mind and of method, and a lifelong commitment to learning new methods, will be prized. Employers will also press for the ability to communicate, to listen, and to formulate convincing conclusions.

Most design firms find the best source of prospects is through their existing staff's contacts. Employees who already know the corporate culture can help find colleagues who would fit as part of the team. These potential employees may be people they have met at conferences or seminars, fellow classmates from their school, or colleagues from previous places of employment. Some may feel apprehension about raiding quality people from other firms; but if your firm can do for a design professional's career what a previous firm cannot do, the entire profession benefits.

The Role of the Interview

The preemployment interview can help obtain information that does not readily appear on a written résumé. Relationship issues should be the central focus. Architecture and engineering are largely team efforts. A potential employee who prizes a cooperative outcome is probably more useful than a solitary player. Ask the applicant to tell you stories about moments of professional fulfillment. Listen for references to other people. Invite an open-ended narrative about his or her dreams for the future; look for clarity of vision and indicators of strong motivation and of a high energy level. In brief, calculate how much money you will put into training a new employee over the next few years and invest appropriately in preparing for the interview.* Many see equal employment opportunity legislation as a restriction on their right to manage. But you can use it to help your firm be open and aggressive about taking full advantage of professional talent independent of sex, nationality, or cultural background. Figure 4.1 is a sample statement of equal employment opportunity policy.

In that pursuit, remember that equal opportunity rules forbid asking certain questions. Interviewers must be careful not to ask questions of women or minorities that they would not ask of all applicants. Do not ask a single woman about her plans for marriage. Do not ask any women about their plans for having children or for

---

*A valuable guide to the interview process is *The Evaluation Interview* (Fear and Chiron, 1990).

In accordance with applicable federal laws and firm policy, (firm name) does not discriminate in any of its policies, procedures, or practices on the basis of race, color, national origin, sex, sexual orientation, age, or handicap. Inquiries regarding the firm's equal opportunity policies may be directed to (principal's name).

Figure 4.1 Sample equal employment opportunity statement.

providing child care. Do not ask older applicants about their plans for retirement. Be verbally, emotionally, and facially even-handed in dealing with every applicant. Figure 4.2 lists questions an interviewer can ask.

Motivation and Rewards

Even as employees are putting increasing emphasis on finding personal fulfillment at work, they see an adequate salary as essential to funding the quest for satisfaction and enjoyment away from work. With commercially published surveys of current salaries in our professions so widely available, most workers will know how their salaries compare with the local market in terms of the level of experience. Some managers are taking advantage of this knowledge by allowing new employees to identify what they believe to be an

- "When did you join this firm?"
- "What was your job description?"
- "What were your daily responsibilities?"
- "To whom did you report?"
- "Did others work under your direction?"
- "Did you have client contact?"
- "What did you learn while working there?"
- "Did your job require any special skills?"
- "What assignment was most difficult?"
- "When did you leave this firm?"
- "How much were you making when you left?"
- "Why did you leave?"
- "Which was your favorite project?"
- "What project are you most proud of?"
- "What was your role on this project?"
- "How often did you interact with the client?"
- "How many people were on this team?"
- "What phases of the project did you work on?"
- "What is your design philosophy?"
- "What would you like to be doing in five years?"
- "How did your current employer contribute to your decision to leave?"
- "How do you like to be given direction?"
- "What do you find frustrating on the job?"
- "Why did you consider our firm?"

Figure 4.2 Possible questions an interviewer can ask. (From Woodward's *Human Resources Management for Design Professionals* (1990), pp. 29, 30.)

appropriate beginning salary, then giving them a period of time to demonstrate their productive worth to the firm. Salaries are then adjusted to match their value to their firm. Other information sources which can help you set salary ranges for each job category in your firm include recruiting firms, classified ads, and the requests of prospective employees themselves. When employees know that pay raises will be tied to doing the very things the company prizes most, it will focus their investments of energy on those key priorities.*

Motivating Exceptional Performance

The difference between a mundane manager and a true leader is that the leaders inspire others to do their best. They expect much of themselves and of others, and they explicitly notice when others have done their best. In the highest sense, bonuses are a concrete way of saying, "*We have noticed* that you have done your personal best." To the extent that the employee trusts and admires the leader, the personal acknowledgment of that leader is as powerful a motivator as is the stipend itself.

Successful design firms are defining a broad range of areas in which they expect their employees to excel. As a result, more employees have an opportunity to be rewarded in their distinctive area of accomplishment. Similarly, there is a strong trend toward diversified, innovative bonuses. For example, a singularly strong contribution by one employee that results in a major income benefit to the company should be acknowledged in a manner proportionate to its worth to the firm. If the principals merely award themselves a cash bonus from this extraordinary piece of work, the employee may leave to start a rival firm.

Seeking to reinforce the ethic of team effort, many companies offer only a companywide bonus at the close of the fiscal year, as the entire company meets or exceeds its performance goals. Others believe that employees prefer a solid, contractually reliable wage throughout the year. This combined with the certainty of a good raise for the coming year simplifies their personal budget planning. This may be preferred to an artificially low wage followed by a year-end bonus.

Still other architectural and engineering firms use bonuses that directly benefit the productive employee's personal career track. For example, some link high productivity with sabbatical leaves for study, underwriting of graduate school costs, or commissioning the employee to accomplish a highly autonomous task within the support structure of the firm and enjoying a larger share of the resulting profits.

Many companies continue to provide incentives in the form of employee stock option programs. This approach is most effective when the employees clearly see how the value of their stock is tied directly to the commercial success of the firm.

Another trend involves giving exceptional employees a special discretionary budget that they can use for purchasing new design software, visiting with colleagues in other firms, attending conferences of

---

*See Mohrman et al. (1989).

special relevance to their task, or even for rewarding their own support staff. The statement of trust involved in granting the employees the freedom to use these funds as they see fit is a powerful reward itself.

But spendable currency cannot remain the only or even the primary performance incentive. So long as more lucrative career options are available for an engineer or architect, it is going to take more than cash to retain their loyalties and motivate them. The best incentive still remains an early taste of success and the expanding arena of personal challenges. If they can rise rapidly to higher levels of responsibility and own a sense of project development completion or design accomplishment, then the work itself will provide its own intrinsic rewards. And, it is these rewards, inherent in a task well done, that speak to that dual concern identified at the beginning of the chapter: young professionals looking for an increasing sense of potency in their own careers, and able to define their work within a larger framework of meaning.*

New Images for Training

Employees in the years ahead will have a stronger sense of their need for continuing education and will take more initiative in defining its form. American industry spends more than $19 billion a year on various forms of employee and management training in a bold attempt to keep pace with new technologies and a turbulent market.

The old concept of a mentor is taking on new forms as design firms address the needs of employee training. Rather than the mentor's entering the employee's life from a position of superior power or authority, the mentor and trainee develop a bond of mutual interests. A defined expectation exists that the mentor will impact the life of the employee. The mentor does not function as a hero into which the less experienced worker fuses his or her own identity. Rather, the mentor beckons the other's emerging vision of self into full, integrated being. The mentor helps the less experienced employee resolve the tensions of sometime conflicting expectations without taking accountability for the direction of that resolution. The mentor's central goal is to empower the employee, making him or her strong enough to face the freedoms of responsibility; the mentor will therefore avoid even the most subtle forms of exercising power over the other. If the less experienced employee finds the mentor to be anchored in a sensible, real world, trainees will allow the mentor to hold them accountable for personal decisions that will result in growth. The mentor usually does not participate in a performance appraisal, because of its major management implications for raises and promotions. But the outcomes of the appraisal are fruitful territory for discussion between the trainee and the mentor as they explore together specific career-enhancing options that the trainee might pursue.

The discerning personnel manager will assist in establishing such

---

*See especially James M. Kouzes and Barry Z. Posner, *The Leadership Challenge,* San Francisco: Jossey-Bass Publishers, 1990, pp. 241ff.

mentor relationships. Though their role is most readily grasped for the entry-level worker, there is probably not a level of responsibility throughout the company that would not be enhanced by the mentor relationship. Often, openness and vulnerability develop between a mentor and a trainee. Awkwardness could result when one party needs to step back from regular involvement. As a result, these relationships should exist for defined periods of time, with formal termination points. This allows the selection of a new mentor who may be more fitting for new areas of interest. Senior managers, who run special risks of cutting themselves off from sensitive feedback, may benefit as deeply as others from engagement with a candid mentor.

Appraisal and Training

With increasing precision, human resource leaders are linking performance appraisals with training. With a view toward the needs of both the company and the individual design professional's career objectives, the appraisal is a helpful communications tool used in an atmosphere of supportive emotional safety, to prompt goal setting and growth.

Seldom does the responsibility belong to the personnel manager for conducting all performance appraisals. This should be the employee's immediate supervisor's task. The personnel manager, however, will support the development of adequate appraisal methods for use throughout the firm, will train managers in their proper use, and will audit the completed forms. Most importantly, the personnel manager integrates the appraisal into an ongoing system that ties the measurement to agreed-upon rewards, to counseling about task-related and interpersonal skills, and to goal setting based on self-acknowledged needs. Employees, however, must not feel that these training goals are being merely imposed on them from above; they know when they have genuinely been empowered and are entitled to negotiate the learning strategies.

The appraisal system will be appreciated by supervisors as they see its power to help them manage, i.e., to improve performance. It will be appreciated by employees as they see its ability to accelerate their personal career development. The critical task, then, for the personnel manager is to negotiate among three vectors of input. First, the manager considers the aspirations of the firm itself. What core competencies does it need as it positions itself within long-range strategies? Given the present staff capabilities, what are the human resource gaps that must be filled to reach the goals? Second, what individual employee's personal career goals most closely align with the needs of the company? Can an acceptable match be arranged given additional training? Third, can that employee's needs be brought in contact with available training resources, both in-house and from training consultants and seminars? Working with area supervisors to obtain specific performance standards will guide in the selection of appropriate learning experiences and also will provide somewhat objective criteria for determining the effectiveness of training programs.

People Skills One large firm reports that of all the reasons that lead to termination of employees, more than 90 percent are related to their inability to get along with their peers, rather than to the lack of any technical skills. As team-based production becomes more the norm, training in interpersonal skills will become even more critical. One informal survey indicates that architects and engineers, as a class, show some tendency to be less assertive, hold a more parochial world view, have more difficulty being persuasive, and tend to resist both giving and receiving personnel evaluations. In our interactive worksites, the absence of such skills can have a direct impact on productivity.

The Changing Legal Environment

The principal or employee who performs the job of personnel manager is intertwined with complex and often volatile legal issues. In many states, employment is no longer considered something that an employer can offer or withdraw at its discretion. Employment is being regarded as an entitlement, and the courts are supporting this interpretation. The totality of interaction between employer and employee—including handbooks, written memos, oral representations, and even regular patterns of dealing with an employee—comprise the elements of an implied contract. Any departure from the terms of this implied agreement, without legally justifiable cause, can be viewed as capricious, arbitrary, or even prejudicial, and can prompt a course of action against an employer. Wrongful termination suits have increased rapidly in recent years, and will likely continue to do so.

Personnel managers, and by extension all supervisors who are involved in performance appraisals, cannot afford to hide behind the desire not to trouble good employee relationships, and thus avoid dealing directly with performance or interpersonal problems they have identified. These problems will continue to fester and drain internal energies. If they eventually lead to termination, the lack of a specific and documented paper trail will increase exposure to litigation for wrongful termination. Even though not all states presently require expressed due process statements relating to dismissal or failure to promote, such requirements appear to be the trend for the future and constitute good management practice as well.

Antidiscrimination Policies Public sentiment has yet to find a firm resting place regarding various endeavors to avoid discrimination in the workplace. This is partly because certain basic employment practice values are in irreconcilable tension with each other. For example, Title VII of the 1964 Civil Rights Act states that it is illegal for a person's employment status to be affected because of race, religion, color, gender, or national origin. The Age Discrimination in Employment Act extended these protections to employees over age 40. Case law has issued affirmative action rulings that assert that unless a particular protected class among a work force is being hired, promoted, and paid at the same rate as the dominant class, discrimination is presumed to be operative. Many employers, either by choice or by legal necessity, have adopted quota systems to assure proportionate hiring practices for all groups.

But, this remedy appears to some merely to present the same problem in reverse, because now issues of race, color, gender, etc., must not only be directly considered in hiring practices, but must in some cases be weighted as more crucial than issues of basic skill and professional competence. Consequently, members of the dominant class are now filing job-related suits claiming reverse discrimination.

While state and federal legislatures will no doubt be giving further direction to this complex societal dilemma, companies can take certain actions to avoid discrimination suits. Failure to take these actions can be counted as prima facie evidence for discrimination.

Use Objective Data   If job-related performance appraisals include subjective measurements, it is easy for human bias to enter into the process. For example, the trait "dependable" is far more subjective than "submits work within time schedules." Also, rankings and comparisons are similarly suspect, as the criteria used to compare one worker with others may not be related to one's ability to perform the job in question but will reflect preconceived prejudices based on more personal factors.

Train Appraisers on the Issues   Any person involved in doing performance appraisals or in conducting hiring interviews should be given printed instructions on how to conduct a bias-free assessment. Also, appraisers should be people who have the opportunity to observe the employee's actual performance. And, their own work should be monitored for any signs of discrimination.

Listen Intently for Internal Signals   When employees who feel they may be the objects of discriminatory practices voice those concerns to insensitive ears, it tends to reinforce their suspicions. While managers cannot base policy on scattered statements of discontent, many legal claims are prompted not by poor policy but by insensitive personal interaction between staff and management.

Communication in the Design Firm

Communication is far more than transmitting data. Every communication event is held under assumptions about who has the power, how safe it is to be honest, and how seriously any suggestion will be taken. In the hierarchically flat and decentralized organizations that are becoming the norm, the communications atmosphere is people-centered and warm, rather than structured and aloof. Since knowledge is power, and since empowering the work force is a primary goal, knowledge is not hoarded at the top but is shared openly and trustingly, with any employee whose responsibilities even remotely touch on the information at issue. In traditional, hierarchical organizations, where the primary responsibility for innovation and problem solving rested with senior management, they decided what junior staff needed to know. As a result, many problems that were best appreciated at the hands-on level were deprived of the creative input of the very people who later would have to implement top management's dictums.

An 80-person engineering and architectural firm in California is a good example of this. Staff are hired for their expertise and are expected to keep up with the latest information in their field. When they become a part of the team, they are given trust and acceptance. Each is expected and encouraged to speak freely, candidly, sometimes argumentatively about controversial issues the firm confronts. No one holds back for fear of rejection, so everyone knows each other's position. Their communication is energetic. They effectively use, and even need, the synergy that comes from their spirited communications.

In multichannel (upward, downward, lateral) communication among design professionals who are regarded as a mature, interdependent team, there are fewer hidden agendas, less need to defend one's power-based turf. Senior partners expect the staff both to be active in obtaining necessary information, and also to use it in a goal-oriented manner with others.

Personnel Manual Good communication patterns often begin with a well-composed personnel manual. The spirit of warmth and candor that surrounds the serious business of the document can set an important tone. The personnel manual defines the working relationship between the firm and each staff member, and as such has major legal implications. Most firms that do not have a well-trained human resources professional on their staff often hire a consultant to evaluate their manual (and any subsequent handouts) before distribution. Many payroll services are now offering human resources and personnel manual consulting on a flat-fee basis.

A complete personnel manual, or employee handbook, should express your firm's position on at least the following areas:

Introductory statements (history, philosophy, etc.)

Recruitment policies (including equal employment opportunity, affirmative action)

Employment policies (records, promotions, appraisals)

Compensation (salary, leaves, holidays, vacations)

Benefits (medical, bonuses, pension, disability, etc.)

Office procedures (hours, location of services, codes)

Travel and reimbursable expenses (procedures, allowances)

Professional development (continuing education policies)

Termination and retirement (procedures, benefits)*

---

*For a detailed expansion of this handbook outline (taken originally from *The Architect's Handbook of Professional Practice,* chap. 1.10) see Woodward (1990), pp. 41–62.

A key to success in design firms is to engage frequently in planning. Even as economic trends can be predicted, so the personnel manager can work with somewhat reliable projections about the future shape and character of the work force. A survey of relevant sources suggests that human resources people in a design firm will face the following issues in the years ahead:

Increasing Benefits Costs Within industry as a whole, employers are paying between $3200 and $3500 per year per employee for health benefits. Some design firms pay as much as $6000 for an employee and his or her family. This will increase sharply. For example, the incidence of AIDS is increasing rapidly in virtually all categories, with an estimated cost per case of more than $180,000. This places a staggering load on the health care system, with costs being passed to those required to pay for health care: employers. There is strong indication that government will mandate some form of universal health care program in the near future but will not pay for it with tax revenues. This cost, too, will likely be passed on to employers.

A 1990 National Conference Board study asked human resource managers what they saw as the pressing issues for the next five years. The highest concern (48 percent) was for controlling employee benefit costs. By comparison, only 5 percent are anxious about productivity, or the introduction of new technologies. Health maintenance organizations (HMOs) and preferred provider programs (PPOs) are a partial answer, though they run the risk of becoming cash-absorbing bureaucracies themselves. Urging employees to look after their own wellness, rather than depending on the system to look after their illness, will also be a necessary attitudinal shift.

The Role of Specialty Service Providers With personnel demands becoming not only more diverse, but more precise, specific service providers and consultants are burgeoning. Some of these services (such as employee drug testing, establishing new salary and benefits protocols, retrenchment and downsizing consultations) that deal with sensitive or unpopular matters are often contracted to an outside firm. Other services, such as executive recruitment or major strategic planning, may come best from outside consultants simply because few firms are able to home-grow their own specialists in these complex areas.

A Changing Work Force Much has been written about the fact that the demographic bulge known as Baby Boomers will begin retiring early in the next century. The traditional mostly white male work force will be no more. By the year 2000, 60 percent of the new entrants into the work force will be female; more than 85 percent of the work force will be women, minorities, and foreign nationals.

Personnel managers will, of sheer necessity, look at the rich diversity of the work force not as a disappointment but as an opportunity. The more they nurture and even celebrate the differences available to them, the more attuned they will be to the realities of the labor market, and to their very pluralistic client base, as foreign investment underwrites an increasing share of the construction industry.

The Feminine Impact   In 1970, women comprised 3.7 percent of the architectural profession. By 1980, this figure had more than doubled to 8.3 percent. Currently, about 30 percent of all architectural students are women, and several large design firms report that close to 50 percent of their work force is female, with an increasing number occupying executive offices.

But these numbers tell only a portion of the story; the more subtle aspect of this trend is that women's ways of experiencing relationships are enriching the workplace at every level. Women, for example, are more likely to combine intuitive activities in their task. While men tend to define their experience through individualism, women prize relatedness, collaboration, and a sense of belonging. As such, women may intuitively be more adept at team building. While men are often prone toward domination, women put their energies toward nurturing and empowering—a style very much in harmony with emerging management philosophies.*

Merging Work and Family Concerns   Family life in America has felt the impact of the dramatic increase in the number of working mothers. We are seeing, however, a resurgence of interest in the health of the family unit, but it will not be accomplished by a return to the old patterns. Women's roles are being defined much more broadly, and a large percentage of children are being raised in single-parent homes.

We will see a more creative collaboration between the home and the workplace. Work-related child care facilities are a growing trend. We are likely to see parental leaves extended for both fathers and mothers. Especially with design firms, we will see flexibility of hours for those caring for both young children and elderly parents.† More professionals will negotiate part-time roles with employers. Others will take their computers and drawing boards home, and work on a piece-basis contract.

In the human resources concerns of the design firm, no one will be able to say that it is business as usual. As is the case in the larger business environment, change is the only constant. In the midst of that turbulence, however, the willing involvement of each employee, as a whole, creative, distinctive individual, will be prized as a company's most valuable asset.

---

*Carol Gilligan's book *In a Different Voice* (New York: Harper & Row, 1986) illuminates some of the distinctive approaches women take to making moral choices. Also see Mary Belenky, Blythe Clinchy, Nancy Goldberger, and Jill Tarule, *Women's Ways of Knowing* (New York: Basic Books, 1986).

†The typical woman today spends 16 years raising her children and 18 years caring for her aging parents. See Ken Dychtwald and Joe Flower, *Age Wave* (Los Angeles: Jeremy P. Tarcher, 1989), pp. 239–241.

Bibliography

1988 ASPA/CCH Survey: Managing the Aging Workforce. Chicago: Commerce Clearinghouse, 1988.

Adair, John. *Effective Teambuilding.* Great Britain: Gower Publishing Company Limited, 1986.

Birnberg, Howard G. *Finding, Keeping and Training Design Office Staff.* Chicago: Birnberg & Associates, 1988.

Blau, Judith R. *Architects and Firms: A Sociological Perspective on Architectural Practice.* Cambridge, Mass.: The MIT Press, 1984.

Broadwell, Martin M., and Ruth S. House. *Supervising Professional and Technical People.* New York: John Wiley & Sons, 1986.

Coxe, Weld, et al. *Success Strategies for Design Professionals.* New York: McGraw-Hill, 1987.

Dyer, William G. *Team Building: Issues and Alternatives,* 2d ed. Reading, Mass.: Addison-Wesley Publishing Co., 1987.

Fear, Richard A., and Robert J. Chiron. *The Evaluation Interview,* 4th ed. New York: McGraw-Hill, 1990.

Gutman, Robert. *Architectural Practice: A Critical View.* Princeton, N.J.: Princeton Architectural Press, 1988.

Haviland, David, ed. *The Firm.* Vol. 1 of *The Architect's Handbook of Professional Practice,* 8th ed. Washington, D.C.: The American Institute of Architects Press, 1988.

McReynolds, Charles M. *Human Resource Management for Design Firms.* Washington, D.C.: American Consulting Engineers Council, 1987.

Mohrman, Allan M., Jr., Susan M. Resnick-West, and Edward E. Lawler III. *Designing Performance Appraisal Systems: Aligning Appraisals and Organizational Realities.* San Francisco, Oxford: Jossey-Bass Publishers, 1989.

Parker, Glenn M. *Team Players and Teamwork: The New Competitive Business Strategy.* San Francisco, Oxford: Jossey-Bass Publishers, 1990.

Schein, Edgar H. *Organizational Culture and Leadership.* San Francisco, Washington, D.C., and London: Jossey-Bass Publishers, 1985.

Stitt, Fred A., ed. *Design Office Management Handbook.* Santa Monica, Calif.: Arts and Architecture Press, 1986.

Tracy, Diane. *The Power Pyramid: How to Get Power by Giving It Away.* New York: William Morrow and Co., Inc., 1990.

Weisbord, Marvin R. *Productive Workplaces: Organizing and Managing for Dignity, Meaning, and Community.* San Francisco and London: Jossey-Bass Publishers, 1989.

Woodward, Cynthia A. *Human Resources Management for the Design Professional.* Washington, D.C.: The American Institute of Architects Press, 1990.

Yate, Martin John. *Hiring the Best: A Manager's Guide to Effective Interviewing.* Boston: Bob Adams, Inc., 1987.

5

New Directions in Business Planning

Ralph J. Russell and Howard G. Birnberg

Future success requires a plan. Unfortunately, few design firms commit their budgets, goals, or strategies to paper. Most leave their futures to chance and as a result fail to sustain growth long-term. Without clear-cut goals you cannot monitor your progress or measure your achievements. This chapter discusses the types of planning and offers approaches to developing your plans, goals, and budgets, outlines the steps to the planning process, and includes a case study of how one firm developed its plans. It shows some strategies for institutionalizing long-range business planning.

Types and Approaches to Planning

The key to success is to have a plan to achieve it. Planning approaches will vary depending upon your goals. Long-range business planning can help you plan and conceptualize future goals and needs for programs, facilities, systems, marketing, personnel, etc. Shorter-term projects will require *operational planning* to prepare near-term targets in areas of budget, sales, equipment, supplies, etc. These are needed to support the long-range plan.

Planning for change in the long term will require *strategic planning* to look at the specific businesses, disciplines, markets, regions, and offices the firm wants to be in and how to achieve them. Short-term plans for change are *action plans* which require detailed and specific plans and programs with timetables and accountabilities in support of the strategic plans.

Contingency planning addresses how best to deal with opportunities, unexpected problems, surprises, or changes that could arise.

This chapter focuses on the long-term aspects of planning. Clearly, the other forms of planning flow from the decisions made in the long-range planning process.

Short- and long-range business planning is a common practice in most major industries. In design firms, however, there is almost a total lack of this activity. Most firms respond to situations with little or no formal planning to direct and allocate resources, provide for expansion of services and service areas, allow for smooth ownership transition, and organize many similar activities.

Long-range planning provides a framework that guides choices. There are four elements to this process (see Fig. 5.1).

1. *Strategies:* This includes the development of broad objectives for accomplishment over the next 3 to 5 years. They must be challenging enough to require significant effort, yet reasonably achievable in the timeframe of the plan. For example, the purchase of a computer or CADD system is not a goal. It's a task. The aim of becoming a highly computerized office is, however, a goal.

2. *Implementation plans:* While strategies describe a firm's broad goals, this element begins to describe how these goals will be implemented. "What" versus "how." This implementation process provides a general guideline rather than a precise game plan for accomplishing the goal outlined. For example, the goal of computerization may require the firm to first develop detailed manual systems or a training program.

3. *Initial objectives:* After broad goals and general implementation plans are outlined, priorities and short-term goals need to be established. Objectives cover detailed activities to be undertaken during 3- to 6-month periods until the goal is finally achieved. Firms typically hold regular planning meetings to review progress toward achieving initial objectives and to estab-

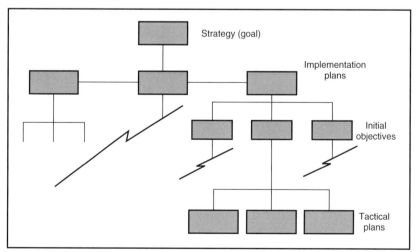

Figure 5.1 The planning process.

lish new ones as others are completed. For example, the goal of computerization may require the development of a regular staff training program. Initial objectives set priorities for this training.

4. *Tactical plans:* These are detailed implementation plans to help achieve the initial objectives and eventually the long-range goal. Tactical plans usually include budgets, detailed work assignments, and other similar items. The training program mentioned previously, for example, will require the establishment of a budget, schedule, etc.

Through this process, decisions can be made regarding organizational structure, market position, methods to improve profits, techniques to develop future managers and principals, and many other issues. A concise definition of long-range strategic planning is determining the essential thrusts and concepts and the marshaling of a firm's resources and capabilities toward achieving them.

Goal setting is the heart of the process. In developing goals, it is a wise manager who begins the process by first focusing on the points of agreement and then slowly narrowing the points of disagreement through discussion. The three basic approaches to establishing goals include:

1. *Bottom-up decision making:* This approach attempts to achieve goals by a democratic agreement of staff and management. Its objective, to achieve a consensus by committee meeting, can result in endless discussions with little actually accomplished without strong leadership and direction.

2. *Pragmatic compromise:* This approach results from a senior manager offering or imposing a set of general broad goals for lower-level managers. These managers are then asked to make proposals or perform activities to achieve these goals. Results may be based upon what lower-level managers think top management wants to hear and will accept. In many situations, this approach discourages any significant change in the firm's direction.

3. *Incremental or continual decision making:* This method involves developing specific goals by a mixture of the two previous processes. Usually, this requires a strong leader who has the support and confidence of senior and lower-level managers. General objectives are developed by a planning group. Other managers can then make proposals for implementation or perform in accordance with goals they participated in developing.

Steps in the Planning Process

There are many different approaches to developing long-range plans. Techniques will vary depending upon whether the plan is developed under the guidance and control of an outside consultant or by internal management. For example, an outside consultant might be used where objective opinions and comments are desired during staff interviews. When the planning process is led by internal management, this step might be eliminated if it is believed that objective opinions would not be given.

Some steps, however, must be completed in all planning processes.

Planning Checklist

1. Write down how you got where you are today, what factors contribute to your firm's present position (both good and bad), etc.

2. Make a fair and honest appraisal of the current strengths and weaknesses of your firm.

3. If you had the resources and opportunity, what would be your ideal firm?

4. What are your firm's most important goals?

5. Once your goals are identified, how is the firm going to implement these, where are the resources going to come from, who will be responsible for implementation, what are the timetables, and other related needs and strategies?

6. What external factors influence your firm? These influences might be the general economic climate, where government funding is available, population trends, etc.

7. What are the internal influences on your firm? These may include the lack of adequate capitalization, lack of experience, illness of a key staff member, disagreement as to the firm's goals and direction, etc.

8. Set your initial objectives. This process involves the setting of some initial objectives. These should be easily obtainable to begin the strategic plan. As these initial objectives are achieved, new objectives must be set. This process is continually repeated until the goals are met, modified, or discarded.

9. Develop a measurement and review process. After setting goals and initial objectives, a method of measuring success or failure must be developed. As an example, consider a firm that offers as a goal 25 percent growth in total revenues (after inflation) for each of the next 5 years. This firm must develop a financial reporting system that will allow it not only to measure progress toward the goal but to evaluate the reasons for success or failure in achieving the goal.

10. Communicate your goals and objectives to your staff. Without fully understanding your firm's goals and objectives and how they are to be achieved, your staff cannot fully support these efforts. Wherever possible, staff members should be involved in the long-range strategic planning process.

Case Study

Most long-range planning initiatives soon stumble. Well-meaning beginnings lead nowhere as planning has not been institutionalized in the firm. Occasionally, a design firm has been able to achieve success in long-range planning. Here's a part of how one engineering practice is beating the odds.

1. Senior management understands the need for planning and strongly supports the process.

2. An outside consultant was brought in to "kick off" the process. He was provided with extensive information in advance about the firm, its clients, and its existing plans.

3. All staff at the project manager level and above were encouraged to participate in the planning process. These individuals attended a one-day program led by the consultant.

   During the morning session, he explained the planning process and highlighted conceptual ideas on design office organization. The afternoon was devoted to breakout groups made up of individuals from various levels in the firm. Each group selected a chairperson and began the process of determining general firm goals as seen by their group. Late in the day, a joint session was held to identify goals common to all groups and to select a long-range planning committee and a chairperson. This committee included individuals from upper and middle management. (See Fig. 5.2 for a sample outline of the planning committee responsibilities.)

4. The planning committee prepared a memo outlining the general

---

HOWARD R. GREEN COMPANY PLANNING COMMITTEE

Recognizing the need for long-range planning, the management and owners of Howard R. Green Company authorized the establishment of a Planning Committee within the firm.

The primary purpose of the Planning Committee is to identify strategies and courses of action to be taken which will assist Howard R. Green Company in accomplishing its corporate mission and goals. The committee will be made up of employees of Howard R. Green Company appointed by the President and approved by the Board of Directors. It will hold regularly scheduled meetings and its work will be ongoing, providing a permanent vehicle for continuous input to the management and Board of Directors of the firm.

If the Planning Committee determines that additional study or research is needed in order to provide a recommendation, it shall notify the President and outline the general nature and extent of the desired information. The President will authorize and monitor the gathering of data, working closely with the Chairman of the Planning Committee. Recommendations from the Planning Committee will be presented to the Board of Directors through the President. The Board of Directors will consider all recommendations and act upon them in a timely manner.

Planning Committee recommendations which have been approved by the Board will be in the form of policy established by the Board of Directors. Implementation of this policy is the responsibility of the President.

Expenditure of financial and human resources needed in the planning process will be authorized by the President. The Planning Committee will establish a financial and time budget for its operations on an annual basis.

Figure 5.2 Planning committee responsibilities. (*Courtesy of Howard R. Green Company, Cedar Rapids, Iowa.*)

goals and suggested action plans. This was distributed to each member of the firm for comment.

5. The staff comments were summarized and a report was prepared by the planning committee, outlining long-range goals and suggesting specific action plans.

6. This report was submitted to the firm's board of directors for review and modification.

7. The proposed goals and suggested action plans were prioritized into several categories including:
   - Those selected for immediate action
   - Those requiring further study prior to action
   - Those on which no action will be taken in the immediate future
   - Those on which no action is intended during the life of the plan

8. This information was communicated to all staff members, and several implementation groups were established. Time schedules and budgets were set. Each of these subcommittees regularly reports back to the planning committee on its progress.

Through this process, the gradual implementation of their long-range plan is achieved. In summary, the keys to successful implementation of a plan include:

1. Interested and knowledgeable senior management.

2. Senior management's willingness to direct the process, not dictate the results.

3. Extensive staff participation and feedback. Time is made available for this participation.

4. Regular meetings, budgets, and deadlines which are set and followed.

5. A willingness to seek outside help.

Institutionalizing Long-Range Planning

Implementing your business plan is the most difficult part of the long-range planning process. Many firms undertake planning with the best of intentions only to fail to follow through on their plans. In some cases, the plan was unrealistic. In other situations, adequate resources or staff are lacking. For many firms, the necessary discipline is missing.

Firms that are successful in implementing their business plans are able to build a constituency to support the program. This support comes through staff involvement and by use of cost-effective outside resources such as an external board of directors. Your staff must be given implementation responsibilities and have their efforts guided through the setting of schedules, budgets, and deadlines. Their efforts must be monitored and encouraged by senior management. They must also participate in update and feedback processes perhaps by involvement in company retreats by key employees and managers.

How Outside Directors Can Help

The vast majority of architectural and engineering firms have nine employees or less. With so few staff some important activities tend to be ignored. Since project work often takes precedence, areas such as long-term planning, financial planning, community relations, and employee development tend to be less than top priorities. Obviously, it is important to focus some effort on these activities.

For many firms, the solution is to utilize an outside board of directors. At very little cost, outside directors can bring skills and perspectives which are not otherwise present in a firm. Depending on the individuals selected, skills can cover long-range planning, mergers and acquisitions, budgeting, data processing, personnel compensation and development, equipment financing, bookkeeping, retirement planning, and providing political contacts. Do not select outside directors for their knowledge of your business. It is better to determine those areas of expertise missing in your practice and select directors for their knowledge of *their* businesses.

Three professions are particularly attractive when seeking outside directors. First is banking. Informally interview your banking candidate before you mention a seat on your board. Also consider using someone other than your own banker if there are concerns about your financial strength. Don't hinder your chances of getting a loan by having your banker too informed. It also puts your lender in a conflict of interest situation if there are financial problems later.

Next is the legal profession. Look for an attorney who is both competent and practical. You want someone with good common sense and practical business experience. Most attorneys may make good legal advisers but are lousy business advisers. If your first choice is your firm's corporate counsel, then expect to pay for time spent attending your board meetings. Other outside attorneys may only require a good meal and a thank you.

Third are accountants. Look for a knowledgeable, but practical accountant. If your accountant sits on your board, he or she cannot then conduct an independent audit. However, other accountants can help in planning, budgeting, forecasting, bookkeeping systems, and other related areas and should be considered for your board of directors.

You may also wish to name some independent business people to your board. These individuals might include a developer, consultant, or a small business owner with some "real world" experience, good contacts, or specialized knowledge.

Once you have selected these valuable resources, you must keep them informed on a regular basis. Let them review your long-range growth plan. Send them your monthly financial statements, quarterly status reports, and other information on the trends in architectural and engineering practice. Occasional telephone calls and quarterly meetings are probably sufficient for a firm that is doing well. An annual dinner with spouses might also be advantageous.

If you expect outside directors to take a serious interest in your firm, they need to feel close to your practice. If possible, do this through personal contact and regular lunches or dinners. Otherwise, consider some cash payment to your directors. A fixed director's fee for meetings is a nice benefit but does not provide them with much incentive to do their best thinking. A fee scaled to the profitability of your firm will certainly provide more incentive.

The initial selection process of directors is critical. The information flow is vital and the care and/or compensation of your directors determines their long-term contribution to the success of your firm.

Retreats

Many design firms organize and conduct weekend retreats for owners and senior managers. Their purpose is to review the past year's performance and make plans for the coming year. A well-conceived retreat can provide a valuable, distraction-free atmosphere. Successful retreats revolve around business sessions and not recreation or other activities. Resort locations should generally be avoided to minimize distractions. As a result, spouses and families should not be invited to attend, as the purpose of the retreat is business, not social.

To make the retreat more effective, consider the use of an outsider (consultant, accountant, etc.) as a controller and expediter. This individual's function is to act as a moderator to keep the session moving and not allow personalities or office politics to obstruct progress. The outsider should be familiar with the firm and also bring to the retreat specialized knowledge on the subjects to be discussed. For a retreat with more than five individuals, it may be advantageous to establish task groups to address certain issues. This will permit faster results than discussions held in larger groups.

As with any effective meeting, it is important to have a chairperson who is also responsible for the advance preparation of an agenda. It is essential that those attending the retreat come prepared. In addition, to be most effective, retreats should be held at least yearly to maintain continuity.

Retreats are an opportunity to work as a team in the development of common goals and strategies. Unfortunately, in some firms, the retreat is used by a senior manager(s) to present the accomplished fact of a plan and goals. Others are invited or required to attend only for the purpose of providing a perfunctory approval and commitment. To be a useful planning and management device, the retreat must involve the combined efforts of all principals and key managers.

The retreat must end with a clear strategy to be followed and should develop activity assignments that include deadlines and implementation plans. Retreats are intended as planning opportunities and should not be confused with an annual meeting. Properly used, the retreat is a valuable management and planning tool.

Resources

Books and Manuals

Ballast, David Kent. *The Architect's Handbook.* Englewood Cliffs, N.J., Prentice-Hall, 1984.
Birnberg, Howard. *Small Design Firm Marketing Manual.* Chicago, Ill., Birnberg & Associates, 1983.

Birnberg, Howard. *Financial Management for Small Design Firms*. Chicago, Ill., Birnberg & Associates, 1985.

Birnberg, Howard. *Project Management for Small Design Firms*. Chicago, Ill., Birnberg & Associates, 1992.

Birnberg, Howard. *Financial Performance Survey for Architectural and Engineering Firms*. Chicago, Ill., Birnberg & Associates, latest edition.

Burstein, David M., and Frank A. Stasiowski. *Project Management for the Design Professional*. New York, Watson/Guptill, 1982.

Class, Robert A., and Robert E. Koehler. *Current Techniques in Architectural Practice*. Washington, D.C., The American Institute of Architects, 1976.

Drucker, Peter F. *Management—Tasks, Responsibilities, Practices*. New York, Harper & Row, 1974.

Haviland, David. *Managing Architectural Projects: The Process*. Washington, D.C., The American Institute of Architects, 1981.

Haviland, David. *Managing Architectural Projects: The Effective Project Manager*. Washington, D.C., The American Institute of Architects, 1981.

Haviland, David. *Managing Architectural Projects: The Project Management Manual*. Washington, D.C., The American Institute of Architects, 1984.

Jones, Reginald L., and H. George Trentin. *Management Controls for Professional Firms*. New York, The American Management Association, 1968.

Stitt, Fred. *The Guidelines Systems Management Manual Series*. (5 vols.) Orinda, Calif., 1982–1983.

Articles

Maister, David H. "Balancing the Professional Services Firm," *Sloan Management Review*, Fall 1982, pp. 15–27.

Quinn, James B. "Strategic Goals: Process and Politics," *The McKinsey Quarterly*, Winter 1979, pp. 35–53.

Sease, Douglas R. "Entrepreneurship 101," *The Wall Street Journal*, May 15, 1987, p. 32D.

Thompson, Roger. "Business Plans: Myth and Reality," *Nation's Business*, August 1988, pp. 16–23.

Tregoe, Benjamin B., and John W. Zimmerman. "Strategic Thinking: Key to Corporate Survival," *Management Review*, pp. 9–14.

Other Resources

The Guidelines Letter, Guidelines Publications, P.O. Box 456, Orinda, Calif. 94563. (415) 254-0639.

The Profit Center (newsletter), Birnberg & Associates, 1227 West Wrightwood Avenue, Chicago, Ill. 60614. (312) 664-2300.

6

Information Management

Susan Greenwald

Goals of Information Management

Design firms increasingly are required to collect and assimilate vast amounts of project, business, technical, and other information. The ability to store and retrieve documents and to use information efficiently is vital to a firm's success. Inadequate information management allows islands of ignorance to exist within the firm, even when the needed information is theoretically near to hand.

The goals of information management are to be able to confirm whether needed information exists, to facilitate access to information, and to control access to information that is legitimately restricted to certain users.

Means of Information Management

"Information management" has become a buzzword that is not always clearly understood. Information, except that which is conveyed directly by speech, is carried by documents; thus, fundamental principles of records management underlie all efforts to improve access to information. The field of records management is well established, and much can be learned from it. Records management includes physical conservation of records, document retention scheduling, filing, document storage (paper, microfilm, and electronic media), document retrieval, disposal, and disaster recovery planning.

Information management goes beyond records management by addressing the broader issue of what information is needed, including but also beyond that contained in business records. An information management approach includes the office library in its purview, and consolidates access to information regardless of the medium that carries it. Information management, in a design firm, seeks to improve access to all of the following:

- Documents created by the firm and its work:

  Project records—current and archived

  Business files—personnel, marketing, legal, insurance, financial

  Professional files—for activities in professional and community associations, lectures, publications, and similar activity files

- Documents used by the firm in producing its work:

  The office library

Product literature	Codes and standards
Association literature	Directories
Dictionaries and thesauri	Books
Periodicals	Slides
Photographs	Samples
Videotapes	Audiotapes
Software	CD-ROM disks
Microfilm/fiche	Telephone and business card files

  Outside information sources

Each of the above document types may be managed in a different way and may be under the control of a different person or people. The goal of information management, as stated earlier, is to organize access to the information in all of the above documents and media so that whoever needs the information can find it quickly.

Costs and Benefits of Information Management

Most firms have at least some sort of an ad hoc system for managing the various types of documents generated and used in their practices. Project files are usually assigned a project number, and documents may be grouped within the project file by document type, such as transmittals or meeting notes. The office library typically groups codes together and files product literature by the Construction Specifications Institute 16-Division MASTERFORMAT or some variant of it.

Nearly everyone, however, finds at times that the information needed is not at hand. For all the talk of the paperless office, to date the computer has generated more paper than it has replaced. In addition, computer files themselves may be lost. Tools are now becoming readily available that will actually help in the management of the morass of information that computers have created.

Such management tools can be measured in strict cost-benefit terms by analyzing the time and expense of implementing and maintaining them versus the time saved by their use. However, as we have all found with other aspects of computerization, the main advantage of many of these systems is in the ability to do things that were virtually impossible before.

The cost of effective information management also must be considered against the cost of poor information management. Failure to find and successfully use information can lead to inappropriate technical decisions that result in construction problems and legal headaches. Legal headaches can also occur when technical decisions have been properly made but have not been documented.

Emerging Technology

Technologies are available to provide a smart workstation that gives access to extensive informational databases, in addition to the computer-aided design and drafting and specifications software already widely used. The design professional soon will be able to sit down and draw a project, incorporate specifications requirements, and ask for and receive technical information, all without leaving the workstation (other than for much-needed breaks!). This section reviews the technologies that are making this possible.

Scanning and Microfilm

While cost-benefit studies still show microfilm to be less expensive than scanning, as costs of scanning and optical storage decrease, the use of scanning will dramatically increase. Scanning systems finally offer the paperless office so long promised. At their most sophisticated, they can be programmed to recognize images and text and to prepare them for manipulation by other programs such as search programs, word processing, and CADD.

Optical character recognition (OCR) and electronic image management (EIM) coupled with character recognition are creating the capacity to scan an image and to convert it to usable information that can be searched, edited, and otherwise manipulated. Images require vastly greater storage space than text; thus, in current systems for small business, images are converted to text by use of OCR or are vectorized for use as CADD drawings.*

With the advent of larger storage devices, storage of images will become increasingly feasible. Images are typically stored in compressed form, using standards called CCITT Group 3 and Group 4; however, images stored by products of various vendors may still not be compatible.

There are trade-offs between storage requirements, frequency of use, and need for information versus need for a true facsimile of the document. Because of these trade-offs, microfilm storage with a computer index or with fully computerized image retrieval is a reasonable interim technology for many firms.

Just as many small firms are skipping straight to fairly advanced use of CADD as the cost becomes reasonable and the software more powerful, many firms that currently file all images in paper only will

---

*Marc D'Alleyrand (1989) presents a useful discussion of the relative computer storage space requirements for index entries only (X), with abstracts (10X), full text (100X), compressed image (4000X), and uncompressed high-quality image (100,000X).

skip to scanning and optical storage as the costs come down and the storage parameters and media stabilize.

Optical Storage Media

CD-ROM is an acronym for compact disk-read-only-memory. CD-ROM, because of its use for SweetSearch™ and SpecSystem™ as well as for NIBS Construction Criteria Base (CCB), has already become familiar to many practitioners and is estimated to be in use in 10% of U.S. architecture and engineering offices. The 5¼-inch CD-ROM format provides approximately 540 Mbytes of permanent, unchangeable storage. CD-ROM is primarily suitable for computer publishing because it is a read-only format. Producing a CD-ROM product requires first producing a master and then making multiple copies from the master. CD-ROM drives are also available in large formats that hold proportionately more information.

WORM drives (Write Once Read Many) have been available for several years and are gaining some acceptance as a medium for archiving data. The WORM drive uses large (940-Mbyte) removable cartridges. Because WORM drives permanently burn the data onto the cartridge and cannot be written over, they are better as legal evidence than floppy disks and other modifiable media, though there is still debate about the extent of their acceptability. Fears have also been expressed that the WORM drive technology may continue to advance, leaving no means of reading cartridges produced with current drives. Thus, for long-term archival storage, the conservative approach is to keep paper or microfilm copies. WORM drives provide vast storage for records that do not require modification.

Rewritable optical drives (sometimes called WMRM) have also recently become available. Their format and capacity is similar to that of a WORM drive, except that they can be modified, just like a floppy disk or hard disk drive. Rewritable optical drives are slower than most hard disk drives, are relatively expensive, and are not yet widely available; however, this is an exciting technology that is likely to be widely used as costs and availability improve.

Search and Retrieval Software

A number of inexpensive programs are now available that will search a hard disk drive for words and combinations of words;* some of these will search for text appearing in word processing, spreadsheet, and database files. Word processing programs are also beginning to include more sophisticated file search capabilities. Other programs† facilitate links between in-house database programs and search requirements so that nonprogrammers can develop reports.

One limitation of free text search techniques is that language is imprecise. A search for "volatile organic compounds" will not find references to "VOCs." Thus, a more controlled vocabulary is helpful in

---

*See the following: "Two for Text-Based Database Search" (Carroll, 1989*b*), "ZyIndex Finds Text Fast" (Weatherby, 1989), and "Navigating Your Disk Files" (Carroll, 1989*a*).

†Such as Friendly Finder, Proximity Technology, Inc., and Popdbf, Bouven Software.

improving the accuracy of computer searches. A thesaurus is built into some search programs to direct the user to related terms. It is theoretically possible to program the computer to recognize equivalent terms automatically; however, most systems currently marketed ask the searcher to select which terms from a list of similar terms should be included in the search.

Trends to look for in search and retrieval software include:

Ability to search over wider terrain (more than one disk drive)

Linkage to a controlled terminology database

Ability to find and view documents created with different programs, including graphics programs

Hypermedia applications that create links between related subjects, for example, allowing the searcher to go directly from a specification that mentions a certain standard to a computer copy of the standard itself

Technical Databases

A number of databases utilizing search and retrieval capabilities are currently available for the construction industry. Following is a summary of major systems currently available:

Sweet's Division of McGraw-Hill has published a CD-ROM disk called Electronic Sweet's containing SweetSearch, an automated index to Sweet's Catalog Files.

The Construction Specifications Institute publishes Spec Data and Manu Spec on floppy disks for loading onto a computer hard disk drive. The system comes with a simple program that allows the user to search by product, manufacturer, or MASTERFORMAT number. Spec Data is product data, arranged in a uniform format. Manu Specs are manufacturers' proprietary specifications. Both can be downloaded to disk as text files or directed to the printer. While these require approximately 8 Mbytes of space on a hard disk drive, they are inexpensive and very useful.

The National Institute of Building Science publishes the Construction Criteria Base (CCB) on CD-ROM. The CCB contains military and NASA specifications, federal specifications, military construction criteria, and similar supporting data.

The Construction Specifications Institute is working on an advanced database, CONI, published on CD-ROM beginning in 1990. The first edition contains information relating to Divisions 15 and 16. CONI will contain master specifications, product data, code information, and standards, in a single package.

A number of product manufacturers have also come out with CADD specifications, and other "electronic catalog" offerings. It is likely electronic catalogs will be consolidated by a publisher that will offer them to architects and engineers with a common interface to facilitate use. Eventually, even jazzy color graphics will be replicable on computer or video monitors in the typical office. Eclat offers an example of the potential power of such applications.

Communications

Fax machines have become nearly universal and may lead designers to computer communications, as computer fax boards proliferate. Large firms are using electronic mail (E-mail) systems, of which the computer fax board is a logical counterpart. These devices have enormously enhanced our ability to obtain information quickly but may also inundate us with queries requiring responses. Voice recognition software is advancing rapidly and may soon vastly increase ties between telephone and computer.

On-line searching is common in medicine and law but has seldom been used by architects and engineers. A number of databases are available on-line, including ICONDA, the Avery Index, Compendex, Architectural Periodicals Index, and the Art Index. ArchiText's Construction Index will be providing data to ICONDA, which is on-line internationally. Several of these databases are also available on CD-ROM.

Computer bulletin boards, which allow users to communicate by modem and to leave notes for each other, are well established in the computer field and are a good source for shareware, vendor information, and exchange of information. The AIA initiated a bulletin board for architects, which was unsuccessful, despite its promise as a central source of information and communications for architects. Was it just ahead of its time? Bulletin boards, if widely used, have great potential. Just as television's America's Most Wanted has brought in a number of criminals, so the bulletin board is a way to find information that you need and that someone, somewhere already knows and is happy to share. A critical mass of users is needed, however, for the system to be useful. Perhaps a system could be developed where users would agree to "meet" electronically once a week.

Applications
for Information Management

Managing Project Information

It is not uncommon, and is perhaps even the rule, for the project manager's desktop to be the principal project filing system (the pile file method), supplemented by hanging files and notebooks used for storage of inactive material. Many project managers are buried in paperwork, and a great deal of time is wasted looking for sheets of paper.

While time management experts have long recommended that nothing should be on your desk except what you are using at any given moment, even the most organized professionals find this to be a difficult, if not impossible, goal to achieve. One of the brightest prospects of computerization is the promise of improved handling of such pile files. This is happening in several ways.

- It is already feasible, and will become more so, to scan each item of project correspondence into the project computer subdirectory and to translate it using OCR software. The user can then find issues discussed in meeting notes or correspondence using simple search programs.

- A second likelihood is increased use of computer fax boards, again combined with OCR software to produce searchable correspondence and note files.

- Also becoming available are integrated communications packages that include telephone autodialers, computer fax, and modem support in a single board + software package. These will permit management of information coming to the office by phone, fax, or modem and will facilitate keeping records of phone contacts.

An additional benefit of such systems will be that, for the first time, project information, except that which may be password protected, will be available to the entire project team. The project manager will not have to devote as much energy to answering questions about what decisions have been made.

Computer tools can also assist in tracking project decisions made within the project team. With an ideally organized decision tracking system, anyone in the firm would be able to determine what decision was made and why for each of the thousands of decisions that go into designing even a simple project. The principal advantage of being able to reconstruct the decision process easily is that often a lot of thought goes into the original decision. When the owner or contractor requests a change, it is often difficult to remember all of the considerations that went into the original decision. Often, the individuals who made the original decisions are no longer with the firm, necessitating a complete reanalysis.

The open information flow fostered by these tools can provide better service to the client. Although not every team member may be qualified to make decisions, any team member would be able to provide information to the owner or contractor about decisions already made.

No discussion of managing project files would be complete without a review of the process of managing drawings and submittals. As these are increasingly digitized or scanned, or originate as computer files, drawing and submittal management will benefit from the searchability of the files. Improved links between drawings and specifications, such as the keynoting system proposed by ConDoc, will greatly facilitate information retrieval. Integration of graphics with other computer applications will also improve these links, and eventually the contract documents as we know them will be superseded by a multidimensional database that includes graphic, numeric, and verbal information.

Project record archives will likely remain as paper or microfilm records for some time, primarily because of legal considerations. Normal computer files, which are subject to change, are not accepted as legal evidence. A possible exception to this may be the WORM drive, though its use is not currently widespread.

Managing Business Information

Internal business management, especially financial management, has already benefited from the use of databases and spreadsheets. Programs vastly superior to manual bookkeeping are widely available at low cost. Even using a simple checkbook program, you can track checks in multiple accounts by check number, payee, date, and other information, can keep track of payroll taxes due, can balance accounts, and can sort and report by chart of accounts categories. Imagine having similar access to information in project files or in library materials!

Advances in computer tools will likely appear in the field of business administration before appearing in the more specialized fields of project management and library management. Thus, the capabilities of business programs can be used as a benchmark for measuring automation of other areas.

Managing the Office Library

This chapter uses the term "library" in its broadest sense, to mean those resources available within the firm that provide supporting information for decision making. The library thus includes, in addition to books, periodicals, and catalogs, such information resources as consultant and contractor lists or directories, and business card files.

Increasingly, managing the library will involve

- Managing a variety of physical formats. In addition to the bulky samples and drawings that architects and engineers have always managed, offices will now also need to manage photographs, videotapes, audio tapes, CD-ROM disks, and other computer files.

- Using cataloging systems. The CSI MASTERFORMAT has been the most widely used method of organizing product literature within the office. However, there has been no system for organizing other information, such as information on drawing techniques, building types, or design and performance issues such as acoustics or design for the elderly.

- Keeping up with new information resources. Journals, periodicals indexes, publications lists, bulletin boards, and directories of associations are all sources to access.

Managing External Information Sources

The Rolodex™ and business card file are still probably the single most valuable means of linking with external information sources. Computerizing the information in these files has numerous advantages:

- Link to auto-dialing
- Facilitate sharing resources within the office (if computers are linked)
- Information can be found based on what you know (for example, you may remember the company name, but not the name of the representative, or you may want to see whether any association is listed under Masonry)

A simple card file database allows the user to search for all wood window manufacturers, all carpentry contractors, and similar data. Enhanced, such a file can keep track of the user's experience with that firm, list catalogs on file, or make note of information provided by manufacturers' representatives over the phone. Shared on a network, it can provide information to everyone in the firm. Information can be added about what projects have used a certain manufacturer or contractor, and the success of the projects can then inform the decision of whether to work with the same companies again.

Increasingly available are on-line databases and bulletin boards. Frequently updated information, such as *Commerce Business Daily*, can be accessed as needed, rather than on a subscription basis.

Promises and Pitfalls

Access to information requires organization of the documents that contain information, as well as development of tools for access. This is equally true in a computerized or noncomputerized environment. Access to information within the office will be vastly improved by sound document management practices, including establishment of

- Criteria for selecting library acquisitions. This includes budgeting, and determining who within the firm will have authority to make selections and how staff suggestions for acquisitions will be gathered and assessed.

- Procedures for updating library holdings. Will codes and standards be replaced whenever a new edition is released? How will the firm keep track of what is out of date? Will new acquisitions be dated when they are filed?

- Cataloging and filing standards. Will project files be organized in a standard way? What system will be used for organizing the office library? How will the variety of media be accommodated? Will there be a computerized catalog for both computer and noncomputer documents?

- A backup and disaster recovery plan. If there is a fire, power outage, or other disaster, how will needed information be recovered?

- Document retention and disposal schedule. Does the firm know what retention periods are recommended by its legal counsel for various document types, such as employee records, financial data, and project records? Does the firm have an organized approach to disposal of unneeded and outdated information (remember, this includes computer files, as well as paper files and library holdings)?

- Document confidentiality policy. Does the firm have a policy about whether all information within the firm is available for any employee to review? Are there adequate security provisions for confidential information? What about disclosure to outside parties? Does the firm have any trade secrets?

- Education of staff about available resources. Are new employees introduced to the resources of the firm? How do staff learn what is in the library? Are there lots of things that are "at Joe's desk" or "on Sandy's Rolodex"? If so, people who've been with the firm several years may know where to find them, but newcomers will not. Cataloging "Joe's desk" and "Sandy's Rolodex" might not be a bad idea.

- Education of staff about where to put things. Once a system has been established, it is likely that a number of people will be involved in filing information, including both computerized and noncomputerized information. Does everyone know where to file things and how to categorize them so that others can also find them?

Computerization will permit your office to remain a series of individual messy desks or to combine the resources of everyone in your office. It will enable you to reach outside as well, and to provide the information needed to make architectural decisions intelligently.

Resources

Bibliography

Anderson, Laurie, ed., "Practice: Information Resources," *AIA Memo,* April 1990. pp. 5–6.

Architectural Periodicals Index, British Architectural Library, London, updated monthly (available on Dialog).

Art Index, H. W. Wilson Co., New York, updated biweekly (available on Wilson line).

Automated Product Information for Architecture, Engineering and Construction, Eclat, Inc., Pleasonton, Cal., updated quarterly.

Avery Index to Architectural Periodicals, Avery Library, Columbia Univ., New York, updated daily (available on RLIN and Dialog).

Ballast, David Kent, *Creative Records Management: A Guidebook for Architects, Engineers and Interior Designers,* Practice Management Associates, Ltd., Newton, Mass., 1987.

Carroll, Charles R., Jr., "Navigating Your Disk Files," *Construction Specifier,* May 1989*a.*

Carroll, Charles R., Jr., "Two for Text-Based Database Search," *Construction Specifier,* August 1989*b,* p. 30.

Compendix, Engineering Information, Inc., New York. (This is the on-line version of *Engineering Index.)*

CONI, Construction Specifications Institute, Alexandria (projected), 1990.

Construction Criteria Base, National Institute of Building Science (NIBS), Washington, D.C., updated quarterly.

Construction Index, ArchiText, Chicago, quarterly with annual compilations.

D'Alleyrand, Marc R., *Image Storage and Retrieval Systems,* McGraw-Hill, New York, 1989.

Electronic Sweet's, Sweet's/McGraw-Hill, Inc., New York, published semiannually.

Guzay, Duke, and James Freehof, ConDoc, A Professional Development Program of the American Institute of Architects, Washington, D.C. (unpublished).

ICONDA, ICONDA Agency, c/o Information Centre for Regional Planning and Building Construction (IRB) of the Fraunhofer Society, Stuttgart, Germany, updated monthly. (Available on CD-ROM by Silver Platter, on-line through Orbit and STN International.)

Spec Data and Manu Spec on Disk, Construction Specifications Institute, Alexandria, updated semiannually.

Weatherby, Richard T., "ZyIndex Finds Text Fast," *Construction Specifier,* May 1989, p. 47.

Associations

Association of Records Managers and Administrators, 4200 Somerset Drive, Suite 215, Prairie Village, Kans. 66208, (800) 422-2762.

Association of Information and Image Management, 1100 Wayne Ave., Suite 1100, Silver Spring, Md. 20910, (301) 587-8202.

The Institute of Records Management, 4415 West Harrison St., Suite 200-C, Hillside, Ill. 60162.

7

Marketing Tools and Devices

Rebecca M. Renfro

Marketing tools are the written and visual expression of your firm. They communicate capabilities, strengths, and resources. The majority of these tools are common to most firms. So how do you set yourself apart from the competition?

Creativity achieves the greatest impact. Resist the temptation to do things the way they've always been done before. Step back and take an honest look at your organization. How are you different from your competition? What strengths do you play up? What weaknesses—real or perceived—need to be addressed? Then, brainstorm alternative ways to communicate your message. How can you do it better than it has ever been done before? What mechanism will grab the readers' attention and position your firm prominently in their minds?

Overall Approach

Many firms fall into the "we need a brochure" delusion. They mistakenly believe that a brochure will solve all their marketing problems. So without further thought or discussion, they rush out and produce a brochure. For the record, a brochure does not bring in work.

It's best to define the problem before determining the solution. Why do you think you need a brochure? Are principals reluctant to go out and make calls without something to hand a prospect? Would they more readily leave the seclusion of their office if they had a 12-page, four-color brochure in hand? Is that the only resolution? What about video, or a four-part direct mail program to hit home a strong message? Perhaps staff members are new to the marketing process. Would they benefit from educational programs or training seminars?

Instead of starting with the end product, follow a process which will ensure the solution (or marketing tool) addresses your specific needs. Be sure to involve the appropriate people from the start—decision maker, marketing person, graphic designer—or hire a marketing consultant to manage this process for you.

- Define the problem.
- Identify the audience.
- Determine the message.
- Brainstorm and concept the vehicle.
- Implement the program.

Define the Problem

What do you want to accomplish? For example, the firm has a new service which it needs to communicate to past, present, and prospective clients. If your definition is simply, "we need a brochure because everyone else has one," stop and rethink your goals.

Identify the Audience

Actually, go a step beyond identifying the audience. Describe them. Are they top-level corporate executives? Middle managers? Governmental entities? Detail-oriented or big picture people? What will speak loud and clear to them? Is "slick" appropriate or risky?

Determine the Message

If the focus is your new service, uncover what you do differently rather than rely on worn phrases and descriptions. Create a distinction in the client's eye. Define the buyer benefits.

Brainstorm and Concept the Vehicle

Let those creative juices flow. In brainstorming, ideas may seem off the wall. That's okay, they often trigger other ideas. The intent is not to say, "We want a brochure." It is to say, "What is the best way to achieve the desired reaction?" Is it a direct mail piece? A poster? A puzzle? What is your angle to achieve distinction? Do you really want to produce a brochure that looks just like everyone else's brochure? Your angle might be humor, stunning graphics, or an unusual device—gimmick sounds a little commercial—but remember, you're seeking attention.

Implementation

After you hit upon the right concept, you're ready to implement the program. Let's examine the various steps in this phase of the process.

Budget If you haven't been working with a budget until this point, now is the time to price your concept. You may have a couple of ideas which will vary significantly in cost, so price them both. A graphic designer or marketing consultant should be able to tell you if the concept is within your budget. Secure cost estimates or bids from all required sources—graphic designer, photographer, copy writer, printer, mail service (if you won't be coordinating in-house), etc. Once you have the total cost, calculate unit cost. If the cost comes in over budget, be prepared to make adjustments or sell the added cost in view of added value the piece is expected to produce.

Schedule   The process from concept to completion will take longer than you think. But it takes forever without a schedule. Establish a realistic timetable based on input from the various people involved; then solicit everyone's cooperation in meeting deadlines. Allow an extra day or two at critical points. Murphy's law often prevails, so give yourself a little leeway.

Design   The fact that you are an architect or engineer and design great buildings or systems *doesn't mean you will design a great marketing piece!* Put this assignment in the hands of a capable graphic designer skilled in designing pieces similar in character to what you're trying to achieve. Benefit from their knowledge, experience, and lessons learned. Make sure you give them clear guidelines and expectations, but it should be a creative collaborative.

Writing and Editing   If you do not have someone with strong writing skills on staff, hire a professional. A technical person may know the subject matter thoroughly but cannot communicate succinctly and with impact. If the message is unclear, rambles, or is laden with technical jargon (inappropriate to the audience), you've lost the reader and wasted an opportunity. It is far better to err on the side of brevity.

Photography   The best advice is to use specialists on every aspect of the project. (*Wonderful argument, where have you heard it before?*) Many a brochure or newsletter has suffered the fallacy that photography doesn't matter—let the architect or engineer take a couple of snapshots at the site. Record photography has its place, but it's not usually appropriate in marketing materials. You're investing money in whatever piece you're producing. Get the most impact for your expenditure. If you can't afford professional photography, consider another source or a different concept.

Printing   Often the graphic designer or marketing consultant will coordinate printing. They are familiar with a variety of printers and can best match the job to the level of skill and sophistication required. Let the printer work for you. They are accustomed to following instructions. But take the time to review the mock-up with them and ask for feedback. *Remember the specialist.* Draw upon their wealth of experience. They may offer an alternative method of printing to better achieve your objective or suggest a comparable but less expensive paper stock (ask for printed samples of suggested alternatives). Ask the printer to price two or three different quantities (1000, 2500, and 5000). You don't need to have copies for years to come, but don't make the mistake of ordering too few. The cost of additional paper and ink is minimal compared with reprinting.

Mailing   You haven't gone through the thrill and agony of it all to let your creative venture sit in a closet. Make sure distribution is equally well planned. Is your mailing list up to date—names and addresses? Material is mailed to people, not companies. You may decide to send to a separate targeted audience—the top 100 fastest-growing companies, or corporate facilities managers within a certain geographic area. This research should start during the initial concept stage of your piece. Leave sufficient time to determine availability, quantity, and cost of securing the data or mailing labels.

This organized approach—*define the problem, identify the audience, determine the message, brainstorm and concept the vehicle, and implementation*—should be applied to whatever marketing tool you are considering or evaluating. The following section explores various marketing tools.

Qualification Materials

Many firms neglect the critical elements that form the basis for daily marketing activity—information on their people and projects. No marketing effort can be sustained without a good set of qualification materials—firm profile, résumés, project lists, project descriptions, and references. Evaluate and compare your materials with those of other firms. If you find them uninviting, difficult to read, or boring, an impartial client will most certainly agree. Remember, the challenge is to set yourself apart. This is true for basic materials as well as brochures and newsletters, and even more challenging because all firms' qualification materials contain the same basic pieces of information.

Format is important. Establish standards which are graphically appealing and easy to read. Narrow margins with long lines of text are not visually inviting. Break up the monotony, provide a narrow column for headers with a shorter text column. Pull key phrases out as a highlight in bold type. Insert an occasional graph or diagram to illustrate a point. Use bullets or listings rather than narrative description. Standards provide overall continuity and consistency. As with most copy, the key is "brief is better."

Firm Profile   This is a one-page synopsis of who you are and what you do. Rather than rambling prose about your glorious attributes, use statistics to make strong points about experience and qualifications. Specifics have more impact than generalities. Make a statement; then support it with facts or examples.

> We have in-depth experience in a broad range of projects including office buildings, retail centers, healthcare facilities, and hotels. The firm has completed:
>
> - 5,000,000 square feet of office buildings
> - 3,500,000 square feet of retail space
> - More than 500 hospitals and healthcare facilities

Review qualification materials with a "new eye" as though you had no knowledge of the firm. What is your perception after reading the information? What would you like to know that was not discussed? Do you have a clear picture of the services provided? How are they different from other firms? An honest appraisal, please. You might be surprised at what you've overlooked!

Résumés A résumé is a record of an individual's personal experience and should include projects from current and previous employment. You may insert a short paragraph stating the person's function and responsibilities, but use a list to highlight project experience for quick and easy reference. Project location and scope add substance. Education, registration, professional affiliations, and honors and awards are standard elements. Omit date of birth and personal data unless pertinent to the submittal.

Project Lists Project lists establish depth of experience and are meant to be scanned. Group projects by type—banks, educational buildings, laboratories, recreational facilities, etc. Project name, location, scope, construction cost, and year of completion are standard components. You may choose not to list construction cost, but if you do give dollar amounts always include a completion date as a reference point.

Project Descriptions A description expands upon the services provided for a particular project and highlights its problem and solution approach. In addition to project name and location, list the owner or client, square footage, number of floors (or corresponding unit such as beds, rooms, and parking spaces), construction cost, and year of completion. Keep the narrative portion interesting and informative—what problems did you solve, how did you save the client money, or fast-track the schedule.

Visuals can break the routine of text-only material. Photography adds valuable impact and graphic appeal. A diagram or illustration would be welcome relief to the reader. We're fortunate to have options today that were not available (or feasible) even a few years ago. Color photocopying has improved greatly and is acceptable in most cases. In a market where photography is judged critically, such as interiors, stick to photographs or color-process printing. Photolabels,* photographs produced on a self-sticking label, are a cost-effective alternative (see Fig. 7.1) and are available in sizes from 2¼ by 1½ inches to 4¾ by 3⁄₁₆ inches for less than $25 for an order of 25. Prices are lower for remakes or larger quantities.

References Don't list a reference without first checking the nature of their comments and their willingness to provide a reference. Develop standard reference lists by project type for quick response. Just because someone gave you a good reference six months ago, don't assume they will give a good reference today. Check and double-check.

---

*Photolabels are available through Photolabels, 333 Kimberly Drive, Carol Stream, Ill. 60188 (708-690-0132; fax: 708-690-0140).

THE MENIL COLLECTION

The Menil Foundation
Piano & Fitzgerald
Three-level museum
- 100,000 GSF
- ductile iron, ferrocement and structural steel system

Houston, Texas
Completion 1986

DESCRIPTION

Designed to house and showcase the private art collection of Dominique de Menil, the Menil Collection is located on two city blocks of a residential neighborhood. The functional program dictated a secure but accessible home for over 10,000 pieces of art, which would include areas for storage and curatorial maintenance, scholastic resources and exhibition spaces lighted by natural light during the day. The owner desired a building which would blend with the neighborhood and showcase, not overshadow, the art collection.

The resulting design is from the "inside out," -- a structural system which is an integral part of the architecture. A system of exposed trusses was created to support the glass roof, filter natural light and house mechanical duct work and electrical wiring. A series of "leaf trusses," composed of a ferrocement shell and interconnected cast ductile iron elements, is supported by main girder trusses. This unique structural system required special structural analytical techniques, new materials research and testing, fire resistance analysis, corrosion research and full-scale load tests.

Figure 7.1   Haynes Whaley Associates, Inc., project description with PhotoLabel.

Boilerplate   In addition to a firm profile, résumés, and project descriptions, off-the-shelf material about the firm is prepared for use in proposals or statements of qualification. This information responds to clients' most often asked questions—design philosophy, cost control, awards, CADD capabilities, or track record on schedule control. Your next request for proposal may ask for different information. Once you've researched and collected specific project data such as number of change orders, original vs. actual budget, and planned vs. actual schedule, be sure to record it in your project database or keep it handy for future reference. Chances are, you'll see the request again.

Maintenance   One of the greatest challenges will be keeping your materials up to date. Think through the process of data collection and develop a manual or computerized maintenance system which works for your firm. There are many database programs on the market. But even those require established procedures for determining what information will be collected, its source, and frequency of update. This assignment is usually best handled by one person, with a penchant for accuracy and consistency.

Packaging   Sending out an envelope full of loose pages is not appealing or functional. How do all the pieces fit together? A pocket folder works well for a small package (less than 10 pages). Flaps should be secured so papers don't fall out or fly across the desk when opened. For qualification packages or proposals, a binding system offers the best means of control and flexibility. Make sure that your packaging system works together and has a cohesive look. Don't be guilty of neglecting the details. Folders, covers, tabs, or divider pages should reflect the same level of quality as your other marketing tools. These elements can make the difference in whether or not your package stands out from the mass of submittals and gets that important second look.

Binding   Wire-o binding gives a professional, polished look. This particular binding machine runs approximately $1000. Many firms opt for GBC-type equipment available for about $250. Velo bind equipment starts at $1700; its main drawback—the pages do not lie flat and must be held open. Three-ring binders for larger submittals work well.

Brochures

Brochures come in all shapes and sizes—from a mini-brochure, scaled to fit a No. 10 envelope, to an oversized coffee-table centerpiece. Regardless of its dimension or number of pages, a brochure should be designed to fit your target audience rather than to impress your peers. Realize that an oversized brochure may get trashed since it can't be easily filed.

General vs. Market-Specific Brochures   A general capabilities brochure educates the reader about your firm and your various services. It provides an overview and highlights your experience in various markets. The most flexible size is 8½ by 11 inches, which can be mailed with a cover letter or bound into a proposal. Length varies from 4 to 24 or more pages. Recent trends seem to be away from comprehensive, perfect bound brochures toward smaller special market brochures. The four-page general brochure can be bound together with a special market brochure on airport facilities along with project lists, selected descriptions, and résumés to create a targeted response to a specific client.

Photography and Visuals Photography is often the most important element in making or breaking a brochure. Visuals grab the reader's attention. Images should be striking, unusual, or vivid. Poor quality, poor reproduction, and poor printing are reason enough *not* to do a brochure! Although you can be creative: one brochure which makes less-than-perfect photography work introduces drawings as a prominent element on each spread. This diverts the focus from photography while adding a contrasting visual element.

Copy As stated earlier, if at all possible, hire a professional. But accept the fact that brochures are usually scanned, not read. Which bolsters the case—if you want it read, make it interesting and informative. A brochure does not give you free rein to philosophize or sermonize.

Cover A cover should draw the reader's attention. Give them a reason to pick up your brochure. Use color, photography, typography, illustration, paper stock, or a combination of techniques to make your brochure stand out. Embossing and foil stamping can add texture and interest. Evaluate options in light of cost and overall impact.

Budget How do you respond to the most frequently asked question, "How much does a brochure cost?" . . . with another question, "How long is a piece of string?" Brochures literally run the gamut in terms of cost. Determine up front what you want or can afford to spend. Obviously, the lower end of the spectrum means fewer frills. A four-page, two-color piece using existing photography may range from $2500 to $4000. A four-page, four-color brochure (existing photography) might run $5000 to $8000. Add a PMS color and varnish and that four-page brochure becomes six-color, increasing the cost by $1000 or so. A 12-page, six-color piece can easily run $18,000 to $35,000.

Consultants mean more money, but if the product is superior, achieves your objectives, and avoids costly mistakes, it's probably a worthwhile expense. They can often ensure that you're getting the most bang for the buck, and their cost is offset by these savings. Set your budget, let creativity have full rein, then develop your concept. Regardless of budget, it can be done and done well!

Newsletters

Newsletters have reached near-epidemic levels among design firms. While everyone may be expected to have a brochure, not every firm is expected to produce a newsletter. So many are currently being done that this "unique" element has lost some of its appeal. What's even more discouraging—there are more bad ones than good ones.

A newsletter is a big investment and, as with any marketing tool, should be evaluated in terms of its impact and ability to achieve desired results. If you're not willing to sustain the effort for two years, don't start. You're committing to your clients that you have something informative and worthy of their attention on a regular basis. The moment that newsletter becomes stagnant, boring, or misdirected, you lose your audience. If repeated, you risk losing your audience entirely ("Oh, another newsletter. What a waste!") as it heads straight for file 13.

Newsletters can be valuable tools when done effectively. The content must be broad enough to appeal to a variety of readers. Even finely targeted newsletters usually go to different levels—CEO, managers, and perhaps facility people. The challenge is to have something of interest to everyone in each issue. A manager who can't find one thing worthwhile won't stick with you for future issues. Focus on problems and solutions for readers to relate to rather than describing your latest project and accomplishments. Cover an unusual topic such as negotiating air rights. Save the personal details of birthdays and babies for in-house publications. However, public interest stories of employees involved in community action are often overlooked.

As discussed previously, graphics are important. Incorporate photographs, illustrations, and diagrams. Don't try to cover too much. Provide headlines for scanning and multicolumns for easy reading, and leave white space for visual appeal.

Costs for newsletters vary greatly. Some can be done effectively with two-color printing. Most rely on photography to carry the graphic message which involves 4- to 6-color process printing in a 4- to 12-page format. Depending on whether or not you use existing photography and have a writer on staff, costs can range from $2500 to $15,000.

Announcements

Firms frequently send out cards announcing promotions, new people, or an award. It's an appropriate excuse to keep in contact with past, current, and prospective clients. Many take the wedding announcement approach—a panel card with "we are pleased to announce." While they are short, simple, and easy to produce, they tend to look alike, but more importantly, they lack flair and imagination.

Recall in the beginning of this chapter you were challenged to approach marketing tools "not as they have always been done before" but "do them better than they've ever been done." Why then would you send an ordinary message when you can do something different? Take a graphic approach and play off your logo or some element of the activity you're announcing. Make a teaser or create a play on words relating to a new person. Or simply adopt a different format for presenting announcements—one that a reader can quickly identify with your firm.

Maximize every communication opportunity. It may cost a few dollars more to do something different, but added impact is usually worth it.

Direct Mail

Direct mail are those special pieces developed to address specific concerns and mailed to a targeted audience. The object is to create a perception or to tell a story in a way that sets you apart from the competition. Consider your own mail. What gets attention? What gets trashed? Odd-sized envelopes are most often selected to open first.

Successful direct mail reflects a clever approach or plays upon the unusual. Day Brown Rice, an MEP engineering firm, realized they had an image problem—lack of name recognition—and used direct mail to achieve fantastic results. You have three common names, in an industry where multiple names are the norm. How do you stand out? Using the Thanksgiving holiday, they presented a solution to the engineering dilemma of what to do with leftover turkey. A cardboard box containing a burlap bag of Day (brand) brown rice accompanied a card expressing their ability to provide creative engineering solutions and offering a recipe for Sum Turkey Casserole (brown rice furnished). Approximately 300 mailers were prepared and sent to developer and architect clients. At meetings and events, they were

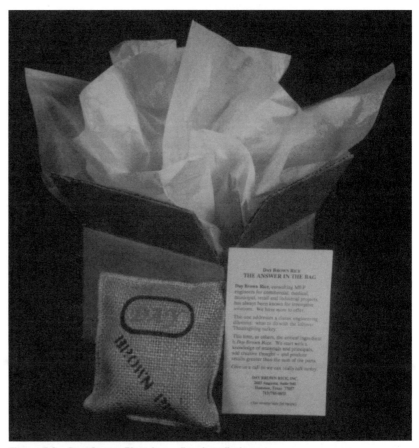

Figure 7.2   Day Brown Rice, Inc., direct mail piece.

Figure 7.3 Wilson Griffin Architects direct mail series—three teasers.

introduced as the guys with the rice bag. They became mementos. Months later, recipients were repeating the story of Day Brown Rice (see Fig. 7.2) as inquirers pointed to the unusual piece on their desk.

Another example of creative direct mail is a series for Wilson Griffin Architects. Partners in a large firm for a number of years, they had only a couple of projects to show under their new firm. A series of three teasers, designed to catch the reader's attention, features the two principals in lighthearted poses using the facilities they designed (see Fig. 7.3). The final, more traditional piece, opens with a studio shot of the two and a philosophical statement. When opened, the unexpected use of color (contrasted with the black and white images seen previously) and dramatic images makes a strong impact (see Fig. 7.4). The last piece functions as a stand-alone brochure. The teaser pieces added significant interest. Without them, the brochure would not have had the same impact. Some peers felt the campaign was irreverent. Clients expressed overwhelming approval. "I know you guys," was a frequent response, which served as an icebreaker and established an immediate relationship with potential clients.

The following year, the firm had a different story to tell. Using the same format of the brochure piece, the two principals are featured on the cover with a statement regarding change. When opened, the piece displays an expansive photograph of the 12-person staff (see Fig. 7.5).

Figure 7.4   Wilson Griffin Architects direct mail series—brochure.

Mailing List

Firms spend thousands of dollars producing a brochure, newsletter, or other marketing piece, often with little consideration given to actually getting it to its intended audience. A mailing list is a vital part of your marketing program. Assign responsibility to one person to make sure that the list is maintained on a regular basis (not just when you have a mailing). Record who within the firm is responsible for each name on the list. The list can then be sorted by contact person for review and update. This accountability is important to ensure that names don't go on the list never to be reviewed again. When someone leaves the firm, if the names from their list remain on the list, then someone should be made responsible for those names.

Make sure all incoming announcements of new personnel, promotions, name change, and address change are routed to the person responsible for the mailing list. It's crucial this person recognize that accuracy is of utmost importance. Regardless of how wonderful the piece, its value is diminished if the recipient's name is misspelled.

If you are mailing to a unique audience on a one-time basis, it's best not to incorporate those names into your regular mailing list.

Volume is not the issue. Don't add all attendees from the convention you just attended to your list. Include only those contacts that you value and intend to maintain.

If you're mailing to a large number, you may want to use a mail service to insert, address, and mail your piece. Seek recommendations from associates or consultants. Check references. Include yourself on the mailing list (to verify when others receive their copy) and ask for documentation or a receipt of postal records to verify the count of pieces mailed.

Reprints

If you've invested time and money in securing good photography and getting your projects published, make sure to budget for reprints. The cost runs about $2 a piece depending on the publication and quantity ordered.

Chances are marginal that your clients and prospects actually saw the magazine. But with a reprint, you can send that message to a tar-

Figure 7.5   Wilson Griffin Architects direct mail follow-up.

geted audience. The third-party credibility generated from publicity creates the perception of "expert" in the reader's mind.

An attachment card or note accompanying the article explains why it's of value to the reader or highlights the project's significant achievement. Have your people sign the attachment card and add personal notes where possible.

Reprints are also included in qualification packets or bound with proposals, as appropriate.

Exhibits

Some firms find that exhibiting at trade shows is a valuable means of keeping in front of a target audience, facilitating new contacts, and generating project leads. But as with any undertaking, if you're going to do it—do it right. You can waste a lot of money with no return on investment without proper preparation and follow-up.

You can expect to pay $1500 or more for exhibit space at a national conference. Prime booth locations run a little more and options such as carpet and plants are additional. A nice but simple modular exhibit system runs about $3000. Then you have the cost of graphics and photography to display your services and projects. Costs of shipping the exhibit materials should be considered. There is also the expense of staffing an exhibit—one or two people for two or three days—with corresponding expenses.

A preshow mailer is a good idea. Again, think creatively! You need materials to hand out at the show. This may be an existing brochure or a piece produced specifically for this target audience. And of course, you need to follow up with at least a letter to all contacts and prospective clients.

The tales of trade show tribulations are many. This is not a venture to enter into without prior investigation. First, attend a conference where you intend to exhibit. Get a feel for what types of people attend, who exhibits, what they exhibit and how. Talk to others who have exhibited at the particular show. Was it beneficial? Then, you'll have a basis for evaluating the perceived value against the costs involved. Exhibiting requires great care and skill to ensure the myriad of details are coordinated. Even with careful planning, expect the unexpected, and be flexible enough to make last-minute adjustments.

Presentation Visuals

Visuals play a significant role in the design profession. Concepts and systems are recorded in renderings, drawings, and photography. Quality visuals go a long way in making your marketing materials effective.

Boards and Overheads   Boards and overheads are great for displaying charts, schedules, and key points (not prose) to small to moderate-size groups. They can serve as a prompt for the speaker but should not be read. For a long presentation, overheads are preferred over slides because you can summarize information and maintain eye contact without dimming the lights. Keep copy to a minimum and incorporate graphics. Photography can be used by framing a 4 by 5 transparency.

Photography and Slides Professional photography makes all the difference. Select a photographer experienced in the type of project you are shooting. If it's an interiors project, ask to see the photographer's contract interior work rather than residential or architectural work.

Plan in advance the number of shots anticipated. If you intend to share costs with other team members, you must notify the photographer in advance of the shoot and negotiate rights. Discuss format of photography (4 by 5 color transparency, 4 by 5 color negatives, black and white negatives, 35-mm slides, etc.). Slides are often made from the 4 by 5 transparency. If possible, walk the project with the photographer prior to the shoot or provide plans with shots marked.

Expect to pay $1000 to $2500 per day for a professional photographer. For architectural (exterior) photography, estimate five to seven shots per day. Interior photography averages three to four shots per day. Some photographers include the cost of their assistant within their day rate; others do not. Film and processing expenses can run $65 to $100 per shot. Don't forget to include travel expenses (air fare, hotel, rental car, etc.) in the budget as well as cost of accessories (flowers, plant rental, vases, artwork) or props to set up the shot.

Photographers hold copyright on the images they produce. Most photographers sell limited rights. Typically, you may use the photography for your own marketing purposes, but requests from clients, consultants, or vendors should be referred to the photographer. You do not have the right to sell an image. Others may negotiate with the photographer for the right to use one or more images. These fees vary according to the use and distribution—say $250 per shot for limited use up to $1000 or more if the image is to be used in advertising. Cost for full buy-out rights (where the photographer gives up all rights and you own the images) can run from 3 to 10 times the basic cost for the photography. Photographers prefer (some insist) that print orders come through their studio in order to maintain quality control. Negotiate!

Secure the client's permission to photograph. Confirm the dates and notify them of who will be present and the times. The client will alert security personnel. Locate master light switches in advance as well as a place to store equipment, if needed. Be sure to leave the space as you found it. And of course, write the client a thank you letter (a set of prints is a nice touch).

Now you have great photography, you must take proper care of it. Originals should be stored in fireproof facilities, preferably off site. At the very least, keep them under lock and key. There are many ways to organize slides—grouped by building type, numbered in sequence by project number. Find a storage solution that facilitates easy retrieval and refiling. This can be as simple as slide sleeves within a three-ring binder or hanging slide sleeves for file-cabinet storage. Special slide storage systems are available in various cabinet models (storing from 1000 to 12,000 slides) equipped with a backlight or light box. Trays pull out for viewing slides. Some models have drawers for storing duplicate slides. Prices for the Abodia* systems range from $775 to $5000.

Video

Advanced technology has pushed video to much greater prominence. Many offices and nearly every home has a VCR. In 3 to 7 minutes you can impart more information graphically, and persuasively tell your story in a way that achieves greater impact.

The key to success is creativity and professional direction. Many believe a marketing video can be produced using a home camera and an in-house narrator. Be realistic—a team of professionals will deliver the best results.

First determine your message. A storyboard illustrates the concept—script and images. Next, write the script. A camera crew shoots the required shots, and final edits are made to the script. An editor puts it all together incorporating voice-over (professional narrator) and music where appropriate.

You may be able to secure permission to use clips from other sources (convention bureau, TV stations, etc.), incorporate slide images or flat art, and combine with segments of your existing video. Successful videos have been produced using solely CADD material and animation.

Most videos are too long. Three to six minutes is usually long enough to effectively communicate any message. Depending on geographic location and expenses (helicopter to photograph aerials, models), cost can range from $1500 to $2500 per finished minute.

Be sure to consider the audience size when selecting equipment. When showing one-on-one, a portable projection unit is sufficient—most commonly used to demonstrate your video brochure. For large audiences, the smaller the image, the less impact. The most expensive video presented to a large audience on a small-screen monitor will pale in comparison with a large-screen, multiprojector slide presentation. Always, know your audience.

Summing Up—New Directions

The overriding theme in this chapter has been *creativity*. There have always been firms that stood out in terms of creative marketing efforts, but they were Lone Rangers. With increased competition, firms are now seeking better ways to distinguish themselves from the pack. Creative, unusual approaches will continue to drive successful marketing solutions.

Architects and engineers have traditionally been conservative in their corporate identity—a simple typeface in black or gray. Use of

---

*Abodia storage systems are available through Elden Enterprises, P.O. Box 3201, Charleston, W. Va. 25332 (800-950-7775; fax: 304-344-4764).

color and unusual typefaces has only recently gained broad acceptance. It's okay to be a designer and for that to be reflected in stationery, brochures, and other materials. As a profession, it seems firms went through a similar color cycle. Brochures were black, followed by the gray period, then the blue era. Finally, the color cycle appears broken. And we should continue to see variation. Many are responding to environmental considerations and using recycled paper.

Video will continue its rise in popularity. Hopefully, we'll carry forward the lessons learned with brochures. They should not be self-serving, laudatory, and boring travelogues of our practice.

Many ask, "How can I do it all?" You can't. We all have limited resources. Develop a game plan of what you want to accomplish. Rather than doing a dozen things halfheartedly or spreading your dollars so thin you can't produce high-quality tools, prioritize your activities and complete them as time and money permit.

Why do clients hire you? In surveys with clients, I frequently hear that they *expect* firms to be technically qualified and to meet schedule and budget requirements. They *seek* firms that exhibit creativity and offer innovative solutions. Let your creativity show, not only within the design and problem-solving arena, but also in your approach to marketing and client communications.

Bibliography

Birnberg, Howard. *Small Design Firm Marketing Manual.* Chicago: Birnberg & Associates, 1983.

Burden, Ernest. *Design Communication: Developing Promotional Material for Design Professionals.* New York: McGraw-Hill, 1987.

Capelin, Joan, ed. *40 Effective Newsletters by A/E Firms.* Newton, Mass.: Practice Management Associates, 1986.

Connor, Richard A., Jr., and Jeffrey P. Davidson. *Marketing Your Consulting & Professional Services.* New York: John Wiley & Sons, 1985.

Coxe, Weld. *Marketing Architectural and Engineering Services.* New York: Van Nostrand Reinhold, 1983.

Edmunds, Jane. *Public Relations for Small Design Firms.* Chicago: Birnberg & Associates, 1988.

Jones, Gerre L. *How to Market Professional Design Services.* New York: McGraw-Hill, 1983.

Sonnenberg, Frank K. *Marketing to Win: Strategies for Building Competitive Advantage in Service Industries.* New York: Harper & Row, 1990.

Spaulding, Margaret, and William D'Elia. *Advanced Marketing Techniques for Architecture and Engineering Firms.* New York: McGraw-Hill, 1989.

Tenney, Sandra M., ed. *PSMJ Design & Building Industry Publicity Directory.* Newton, Mass.: Practice Management Associates, 1989.

Travers, David. *Preparing Design Office Brochures: A Handbook.* Santa Monica, Calif.: Arts & Architecture Press, 1982.

8

Marketing as Process: Proposals and the Concept of Negative Positivism

Thom McKay

Proposals are the great engines driving most marketing groups, too often revving when they probably should be idling, conserving fuel. This may be because marketers can latch onto proposals, and producing them gives justification to a profession that relies so heavily on things intangible. When a partner asks, "What did you do last week?" it's comforting to stand before a stack of proposals and point. "That, that's what I did last week." The 5-foot stack sways. Everyone nods. The partner snorts approval. Smiles all around. Jobs are safe.

But churning out proposals is no measure of marketing success. Winning jobs—winning good jobs, the jobs you want to be doing— is the goal here, and proposals are one small step to that end.

Direct marketing is indeed a series of steps, a process or continuum, with an ambiguous beginning and end. Proposals represent a single step of that process. The purpose of each step, quite simply, is to get to the next one. It's that obvious. The goal of a statement of qualifications is to move to the proposal stage; from the proposal stage to the interview stage; from the interview to selection and negotiation; from negotiation to work; from work to the next job. Unfortunately, each step is frequently misunderstood or, worse, we grow impatient and try to skip a step: proposals are written and presented as if they were going to land the job. It is questionable that many major commissions are awarded based on the quality and literary pyrotechnics of a proposal; but surely too many projects have been lost because of a shoddy proposal.

Hence the concept of negative positivism—a proposal probably won't win the job, but it certainly may lose it.

Definitions

Because there is a tendency to misinterpret, to treat everything as if it will "get you the job," it might be important to define each aspect of the process. Margaret Spaulding and William D'Elia do this very well in their *Advanced Marketing Techniques for Architecture & Engineering Firms*:

> A *statement of qualifications* (SOQ) uses boilerplate material primarily and is often submitted as part of a preselection process.
>
> A *proposal,* written in response to a request for proposal (RFP) or questionnaire, includes much original information and modified boilerplate to respond to a client's stated concerns or direct questions.
>
> A *scope statement* with fee proposal identifies the services in detail (often including a schedule) and provides a fee related to the scope of work. These can be part of a proposal or follow as a final submittal to obtain a project.

The level of effort in assembling the package increases from the SOQ to the fee proposal, as does the measure of negative positivism.

The Statement of Qualifications

Most firms have adopted some method of assembling an SOQ, responding quickly and with some degree of specificity to an outside request. The more tailored the SOQ can be to the actual request, the more powerful the response. There are many ways to do this. Preprinted project sheets—either color or black and white and providing adequate information on a particular commission—are very popular, especially when the pages can be bound in some way to allow for flexibility. Brochures serve as good overviews, but most lack the necessary detail. Some brochure systems, where certain specialized components of a particular firm (highway engineering or university work) are highlighted, are often more successful and more flexible.

In these days of faxable gratification, response time seems to have become the highest criterion in reviewing SOQs. To consider it cynically, how quickly you respond is typically more important than how you respond. Of course, not every firm needs or can afford full-color, full-blown brochures or project sheets on every aspect of their firm, but few firms can afford not to have some method of responding quickly and professionally to a basic request for qualifications.

If the SOQ hits its mark, a firm is usually asked to submit a written proposal. This is a more specific document, typically in response to a defined scope or a series of pointed questions. But, before the great proposal machine begins to hum, ask the probingly important but most often ignored question in the whole marketing process.

Do We Really Want This Project?

The "go/no go" decision may be one of the most difficult decisions for a firm to make; consequently, it is typically ignored, causing the proposal engine to rev a little higher, a little more inefficiently. For whatever reason, most firms would rather file for bankruptcy than pass on an opportunity to submit a proposal, even on a project for which they're unqualified. Proposal preparation and assembling is no small affair. When done properly and effectively, it takes time and commitment. Churning out unwinnable proposals for unwanted projects only burns out a marketing staff. Focus on, and fully understand, what you are chasing, why you are chasing it, and what it will bring you once you get it.

Only a few fundamental questions need be asked when considering a project. In no particular order, they are

Are we capable?

Do we have a chance of winning?

Can we staff the project?

Is it a good client (can they pay, are they interested in quality, etc.)?

Is it consistent with our marketing plan (or long-term goals)?

What does submitting bring us?

These are basic questions, and if your answers give you pause, it is probably best to pass on the proposal.

The Preproposal Workout

The firm that believes a proposal alone is going to win the job is sadly out of touch with today's business climate. Proposals are far from the most important (though they are potentially the most destructive) element of the marketing process, and there are many far more useful activities that will help in the quest for a project.

The most important component of a proposal comes from the work done leading up to the proposal—the homework that brings a proposer knowledge of the client. In an article in *Engineering News Record* entitled "Marketing Ain't What It Used to Be; It's More," Judy Shriener reports that the "organizations that stand out in clients' minds are the ones that go the extra mile to make sure they know the client. . . . They do more homework than their competitors." Today, with fierce competition and markets driven by uncertain, fickle economies, this could not be more true. The more you know, the better off you are, because it is knowledge and understanding of clients and their needs that allow you to develop a truly responsive proposal.

Find out everything you can about the client, their business, their philosophy and goals. Are they small but growing? Large and downsizing? Are they cost-conscious? Design-conscious? Time-conscious? Who are the decision makers? Find out who reads the proposals, who screens the slate of proposers. Is it a long list (20 or more) or a short list of three or four prequalified firms? Find out the personality of the client. Do they have a sense of humor? Are they socially conscious? Progressive? Do they respond to statistical information? Sexy photographs of projects? Have they hired professional services before? Or is this the first time they have done something like this?

On top of client information, try to uncover data on your competition, if only to give you an idea of what distinct qualities you offer. While this is helpful, you needn't be obsessive about it.

There are of course many ways to uncover information, and working a well-developed network of contacts is probably the best. Laurin McCracken, whose network of contacts is world-renowned in marketing circles, is a recognized master in gathering information about a project. Of course, you can always ask the client directly, but for reasons not altogether clear to me, this method seems distasteful and vulgar. Once the information is gathered, the proposal can begin to take shape.

The Proposal

Proposals are about four things, in ascending order of importance: writing, packaging, logistics, and content.

Writing

Because a proposal must not only respond but convince, good writing is essential and persuasive writing is the goal. "The proposal is an exercise in written salesmanship," to quote Herman Holtz, and poor writing offers just another reason for a client to stop midsentence and prevent you from getting to the next step. The ability to convince, to elicit understanding, to persuade—this is the aim of proposal writing. It needn't be the stuff of a Pulitzer, just clear, factual.

Use the language of your clients; write sentences they will understand. While style can be a dangerous thing, writing should at the very least express some of the proposer's personality; a personality that, ideally, meshes with that of the client.

Never underestimate the intelligence or sophistication of your client. Few are taken in by vague, sweeping generalizations, and most would much rather read cold, hard facts. It's easy to spot fluff, however disguised, and it does not belong in proposals, though that is where it is most often found. For example, the claim "XYZ is one of the most experienced firms in the country" is effete writing. It offers little information. To say, "In the last 5 years, XYZ has completed eight projects similar to the one at hand," is another matter, especially if you go on to describe those projects and how they were similar to the one proposed.

There are, of course, countless rules for good writing and innumerable books imparting wisdom and guidance on these rules and the so-called proper way to write a proposal. Some books are better than others. It is not the intention of this chapter to go into depth on how to write persuasively, only to let you know that it is critical. Indeed, the first rule of good writing should be that you cannot learn how to write by memorizing rules. Writing winning proposals takes practice, rewriting and editing, and a gift for communicating. It's a difficult process, one to which many people have dedicated their lives. Fortunately for those who lack the gift, writers and editors can be hired easily.

Packaging

Some major projects fetch as many as 50 responses. Try to envision a stack of proposals piled on a table, and it is your task to wade through them. The one that looks the best starts with an advantage. It caught your eye, impressed you already. You open it gladly and thumb through the pages. You may even read it thoroughly. It makes sense that your proposal try to stand out in some immediate way. More importantly, packaging—what your proposal looks like, inside and out—reflects on the proposer, which is the strongest reason it is important. Binding, printing, color, what your cover looks like are all part of the effort, and these things must come together in some attractive, legible format. They must urge the reader to pick up the proposal, open it, and read it, the goal of course being not only to get someone to pick up your proposal but to move the reader along, easily and logically, from one section to the next, so the entire breadth of the proposal is absorbed and your full, persuasive case can be made.

Personal computers have made technology accessible to virtually everyone in the business world, and desktop publishing has wrought its own type of visual revolution, so there is no excuse for a written document not to look professionally produced. Typewriters—and the visual mediocrity they spew—have been rendered obsolete. The days of one or two typefaces are long past; now hundreds are available—each conveying its own nuance—that must be considered. But, obviously, typefaces are not the only things to worry about.

A number of basic elements of a proposal are worth mentioning, if only because they are too often overlooked:

The cover—print the submitter's name (usually just the prime), the client's name, and the project. This is minimum information. You can get clever and emblazon some type of slogan or design, but remember you want to stand out, not appear vulgar or ostentatious.

Title page—maybe not necessary, but adds a touch of professionalism. Also allows you to offer any information not appropriate for the cover, such as the full listing of subconsultants.

Table of contents and tabs or dividers—every reader will have his or her own agenda, some interested in the individuals assigned, some in past experience, some in the fee proposed. Whatever. Give them opportunity to find it quickly.

Numbered pages—picture the selection committee sitting around a large table, each with an individual copy of 25 proposals. The selection committee chairperson asks that everyone turn to page 10. People flip pages furiously only to find that the pages aren't numbered. In unison, all 25 copies of the proposal are tossed on a heap of rejects. Number your pages. It makes it easier for people to navigate through your work.

It is much easier to say something with an image or a graphic than with a page of text, so incorporating a healthy dose of graphics can help a proposal visually and legibly. Organization charts, schedules, matrices, and sketches are all good examples of graphics that can be incorporated.

As with all good things, there is a point of diminishing return. Desktop publishing and accessible graphic software have made designers out of too many people. Designing a page layout, formatting a proposal, and developing clear, legible, and attractive graphics is an art, botched by too many. Whoever is charged with assembling the proposal and generating the artwork should have a strong visual sense as well as the ability to write and edit. Remember, your competition has probably mastered the art and submits proposals and other documents that look professionally prepared. If you are going to keep pace with your competition, take pains to master the art, or hire someone who can.

Logistics

Because proposals often involve too much information and material for one person to handle alone, there is something to be said for scheduling and orchestrating the various efforts. This includes the writing, graphics, and artwork (including cover and binding), collating all the materials (including résumés and other preprinted materials such as project information sheets), and, finally, delivery. Different firms have different ways of managing their marketing work, and there certainly is no right or wrong way to go about it, just that it gets done. Figure 8.1 shows a possible marketing organization chart.

Your proposal, and the toil you poured into it, counts for nothing unless it arrives on time. Just getting it there can be the hardest job of all, and it makes sense to be as diligent about delivery as you are about content. It is inadvisable to rely on standard U.S. mail delivery if time is an issue, and it almost always is, unless of course the project is for a postal facility. (A story famous among marketers recounts a firm, which always goes nameless, sending in its proposals to the Postal Service via a private overnight courier. It took several submittals before they figured out what they were doing wrong.) In the public sector, and sometimes in the private sector, selection procedures are quasi-legal, and all submission criteria must be scrupulously observed for fear that the award might be protested.

Content

Inasmuch as your proposal is well-written, looks good, and arrives on time—and no matter how cynical we can be about a proposal's real worth—the content is always the most important element. At the risk of sounding axiomatic, you have to say what the client wants to hear. (If you cannot, for whatever reasons, return to the go/no go section of this chapter.)

Clients these days seem to know exactly what they want, and the actual content of a proposal is often dictated in the RFP. More and more frequently RFPs outline not only the specific criteria of selection, which all good RFPs should, but also the format of the proposal to be followed. Some proposals even limit the number of pages to be submitted, all but forcing you to avoid marketing babble. It makes great sense not to tinker with a format suggested by the client—remember, just another excuse to throw you out of the running—and to answer the questions or address the issues in the order in which they are posed.

There are several basics in a proposal, and it is advisable to include them, whether requested or not:

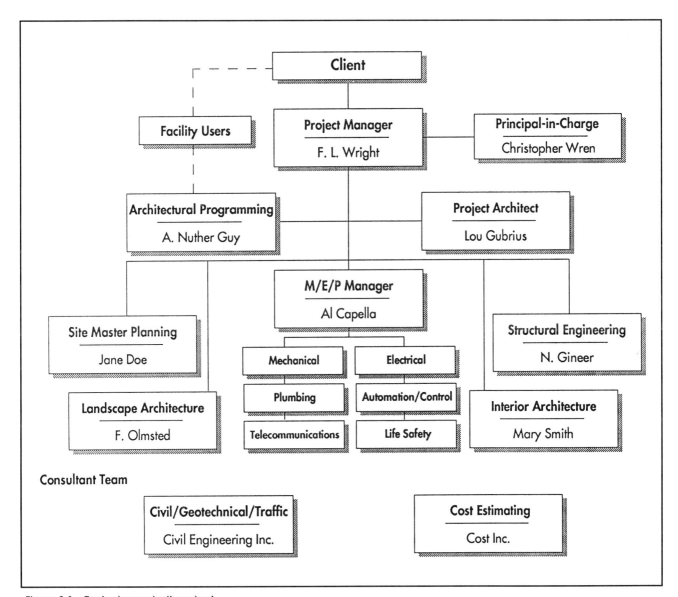

Figure 8.1   Typical organization chart.

Cover Letter   There is an ongoing debate about the cover letter. Is it necessary or just a waste of time? Perhaps they are more appropriately called transmittal letters, and their purpose is simple—to transmit the document. It is one page, identifies the project, the submitting firm, and a phone number and address of a person to contact. That's all. Don't confuse a cover letter with an executive summary or project approach; it's a waste of time.

An executive summary is an excellent way of quickly serving up (with either bulleted text or highlighted sentences) the meat of your proposal. The summary should be brief—no more than one or two pages usually does it—and serve as a road map for the proposal to follow. Executive summaries often are not requested, but they are very useful in larger efforts, serving as a welcome relief for those readers who haven't the time or the disposition to trudge through an epic tome, however well written it may be.

Project Understanding   It's surprising to see how many proposals neglect to exhibit a true understanding of the project at hand. A terse half-page synopsis needn't be a pure regurgitation of what the client has proposed; it should simply illustrate a firm grasp of the project at hand. This is also an excellent place to include the information you gathered in doing your homework on the client. For example, if budget is a concern, let them know that you know.

On some projects, particularly those where design plays a major role or some important aspect is at issue, I've entitled this section "Project Vision," and have waxed poetic on how we have interpreted the client's sublime, aesthetic goals, on how we "share the client's vision." Other sections, such as "Design Philosophy" or "Firm Philosophy," serve a related purpose.

Qualifications   Some clients tend to rely solely on past experience for a project ("Before I select you for my wastewater treatment plant, I want to know how many other wastewater treatment plants you've done."), but thankfully this is changing somewhat. While more sophisticated clients rely on a range of criteria, some believe that if you haven't done ten of their type of projects, don't bother to submit. Whatever the case, relevant experience is almost always a major part of a proposal. Figure 8.2 shows a sample team responsibility matrix.

A required format is typically requested—general description, principal-in-charge, date completed, estimated versus actual construction cost, references. As with the statement of qualifications, it makes great sense to have all this information readily available, whether in a database or file, to tailor directly to the client's requested format.

Approach   There are normally two types of approaches to a project: the management approach and the technical approach. Technical approach refers to the actual progress of the work, what will be done, how it will be done, when it will be done, and so on. It can be presented as text or outline (i.e., a task-by-task narrative) or in a more graphic format (flowchart or bar schedule, for example).

A management approach is more a description of how the project

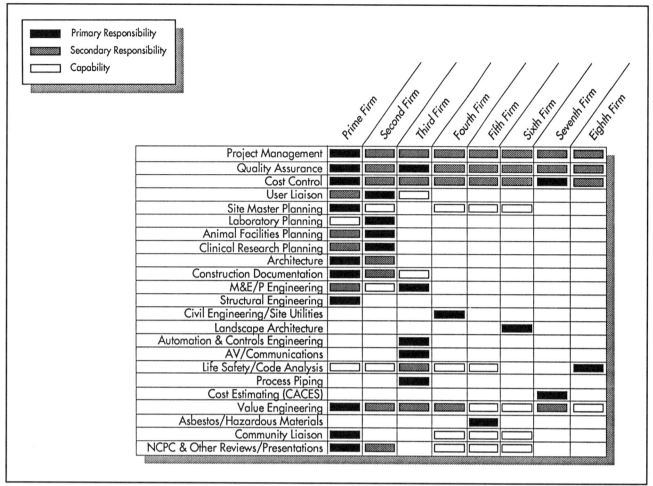

Figure 8.2 Team responsibility matrix.

is to be coordinated. Quality assurance, cost and schedule control, and methods of communication among team members are all management concerns that are sometimes worth sharing with a client, particularly those interested in project delivery.

Staffing In the end, the client hires people, not a firm or a mystique or a design style. Given this, the project team section is arguably the most important. Many firms structure their teams differently (and surely there are as many team formats as there are projects), so there is really no preferable way to present your people. One given is that the proposed project manager, or whomever you assign as the single point of client contact for the project, must have demonstrated, proved experience in the work at hand. Further, that individual probably will be required to dedicate up to 100 percent of his or her time to the effort, depending on the project's scope and complexity.

Résumés It is assumed that the people assigned to the project have some degree of familiarity with the project at hand, whether it be an office building, highway, or HVAC system. Résumés are almost always requested, with certain facts registering more importance—listing of relevant experience, education, teaching experience, registration. All this information can be preprinted or formatted individually; it can be one page or go on ad infinitum; it can include the sublime and the mundane. Whatever the case, the information will be requested.

Federal Selection

Most firms approach marketing to the federal government (as well as state and local governments) as if the client were a medieval castle protected by vast defenses buckled up tight. In the world of architectural engineering procurement, the federal government may actually be easier to understand than the private sector, if only because the selection criteria are, as a matter of law, made painfully public and the method of selection is kept as open and obvious as possible. Procurement integrity is a concept well adhered to in the government, as the last thing any procurement officer wants is for a selection to be protested—a most unfortunate occurrence that plummets even the most well-meaning project into the deepest, darkest depths of bureaucratic hell.

Federal procurement relies almost entirely on three things: past experience, the people proposed, and formsmanship. If you or your firm has not worked on more than five or six similar projects, there is very little use in submitting, especially for the larger commissions (construction cost of $10 million and above). Again: "Before you get my wastewater treatment plant, show me how many other wastewater treatment plants you've done."

Many believe that submitting on projects they know they are going to lose is valid because it serves as an introduction to the contracting agency. This is a ridiculous notion. If you want to introduce yourself to a contracting agency, pick up the phone and make an appointment. They are obliged to answer your questions.

Formsmanship—
Standard Forms 254 and 255

Federal architectural and engineering procurement focuses on two forms—the Standard Form 254 and the Standard Form 255—both of which hold no great secrets. The obvious is too often the greatest hurdle. The SF254 is considered a general form and serves as introduction to a firm. The SF255 is specific and is completed and submitted for a project announcement advertised in the *Commerce Business Daily,* a daily publication of the U.S. government which lists all federal procurement activity.

The Ten-Minute Window

Perhaps more than with a private-sector proposal, the concept of positive negativism works more heavily on an SF255. That is, your submittal has a greater chance of disqualifying you than of getting you selected. The reason for this is that the form is very rigid in what it requests; those reading the forms are also very rigid—if the information is not there, or it is not clear, or it is there only in part, it is tossed in the ash heap of discards. The contracting agency cannot judge based on any knowledge apart from the form; only what is in the SF255, and only if it is relevant to the job at hand, can get you short-listed.

The SF255, the Brooks Act selection procedures, and the Federal Acquisition Regulations serve to make the architectural and engineering selection process somewhat more equitable in the federal arena than in the private sector. Given the forced consistency among submittals, most juries can go through an SF255 with some measure of dispatch. Indeed, with the likelihood being that more than 50 submittals will be made, most juries are forced to go through an SF255 with a *great* measure of dispatch. Jon T. Adsit, in an article in *Architecture Magazine,* "How A/E Firms Lose Federal Jobs," calls this a "ten-minute window," meaning each jury member will give each submittal about ten minutes and is probably "more eager to find reasons for throwing out, or marking down, a submission" than moving it to the short list.

To their defense, it may be because it is the task of an administrative staff member (i.e., someone with little knowledge of the project or the service being procured) to read the submittals and make sure the basic criteria are met—that the forms are signed and dated properly, the firm is within the appropriate geographic boundaries, the team has the needed number of people. It seems astonishing that a multi-million-dollar project can be selected on the basis of a ten-minute review, or one can be lost for want of a signature, but this is often the case, and we needn't quibble about it here.

Of course, each judge will devote his or her ten minutes either to a few critical areas or to a quick, cursory pass over the entire form. Some are interested only in the proposed team, some only in the relevant projects. Again, they are looking for reasons to throw you out of the running, to cut their ten minutes to five, and the reason for being bounced need not be egregious. How many firms have gone down because a form was not signed or because the numbers of registered professionals did not add up correctly?

Because even the smallest detail can count, following the logic of the form is far more important than trying to make a bold marketing statement. (Remember: The purpose of this step is to move to the next step, and, typically, the next step in federal procurement is the interview. Leave the bold statements for the interview.) Clarity becomes critical; confusion and ambiguity sound the death knell.

At the very least, you must respond to the questions being asked on the form (Blocks 1 through 10) as well as the selection criteria outlined in the *Commerce Business Daily* announcement. Moreover, within the framework of the form, you must also exhibit understanding of the type of work being proposed.

Since the SF255 is actually not a proposal—it is a method of transmitting qualifications and resources—past experience and the proposed team are perhaps the two most critical areas. When the form asks in Question 8, "Work by firm or joint-venture which best illustrates current qualifications relevant to this project," it means exactly that—relevant projects. With your competition numbering around 50 firms on most projects, having only four or five vaguely similar projects probably won't get you to the short list.

The Morning After—
Getting Debriefed

A formal debriefing is perhaps the most instructive component of the proposal process. By finding out "why you weren't selected" or "why you did not make it to the next step," you can assess your approach and improve it for the next effort. In the private sector, this might be as simple as a phone call, though any time you have an opportunity to visit a potential client it is usually worth the effort. With federal proposals, the scenario is more formalized and typically cannot be instituted until a contract has been negotiated and signed.

Protesting

Lodging a formal protest is a last resort for firms that feel they've been unfairly judged. With federal proposals, protests are lodged with the Government Accounting Office (GAO), Congress' watchdog agency, which will investigate and adjudicate the matter. Protests are almost always the wrong thing to do. Very little good ever emerges from protesting an award, particularly in the public sector, where grudges linger longer than in most areas and the red tape involved can entangle and delay an award for decades. Everyone suffers. Protests serve their purpose only in very rare situations.

The Future

In the years ahead, as the selection process and clients become even more sophisticated and projects grow more complicated, the emphasis on proposals will probably diminish but never fully disappear. It will diminish in that selections today seem to be becoming more a question of chemistry, of relationships, of being able to work with someone; and this foists the marketing onus on the presentation and interview. Firms should rely less on marketing puffery, sit down and listen to their clients, and uncover what is really needed and wanted. Kohn Pedersen and Fox's Gene Kohn has a famous marketing quote in dealing with prospective clients—"You want to make them like you." Kohn really hits the point of direct marketing. If they—meaning the clients—truly like you, then all the proposals in the world won't change their minds.

Proposals will always be with us, however, keeping marketers busy and stressed because the one true purpose they serve flawlessly is . . . documentation. Proposals are words on paper, and paper leaves a trail, and a trail can be followed in case anyone ever questions a selection. There is a security in having something down in writing and storing it in a file where it can be easily retrieved. And the security of a proposal is something few would give up, even if the proposal goes unread forever.

Bibliography

Adsit, Jon T., "How A/E Firms Lose Federal Jobs." *Architecture Magazine.*

Burden, Ernest, *Design Presentations: Techniques for Marketing and Project Proposals.* New York: McGraw-Hill, 1984.

Holtz, Herman, *Government Contracts: Proposalmanship and Winning Strategies.* New York: Plenum Press, 1979.

Holtz, Herman, and Terry Schmidt, *The Winning Proposal: How to Write It.* New York: McGraw-Hill, 1981.

Jones, Gerre, *How to Market Professional Design Services,* 2d ed. New York: McGraw-Hill, 1983.

Schriener, Judy, "Marketing Ain't What It Used to Be; It's More." *Engineering News-Record,* Feb. 8, 1990.

Spaulding, Margaret, and William D'Elia, *Advanced Marketing Techniques for Architecture and Engineering Firms.* New York: McGraw-Hill, 1987.

9

Effective Public Relations

Patricia P. Rosenzweig

Designers generally believe that public relations simply means getting their work published in magazines. But public relations encompasses a number of other potentially effective tools and tactics that introduce a firm to its marketplace. Public speaking, networking, advertising, and even video taping can work to increase a firm's marketing productivity. The combination of methods chosen depends on the firm's objectives and resources.

Defining objectives and honestly assessing resources are two major components of a marketing plan. A public relations program is not merely asking for more work. You may want to try to obtain additional work or referrals from clients or associates. You may need to smooth the ruffled feathers of clients. You may want your public relations program to emphasize new leads. Or you may want to change the image of your firm. All of these (as well as other marketing or business interests of the firm) are legitimate public relations objectives. Each requires a different marketing technique.

The term "resources" is usually thought to refer to a firm's ability to pay for an effort. This is partly true. Selection of the proper public relations tactic relates directly to a firm's ability to pay for its superior execution. Proper selection also depends on the firm's ability and willingness to devote time to the effort. Some activities can be delegated to staff or to outside consultants, but others must be carried out exclusively by principals. All PR efforts require some of the principal's time—time that he or she, in all likelihood, would prefer to spend elsewhere.

A firm's work is its primary resource. The quality and scope of a firm's past experience and the probability of the market to appreciate its merits dictate the selection of PR tools. For many principals, this resource is the most difficult to assess objectively. At interviews, frustration results from the prospective client's questions about your ability to do a project twice the size of any done before. Magazine editors and seminar coordinators will have similar doubts if pursuing a topic in an area where your depth is weakly documented.

If your objective is to obtain work in a service or building area in which you have substantial experience, being published in a design publication or in the trade press of your clientele is a legitimate avenue to consider. On the other hand, if seeking work for a new service or building area, publication is nearly impossible. Networking, public speaking, and creating a newsletter to rationalize why you should be seriously considered for something you have never before done will be necessary . . . all in a marketplace that starts a discussion by asking, "*How many* have you done?"

Thus, public relations is not limited to publication, nor is publication the correct response for every situation. Management selects key personnel for specific skills and talents and for the abilities to fit into the firm's culture. Therefore, the public relations program must be designed to achieve corporate objectives in a manner consistent with the firm's culture and economy.

The Cost Benefit of Public Relations Tactics

Public relations is situational. What situations call for which activities? What are the range of possible activities? Some activities may seem old-fashioned, but they are still effective when performed properly and at the appropriate time. Other techniques are still being tested by the design professions.

The Print Media

Having work published, however briefly or extensively, projects an image of importance. Those articles that feature a firm and its work make the firm appear to be an expert in that kind of service or project. They are a third-party endorsement that says, "What you do is significant."

Even so, expectations for translating an article directly to a job should be held in check. The primary purposes of obtaining favorable coverage are

> Increasing name recognition so that telemarketers will have an easier time

> Raising consciousness so that people who already know you realize that you are still around and doing good things

> Inducing a facility manager to keep the article for future reference when next compiling a long list

> Making reprints that can be used in a direct mail program

> Supplementing (or creating) a brochure system

Rarely will you get a phone call as a result of an article asking you to come out for an interview immediately. It does happen occasionally, particularly if the publication is prestigious and has the right readership and if the article focuses on a real market interest.

Reprints are important, since you cannot assume that a high proportion of your target market will read the article. Similarly, you cannot always be published in your ideal publication. A reprint allows you to retain the advantages of a third-party endorsement while controlling the readership.

Local news and business press, design and construction industry magazines, trade publications of your clientele, and your clients' newsletters or their professional organizations are all opportunities to appear in print. The value of each opportunity depends on what is printed and the nature of your marketplace.

If your objective is to appear successful and active, then even brief, straightforward announcements are useful, particularly if you issue these releases frequently. Releases can cover new personnel, new officers, and new offices (see Fig. 9.1). The amount of coverage depends on the size of your community and the significance of your practice. A major firm's hiring of a new officer may be printed in the national design press, while the same title in an unknown firm would not be covered by that press at all. Even a new president of a fairly well-known firm would get only a couple of lines in the business press of a major metropolitan weekly. A lower-level hiring, on the other hand, might get a few inches of space in the neighborhood press of a major city or in the daily press of a smaller market.

It is sometimes worthwhile to make a bigger deal out of what could be a simple announcement. Some recent examples:

A well-known firm recruited an executive vice president to head an operating division and received "headline" coverage in several valuable publications in a large metropolitan market by focusing the release on his plans for expansion.

A mid-sized firm whose founder was retiring obtained coverage in the form of announcements, but also received coverage as experts in ownership transition. The press release liberally quoted the founder and his successors on the subject of the transition process.

A large firm that had changed hands a number of times received widespread coverage by "batching" lower-level new hires that, in their marketplace, would not have been picked up individually.

**ABC CORPORATION ANNOUNCES NEW VICE PRESIDENT
FOR QUALITY CONTROL**

John Jones, President of ABC Corporation, today announced the appointment of Jane Smith, 37, a resident of Everytown, Ohio, to the position of Vice President for Quality Control. Formerly Smith was the firm's Senior Job Captain, and previously an architect at QRS Company, also in Everytown.

ABC Corporation is a 35-year-old, 15-person mechanical and electrical engineering firm specializing in renovation of office buildings. Some of their recent projects include the Terrific Lofts for Jack Sprat & Co., First State Bank, and the physician's office building for St. Joe's Hospital in Somewhere, Kentucky.

Figure 9.1 Sample announcement press release.

This left the impression that the firm was, contrary to popular belief, extremely healthy.

Announcements are easy to issue. They follow a standard format that can be submitted by administrative staff to a press list that includes the name of the appropriate editor.

A feature article that discusses your practice or your projects is another matter. First, as a general rule, only completed projects will be reviewed favorably by editors, unless the assignment is limited to programming or planning. Thus, ordinarily getting published is a viable alternative only if your objective is to expand a market in which you already have some experience. It is generally *not* viable as a means to obtain work in a new project type.

An exception to this general rule exists. If you are going to change the way a service is provided, you can survey the marketplace and report on your findings. You can position the service in the terminology of the marketplace, demonstrating your knowledge, even leadership, in that market. After reporting on the study's conclusions, you can then say, "Based on the need expressed by the facility managers surveyed, ABC Corporation is introducing. . . ." This way, *you* are not saying your new service or innovative process is needed; your *clients' peers* are saying it.

Similarly, if you want to enter a new marketplace, for example, shopping centers, you can survey shopping center developers and property managers, systematically inspecting existing centers and reporting on successes and failures. The press loves statistics.

The second difficulty with a feature article is that, unlike an announcement, it is *not* formula writing. Unlike a "boilerplate" project description, a feature story must reflect considerable thought regarding which aspects of the project are publishable. For example, editors do not care that something is blue, unless blue has been found to increase productivity in this kind of space by 35 percent. The structural engineering required to restore the statue on top of Chicago's Board of Trade was not what attracted press attention. For some, the limited circumference of the statue within which the engineers could do their testing attracted interest. Others cared about the height of the statue and others about its historical interest. *You* are rarely "the story." Your client is.

Before considering a potential feature article, apply the "Who cares?" test. First, do you care? Will the projects that are publishable (well-photographed, well-documented, completed within the last year or so for a pleased client who will allow you to publish it) be of interest to the market you are targeting? Are the projects consistent with your marketing plan with respect to the type of client or type of service? Are you so well known in that area that it would be wiser to spend your money on something else? Did you lose a fortune on that kind of project and therefore have no interest in getting any more work of that type? Does it position you properly . . . will the reader see you as you want to be seen?

Many smaller design firms have a number of publishable residential projects, but their marketing plans and limited budgets focus on commercial work. Another published residence would not help them. It may boost their egos, but it will not advance their business plans.

Similarly, a mid-sized firm that wishes to increase the size of its projects should consider publishing widely almost any large job and should strongly consider refusing an opportunity to publish almost any smaller one.

Second, will editors care? or which editors will care? Almost any project is publishable somewhere. However, "somewhere" may not necessarily be exactly where you want it published. Most projects fall short of the standards imposed by the professional design press, but some planning aspect is likely to be interesting to your client's trade press. The more important the client, the more likely it is that the work done for them is publishable in the design, facility management, and your client's trade press—hotel, banking, medical, etc.— and in major metropolitan dailies. If a client is a major force, whatever that client does is important and publishable (Fig. 9.2).

Whoever the client, the presentation of the work must be oriented to provide specific responses to client objectives. How did your work solve a marketing, cash management, maintenance, or safety problem? What was the image with which the space or building had to be consistent? What can your client's peers learn from the problem-solving process? Generally, larger projects have better chances of publication than small ones. However, if you can position a small project as part of a trend, you have an increased chance of getting published (Fig. 9.3).

Award winners are definitely publishable. The awarding organization (AIA, Masonry Council, etc.) will publicize it to the design press. Make sure the client's trade press is notified. A project that was originally submitted and rejected was published when, after receiving an award, it was resubmitted with exactly the same copy and photos, but with a heading "award-winning. . . ."

For the interior design and architecture press, if you do not have superior photography, do not bother to send materials. In addition to using published projects for reprints, list them in your brochure system, even if it is just a captioned photograph.

Do not forget to submit projects for awards. If you know that the project cannot win the more prestigious awards, such as from the AIA, consider the lesser-known programs. If it is a hospital, health care publications have annual awards programs; law publications have law firm design awards; etc.

Finally, if your marketing objective has a strict and limited time frame, you should not count on a media placement to meet your need. Even if the article is accepted, you have no control over when it will be published, if it is published at all.

Some publications, such as the major architectural and interior design press, require exclusive rights to a project or a story. Ordinarily this means that the publication has the right to publish the project first, before any competing publication produces the story. Generally, however, you are free to publish the project in local media and in your client's trade press. When you have accepted an exclusive, it is your responsibility to monitor how long the publication has held the project and whether it is still being considered so that you can request withdrawing the project before it is too old to be considered elsewhere.

Fed Reserve building gets a facelift

By Steve Kerch

Ever seen $1 million in $1 bills before? Ever seen $89.4 million in office renovation before?

You can see both if you see the newly rehabbed and expanded Federal Reserve Bank of Chicago, with its office and processing headquarters on the northwest corner of LaSalle and Jackson Boulevard.

The renovation of the 1922 structure and a 1957 addition, along with construction of a new 14-story tower on the northwest corner of the site, includes a new

Commercial notes

public display, $1 million and all, on the history and workings of the often mysterious Fed, as the United States central bank is called.

"The renovation gave us an opportunity to open some public space in a building that most people wouldn't think of as public," said Nancy Goodman, assistant vice president for information services at the bank.

"The display gives us a chance to tell people what the Fed is about, not an easy task."

The renovation also modernized the Fed's nearly 1 million square feet of offices for 1,900 employees, opened a three-story main atrium to the executive offices on the columned second and third floors and reclad the aluminum-sided addition to match the limestone on the 1922 original.

"After 60 years, the building was functionally inefficient," said Silas Keehn, president of the bank. "But with the expansion and renovation we look forward to being a permanent fixture in the heart of Chicago's financial district and to stimulating the preservation of the character of the area."

Unlike other large banks, the Fed has retained almost all of its processing operations in its Loop building. Goodman said bank officials studied the idea of building a new facility or moving part of the operations to the suburbs before the project began 3½ years ago but decided the best location was the one it had.

The Fed hired Holabird & Root to provide architectural, interior design and structural engineering services on the project.

Sharon Gonzalez, director of interior design for the architectural firm, said that no two floors in the building were laid out the same way before the renovation.

Now, there are common hallway schemes to make it easier to traverse the floors and interior atriums to brighten the office spaces. Accent colors are varied from floor to floor, although none is the color of money.

Even the new boardroom is lighter in color and feel than one

The Federal Reserve Bank building in Chicago has completed a 3½-year renovation and expansion project updating the central bank's office and processing space on LaSalle Street.

would expect from an institution such as the Fed.

"We wanted more openness and more accessibility, but we still wanted to maintain the air of tradition about the Fed," Goodman said.

The new public display is open from 8 a.m. until 5 p.m. Monday through Friday. A new 65-seat auditorium is available for bank functions, and guided tours of the bank are available by reservation.

The openness does not extend, however, to the vaults.

Figure 9.2 The largest interior renovation project in the region received wide coverage by dint of project size and power of owner. *(©Copyrighted, Chicago Tribune Company, all rights reserved, used with permission.)*

Cluster housing at the Woodlands of Darien, 68th Street and Cass Avenue, Darien.

Cluster homes add up to value

By Jim Sulski

Despite an early resistance by buyers, cluster housing has recently become one of the strongest types of residential real estate in the Chicago area, according to several developers.

Cluster housing, which combines the easy maintenance of a townhouse with the prestige and privacy of a single-family home, can be found in many shapes and sizes, as well as dozens of configurations.

As the name implies, cluster housing consists of closely grouped homes. They are usually smaller than the average dwelling and built on downsized lots. They can be arranged around cul-de-sacs, in T-formations and even along straight streets. Cluster housing is also known as zero-lot-line housing or high-density housing.

But the most successful of the various types of cluster dwellings has been the detached single-family home, although the definition of cluster housing includes attached townhouses and condominiums.

More important, the appeal of these smaller homes has been growing steadily, much to the benefit of both builders and buyers.

"For the developer, cluster housing means maximizing the density on a site while still giving the buyer something of a semblance of what they consider to be the American Dream: the detached single-family home," said Mark Hopkins, president of Otis Associates, designers of many cluster home projects around Chicago.

Because they are smaller, they are less expensive to build. Developers say cluster housing allows buyers to own single-family homes at prices near or slightly above attached townhomes or luxury condominiums.

"You can serve more people and yet cut your development costs," said Richard Van Schaardenburg, president of Town & Country Homes, which is building cluster

homes at the Enclave in northwest suburban Arlington Heights.

"But the tradeoff is that you need to provide recreational space or additional green space someplace else in the development."

The Enclave consists of 102 single-family detached condominiums, ranging in size from 1,550 to slightly more than 2,000 square feet.

Despite the austerity angle, cluster homes are not bargain basement developments, say the developers. The interiors of such dwellings are usually replete with amenities. And the small exterior spaces are given a lot of attention.

"We strive very hard to give the buyer a luxury interior," said developer Robert Ranquist, who has five cluster housing developments underway in the western suburbs.

"And we strive to provide them with enough yard space and exterior space to entertain and have adequate privacy."

Plenty of upscale cluster housing can be found in the Chicago area, too, including the dwellings being built at the Wynstone development, a 750-acre North Barrington residential community built around a Jack Nicklaus-designed golf course.

There, cluster homes, from about 3,100 square feet to 4,400 square feet, start at $400,000 and cost as much as $750,000. "These homes have a classic curb appeal that you would find in most upscale single-family developments," said Norman Hassinger Jr., chairman of the Hassinger Companies, whose home-building subsidiary, Hoffman Homes, is one of the builders at Wynstone.

Hassinger's Wynstone houses will include the Falls, 36 dwellings around two lakes; and the Grove, 27 homes to be built along the 10th hole of the golf course.

One reason for the upscale nature of some cluster housing is the market it draws: sophisticated

movedown buyers, including active retirees or preretirees and empty-nesters.

"The movedown buyer has already owned three, four or five homes, so they're a little older and a little wiser," said Jerry Hoskins, director of sales and marketing for the Zale Group, which has built cluster housing at the Woodlands of Fiore, a development in Buffalo Grove. "They're not exactly price buyers. Instead, they're buying lifestyles, amenities and location."

Multifamily residences at the Woodlands of Fiore will include 136 townhouses and 252 carriage homes.

What greatly appeals to the movedown buyer is the cluster home's single-family familiarity.

"The empty-nester wants something that lives like their old single-family home," Hopkins said. "Something that has nice large spaces. But not a lot of spaces."

In addition, they're attracted by the low-maintenance programs, usually associated with townhouse and condominium developments.

"Buyers have become more conscious of their leisure time and they no longer want maintenance worries," Hoskins said.

In addition to empty-nesters, the cluster housing concept appeals to young professional couples, also lured by the attraction of a single-family home and low maintenance.

Another big draw of the cluster concept is the seclusion afforded by a single-family setting.

"The big issue is privacy," said Van Schaardenburg. "No matter how soundproof an (attached) home is, people are still concerned about hearing their neighbors through the wall. And typically with detached housing you can create more private back yards and patio areas than you can with attached housing."

With the graying of home buyers, developers believe the concept of cluster homes will be going strong well into the next decade.

Figure 9.3 No one project reported here was large, but all who were quoted are experts.
(©Copyrighted, Chicago Tribune Company, all rights reserved, used with permission.)

Whether or not you are involved in an exclusive relationship with a publication, if it is important that you hit the market with something within the next business quarter, you should consider another avenue of publicity.

Speaking

Making speeches and participating in seminars can be effective in generating new business. Similar to appearing in print, being a designated speaker makes you an expert, not just to the people who attend, but to everyone to whom the event is announced. The largest commission that came from one panel discussion did not come from someone who attended; rather, the client saw the announcement for the seminar on someone's coffee table and called one of the participants.

Good results can be obtained through speaking because generally the audience is already interested in your subject, or they would not attend. These opportunities also allow you to follow up leads by collecting cards, obtaining the registration list, etc.

Making speeches has several results with respect to the press. Your participation in the event can be announced to the press. The speech can be recycled as an article for a magazine, often with better results than offering to write an article on the same subject without the prior endorsement of another body. Then you can make a reprint of the article to circulate to your mailing list, etc.

Such success is contingent on the compatibility between the audience and your subject matter, and the extent to which both are suited to achieve your practice's objectives. The more helpful the speech is to its audience, the more tangible your results. "How to . . ." or "New methods of . . ." will be far more likely to generate a specific client than "Theories of. . . ." The issue is simple: People who attend a speech want to learn something concrete that will help them solve a problem. If they think they need help doing something correctly, since your speech gave them an idea, they are likely to call you.

Possible subjects include the applicability of a particular design solution to various circumstances, effective methods of managing the design process, responsibilities of participants as the result of a reconfigured owner, design, and construction team, or a case study of how a particularly sticky problem was solved.

For most firms, the ideal audience is one composed of potential clients: trade associations of those industries in which your firm works, such as conventions and meetings of the American Hospital Association or the various state school board associations; the professional organizations of decision makers within your client base, such as the International Association of Real Estate Corporate Executives, the International Facility Managers Association (IFMA), or architectural and engineering organizations *populated by those professionals who are employed by industry*.

Selecting an audience of peers makes sense for several good marketing reasons. In addition to an obligation to contribute to the profession, some firms feel it is important to elevate their image in their professional community. It helps recruitment and it looks good on credentials statements to see that a member of the firm has been selected to speak before its own professional organization. High school career days, marketing peer groups, such as the Society for Marketing Professional Services (SMPS), Rotary, and other service organizations are examples of groups that will not necessarily generate work but are terrific speaking practice for younger, less experienced members of your firm. It is training for the IFMA speech he or she will give in a couple of years. Since it gives exposure, presenting any good speech has a marketing benefit. New contacts will be made in a positive context.

Many firms are teaming up with allied professionals to sponsor seminars: architects, telephone consultants, and accountants on cost-efficient facility management; developers, mechanical engineers, and lawyers on building renovation. They share mailing lists and promotional costs and solidify bonds within their referral networks. It is, however, extremely time-consuming. If you have not done it before, consider teaming with someone who has, probably a large accounting firm or law firm. They often tackle these endeavors.

Advertising

In earlier days, advertising was anathema to any professional services firm, from lawyers to architects to accountants and engineers. Long before the word itself was accepted, professionals were advertising, though not through display or electronic media advertising. Many sent newsletters and announcements, and nearly everyone sent Christmas cards. All of these are direct mail advertising.

Print and Electronic Media   Conventional media advertising is today considered more acceptable to professional services firms than it was in the past, but it is still used only by a limited number of design firms. This is not necessarily for lack of imagination, but for lack of funds. Television, radio, newspaper, and magazine advertising is costly, even if done poorly. In the print media, space costs $1500 to $8000 per insert, depending on the dimensions of the advertisement and the size of the publication's readership. A one-third-page ad in most national trade publications whose readers concentrate on your market is likely to cost between $2500 and $4000 each time the ad runs (Fig. 9.4).

Running an ad once is not enough. Repetition is the heart of advertising (display, electronic, or direct mail). And the costs do not end with placement. Concept design fees, typesetting, artwork, and, ideally, market research to ensure that message and the medium match ordinarily cost at least as much as one or two placements (Fig. 9.5).

One small general contractor was able to launch a 6-month advertising program in an AIA chapter newsletter for a total cost of $2000. That is exceptionally rare. Some major design and construction industry press have special services advertising sections where design organizations may obtain special rates in specific editions. Often these publications permit copy to be in "editorial style" (called "advertorials"), so that they are suitable for reprints, and often the publication, at no charge, will design a layout. Some design firms are emulating the real estate and finance industries and taking out "tombstone" ads (type only except, perhaps, a logo) announcing that they have obtained a new commission, and perhaps thanking the new client for the confidence placed in them.

Ordinarily you should not embark on advertising as a significant part of marketing with a budget any less than $50,000 per year for advertising alone. If the firm can afford this level of effort, some further issues must be considered.

- If you are strictly building name recognition, a highly specific statement of your services is not crucial; that you do corporate interiors can be conveyed through an image and your name.

- If you hope to get inquiries as a result of the series of ads, the more limited and specific the message, the more impact it will have. "Consulting Engineering" and "Architecture and Planning" are simply not enough. Instead, consider: "Structural Engineering for Garage Owners and Managers" and "Matching Shopping Center Design to Community Character."

- If you want people to notice and respond to your ad, it must be boldly designed and large enough to compete with industry ads. While you may be scared of advertising, if you do it, you cannot be timid.

- If you want to know if the ad is worthwhile, establish a monitoring system to track the phone calls that come in as a result of the ad. That means training receptionists and anybody else to whom requests may be funneled to determine the source of the call and

Figure 9.4   One architect in a recruiting mode placed an ad in a regional design magazine to elevate awareness of the firm among young architects. *(Courtesy of Prisco Duffy & Associates, Ltd., Naperville, Illinois.)*

Figure 9.5 Bold ad draws on facility managers' need for strong references. *(Courtesy of Construction Technology Laboratories, Inc., Skokie, Illinois.)*

to keep track of various sources. It means tracking reader response cards (the cards the magazine provides for the reader to request more information) and tying responses to the date, content, and location of the ad.

Radio advertising is similar to print advertising. In smaller markets, the costs may not be as prohibitive as in major metropolitan areas, but the need for specific subject matter and extremely well-written copy still predominates. The listener must know what you are selling.

Several major firms have used public television as an outlet for image-building advertising, sometimes through conventional sponsorship, sometimes more subtly. In Chicago, Skidmore Owings & Merrill provides its CADD-generated Chicago skyline for use as the introductory and closing graphics on the local version of "Washington Week in Review." SOM is credited at the end of the show.

Newsletters Formatted as a magazine, a newspaper, or a bulletin, black and white, two-color or full-color, newsletters are becoming increasingly popular in the design and construction industry (Fig. 9.6). A newsletter is the most substantive form of direct mail advertising. Its objective is to expose the firm regularly to a controlled audience with a controlled message. The content hopefully will stimulate the reader to circulate the edition among his or her colleagues and to look forward to the next edition.

Developing a newsletter offers two advantages over relying on press coverage to tell a story. The first is control—you control how a subject is treated, who the audience is, and when they will see it. The second advantage is the opportunity it provides to report on a project type in which the firm does not yet have experience sufficient to obtain press coverage. The press will rarely publish a project that is still in design, particularly if it is the first one of its kind for your firm. In your newsletter, however, you may report on any project you wish at any stage of its development. You may draw analogies, just as you would in an interview, that demonstrate how this project type is not new for you after all. For example, you have done labs for colleges; they are just like the labs for this industrial research lab you have just been retained to design.

A newsletter ideally has two components: first, a small section containing straightforward advertising, usually in the form of announcements of new projects, recently completed projects, and recently received awards. Second, an outstanding newsletter will devote the majority of its space to educating the reader. Within this context, some will have outside contributors give advice, usually on the management of the design or construction process.

The reader can be educated in a number of ways. Environmental and other engineers that deal with often-changing regulations report on these events. This is also a topic for specialty architects who monitor regulations affecting particular owners, such as asbestos in public facilities or new land use policies in a section of a metropolitan area. New techniques that make a project run more smoothly for the client can be reported. Cost- and time-beneficial applications of CADD is another subject for a newsletter.

TurnerAction

Attention to Client's Daily Activities Drives Hospital Renovation

On three diverse assignments for Rush-Presbyterian-St. Luke's Medical Center... a recently completed 70,000 square foot perinatal department, its accompanying 5-story physical plant, and a new 11-story professional office building currently in progress... Turner Construction addressed the need to minimize disruption to staff and patients while working in and around existing, functioning buildings. "Construction within a hospital takes second place to the primary business of running a health care institution," stated George Hoehl, Turner's Project Executive for all three assignments. "The construction team has to respect and work with the hospital staff. It requires coordination, flexibility and teamwork."

The Perinatal Department

Providing general contracting services for the renovation of the hospital's sixth floor into a new 70,000 square foot perinatal department, Turner's intensive coordination with the activities of staff and patients allowed the fifth and seventh floors to remain fully operational during construction. Potential problems in transporting workmen and materials on hospital elevators was alleviated by installing an exterior hoist which brought both materials and men onto the sixth floor.

(Continued on Page 5)

Marco Lorenzetti, Hedrich-Blessing

The Special Care Nursery in Rush-Presbyterian-St. Luke's Medical Center's new perinatal department provides state-of-the-art care for newborns.

INSIDE

Figure 9.6   Newsletter articles point to challenges posed by projects. *(Courtesy of Turner Construction Company.)*

A project description must place priority on the owner's objectives and the ways the firm's activities have contributed to meeting these objectives. Care must be taken to accept credit for only your areas of responsibility, not an aspect of the job under the domain of another member of the team. An engineering firm can report on an AIA award received for a project on which it worked. It is more credible, and more fair, to congratulate the architect; and the architect should do the same for an ASHRAE (American Society of Heating, Refrigerating and Air-Conditioning Engineers) award-winning engineer.

Newsletters are time-consuming, and doing them well is expensive. Just as with a brochure, if there is photography, it must be of excellent quality. Good typesetting is essential. The design of the newsletter is especially important for architects and interior designers.

Other Direct Mail To have your name seen frequently by existing and prospective clientele is the objective of direct mail. In the past, it was customary to send a wedding invitation–like announcement for new key personnel, new principals, a new location, or an award. This is still being done. These pieces are increasingly attractively designed. If announcements or other materials appear to have been thrown together, you may leave the impression that you do not care how they look.

To make creating announcements easier, firms are establishing a rigid announcement format so that information can simply be slid in. Firms often preprint large quantities of small, well-designed folders and then print the announcements on tissue or card stock for insertion in the folder (Fig. 9.7). Batching techniques not only save time but usually substantially reduce the unit cost.

Visibility

The foregoing discussion was limited to getting your name before your clientele, principally through a formal medium of communication. For most firms, however, most public relations efforts were, and are, in person: "The Old Boy Network." If the volume of work needed to maintain and grow a practice were not prohibitively large, meeting people would still be the preferred public relations tool, even to the exclusion of all else. Professional services relationships are built on trust. No other form of marketing rivals personal contact as a means to establish the necessary relationships for gaining new work.

With competitors' increasing sophistication, meeting people cannot stand alone. It must be supplemented with other public relations techniques. It is important to remember that, to the degree there is time to meet people in person, these opportunities need the same level of strategic thinking as do the other more formal techniques.

Activities to maintain and further relationships with acquaintances are different from creating opportunities to meet new people. The people you know—your clients, associated firms, the press, your banker, lawyer, accountant, dentist, insurance agent—can be courted through conventional entertainment. Conventional does not mean without thought. Your banker wants to know your developer client and a law client will want to know a banker and a developer. So if arranging a golf game, try to put together a group that wants to meet each other. You are the catalyst. Thus, you are a valuable person to know.

Giving a party is primarily a means to say thank you to your clients, associates, and those who refer new business. An annual party will be attended if it is in an interesting place, has reasonably good food and an adequate amount to drink, and provides good contacts for your

Figure 9.7 A small firm ran four announcement cards at the same time to save costs but will mail them at 1-month intervals. *(Courtesy of Empeco, Inc., General Contractor, Northbrook, Illinois.)*

guests. If the room is too big or too cold, or if you exert no effort to introduce people who should know each other, people will not attend your next event.

Meeting people you do not know takes a similar effort. Join organizations to which you are willing to commit time and that include people who are either themselves potential clients or are in a position to refer clients. With a commitment of a few years, you should be able to get some work if you have selected the group wisely and have assumed some level of leadership.

Selecting an organization to join depends on the nature of your work. For example, one recreational facility architect is an active member of every golf club he can afford. In addition, a woman principal of an interior architecture firm is active in every executive women's organization that meets regularly. She is also a member of the most prestigious speaking club in the area, to which she regularly invites clients to hear major national speakers. Few new prospects arise where she is without someone to call to get more information.

If the group has a regular speakers program, you can work to become a speaker. It is also effective to be on the committee that invites speakers. It provides an excuse to call people and do them a favor, even if they decline to speak. The same principle applies to groups that publish a newsletter. Try to become a member of the editorial board so that you can invite people to contribute articles.

Techniques That Bridge Public Relations and Sales

Some marketing tactics are principally sales tools. They generally are designed to address specific new project opportunities and are introduced only when a specific prospect has been uncovered or as a part of the lead-generating (rather than image-building) process. These tactics include corporate brochures, videotapes, and convention exhibits. Each of these has a public relations component and can be used judiciously in a public relations program.

Video

Video has not yet found a comfortable niche in marketing design services. Many firms have experimented with video presentations, some with success. Video allows the presentation of a tremendous amount of information and images in a very short time. With video you can create the impression of a larger volume of work than you actually have by using dynamic motion in tandem with a tight script to capture the attention of the audience. With exciting graphics, a video can present the design process so often required in formal interviews more effectively than can most architects or engineers in person.

Most firms have found video to be too expensive, except in the most important sales opportunities. One architectural engineering expert in sports stadia shows NFL and NCAA tapes of games that have occurred within stadia the firm has designed. They never have to say "if the firm's good enough for all of these championship teams, it must be good enough for you." The message is clear and the audience is rapt.

Another large national firm used video to convey two impressions considered critical to being awarded a specific downtown bank project. Although the primary competition for the job had done many more banks and highrises than this team, they had a reputation for devaluing local associates. Proper consideration of the local associate was key to this job. Through the careful use of scripts and pace of visuals, video allowed the firm to project an image of having long experience in designing buildings of lasting quality. In addition, the local associate narrated the tape, thereby subtly confirming that the associate was a valuable member of the larger firm's team. After the formal presentation, each member of the selection panel received a copy of the tape.

For virtually any firm to make the use of video cost-effective, a by-product beyond a specific interview is beneficial. In the case of the stadium, the tape is generic; it can be used at any interview for a stadium. For the banking tape, however, the voice-over was edited to be less project-specific and the tape was subsequently used as the focal point at exhibits and at firm parties.

Exhibits

Firms of all kinds increasingly are exhibiting at the trade shows and conventions of potential clients. Environmental engineers exhibit at structural engineering and architectural meetings; architects exhibit at shopping center, school board, park district, health facility, and real estate conventions. This is technically part of the lead generating and sales effort. For every business card you collect, however, some very high multiple sees your exhibit and assesses your quality, sophistication, and success based on what they see. Thus, exhibits flow into the realm of public relations.

Brochures

Firm brochures generally are used only once a prospect is identified. They usually are, or should be, too expensive to use in direct mail. However, if you have a flexible brochure system, one that dedicates a page per project (tear sheets), or one that dedicates a unit (one page or four) to a service or building type, it is feasible and useful to use selected parts of your system for direct mail, usually accompanied by a letter. It may be more economical to use a brochure page, produced in quantity, as a new project announcement than to design and produce a separate project announcement card in a limited quantity. In all likelihood, you would not do the latter.

Future Trends

As architectural and engineering firms come to recognize that they are businesses and professional service is their product, so too they will emulate the methods and style of marketing in industry. They will accept marketing time and materials as necessary costs of doing business, and they will do all aspects of marketing and sales more deliberately and more creatively.

Increasingly they will use outside graphic design, public relations, and advertising agencies to design and implement their press relations, direct mail, and brochure programs. Even small firms have begun to acknowledge that their business is doing architecture or doing engineering and that their interests are best served by spending time on serving clients and meeting prospective clients. They are letting promotional communications professionals advise them on the appropriate tools to obtain new work. As a result, their communications materials are becoming more and more creative, and the level of creativity will continue to increase. In speaking, press, direct mail, and brochures, there will be fewer project descriptions and more client-benefits-oriented copy. In direct mail and brochures, there will be fewer definitive photographs and more conceptual artwork. All materials will be tailored to specific markets. For many firms this means developing several brochures, several mailing lists, and multiple systems to target the specific needs of each client type, building type, or service type. All of this will cost more.

Telecommunications and video will be used more extensively. Videotapes rather than print materials will be sent through the mail to announce the completion of new projects, tour an award-winning project, introduce new staff, or tour new offices. In the foreseeable future the American psyche will continue to pay more attention to video than to print. Thus, a message on video has greater impact. Similarly, until video mailings become routine, it will be the rare recipient who will throw away a video.

The professions haven't begun to tap the promotional opportunities of facsimile transmission. As more companies obtain equipment that receives on ordinary paper and has programmed transmittal to allow lower-rate nighttime transmittal, and as color FAX is developed, companies will distribute direct mail over the phone lines. For many types of communications, quality will not be compromised and costs will be reduced.

The future will be characterized by increased sophistication in business methods and in the use of technology, much of which we cannot even contemplate today. The techniques available to introduce a firm to its marketplace are endless. The only limitations are your imagination and your understanding of your own objectives, financial and personnel resources, and in particular, the interests of your clients. No professional firm can be criticized for aggressive marketing and public relations as long as its tactics are tasteful, honest, and relevant.

Bibliography

American Consulting Engineers Council (ACEC), "The Brochure on Brochures," Washington, D.C., 1983.

American Consulting Engineers Council (ACEC), "The Industrial Market for Consulting Engineers," Washington, D.C., series of four produced 1985–1987.

American Consulting Engineers Council (ACEC), "Membership Directory," Washington, D.C.

American Consulting Engineers Council (ACEC), "Public Relations Guide for Consulting Engineers," Washington, D.C.

Architects Handbook of Professional Practice, vol. 1, chap. 1–14, "Marketing and Public Relations Services," The American Institute of Architects, Washington, D.C., 1988.

Bertrand, Kate, "Divide and Conquer: Identifying Market Segments and Catering to Them Can Increase Profit—in Most Any Industry," *Business Marketing,* October 1989.

Birnberg & Associates and The Profit Center, *Small Design Firm Marketing Manual,* Chicago, 1983.

Birnberg & Associates and The Profit Center, *Public Relations for Small Design Firms,* Chicago, 1988.

Coxe, Weld, *Marketing Architectural and Engineering Services,* Van Nostrand Reinhold, New York, 1983.

Creel, Diane, *Indirect Marketing: Marketing Information Report 4,* Society for Marketing Professional Services, Alexandria, Va.

Kotler, Phillip, and Paul N. Bloom, *Marketing Professional Design Services,* Prentice-Hall, Englewood Cliffs, N.J., 1984.

Levitt, Theodore, *The Marketing Imagination,* The Free Press, New York, 1983.

Lord, Barbara, ed., *The Design and Building Awards Directory,* Lord Communications and the A/E Marketing Journal, Newton, Mass., 1984.

Lord, Barbara, ed., *The Design and Building Industry's Publicity Directory,* Lord Communications and the A/E Marketing Journal, Newton, Mass., 1989.

Marketing Architectural Services for Health Care, Profile 85, Official Directory of the American Institute of Architects, Washington, D.C., 1985.

Neuman, Connie, "The Lady Moves Engineers, Long in the Wings, to Stage Center," *Public Relations Quarterly,* vol. 32, no. 2, summer 1987, pp. 17–20.

Neuman, Connie, *Performance Marketing for Contractors: A Comprehensive Guide to Selling Construction Services,* Builders Association of Chicago Marketing Committee, 1989.

Rosenzweig, Patricia P., "Public Relations and Promotions: What's Right for My Firm" (transcription from SMPS Marketing Coordinators Workshop), May 17, 1986.

Rosenzweig, Patricia P., "Selection Criteria: Which of Your Projects Is Publishable," *CCAIA Focus,* 1987.

10

Trends Affecting Profits in the Near Future

Steven A. Etkin

The methods used during the 1980s for annual profit planning need to evolve from their emphasis on billable hours to assets under management. The approach used in the 1980s was based on an estimate of revenues from work under contract, outstanding proposals, and requests for proposals. The revenue projection was translated into billable hours. Billable hours were then used to develop billing rates. The combination of billable hours and billing rates formed the annual profit plan. Because projected profits were at the end of this chain of calculations, this approach seemed appropriate for firms attempting to assign all their staff hours or where profit planning was of secondary importance.

For firms that wish to place a greater emphasis on profits, the annual profit target should serve as the primary input to the planning process rather than as a result of billable hours. Before this approach is explained, it is worthwhile to characterize the billable hours process used in the 1980s.

Billable Hours Approach

The billable hours planning approach of the 1980s employed a four-step approach:

Revenue projection

Staffing requirements

General and administrative expenses

Billing rates

Revenue Projection

The first step in the conventional approach called for developing an estimate of revenue to be earned by the firm. The revenue projection established anticipated revenues from projects under contract and those in negotiation, and a probabilistic approach to those being bid. With the estimate of revenue available, the second step is to develop the staffing requirements.

Staffing Requirements

The staffing requirements are developed based on the amount of professional services that are required to meet the project's needs and to generate the anticipated revenues. These requirements are developed through a matrix approach that takes into account the number of professional billable staff, their salaries, and their number of billable and nonbillable hours.

General and Administrative Expenses

The general and administrative expenses account for all the remaining expenses that are not directly billable. Professional direct billable hours often are used to estimate the general and administrative expenses. They are based on what would be needed to support the project staff and nonproject specific activities, such as marketing, accounting, and office management. While these expenses are nonreimbursable, they do need to be accounted for when determining profitability.

Billing Rates

With the revenue potential calculated in the first step and the expense estimates developed in the second two steps, the traditional approach calls for developing billing rates. In this final step, billing rates for direct labor hours, which incorporated direct and indirect expenses plus a margin for profit, are developed. The profit margin is the amount that is added to the billing rate in addition to the direct and indirect expenses.

This approach is acceptable in an environment where the firm wishes to sustain its position or whose value structure is based more on maintaining billable hours. It is not the type of approach whereby a firm places an economic value on its asset base and services, and then seeks a return on this "investment" comparable with what the financial market might offer at a similar level of investment and associated risk.

An investment value basis to business planning should follow these steps:

Profit target

Business volume target

Annual budget

Compensation methods

To help illustrate the investment value approach, a hypothetical firm with the following characteristics is used:

The Hypothetical Firm

Staff

Principal or partner	2
Manager	3
Architects	10
Technical staff	4
Nontechnical staff	1
Administrative and clerical	2
Total	22

Direct (billable) labor hours   22,900

Total (gross) revenues	$1,500,000

Less:		
	Outside consultants, e.g., engineers	(275,000)
	Reimbursable expenses	(65,000)
	Project equipment and furnishings	(35,000)

Net (operating) revenues	$1,125,000
Net profit before taxes	$47,300

Assets

	Current	$383,000
	Other	128,000
	Total assets	$511,000

Liabilities

	Current	$170,000
	Long-term	80,000
	Total liabilities	$250,000

Equity

	Capital	$ 35,000
	Retained earnings	226,000
	Total equity	$261,000
	Total equity and liability	$511,000

Historical information

Net profit before taxes on net revenues	4.2%
Net profit before taxes per direct labor hour	$1.75
Direct expenses* per direct labor hour	$15.50
General and administrative expense per direct labor hour	157%

*Includes direct nonreimbursable expenses

Establishing a Profit Target

The profit target is the first step of profit planning. To establish a profit target, an expense basis must be chosen that is compatible with how the firm is managed. There are at least three bases to choose from: annual operating expenses, equity or investment, or assets.

Choosing an Expense Basis Some firms prefer to keep the equity account to a minimum. Hence in those firms, the equity basis would not be appropriate. Other firms may choose a strategy to have a low asset base and lease their equipment and office space. The choice of expense basis also depends on which other businesses the firm wants to compare its financial performance with. As an example, professional services firms tend to value their financial performance based on the level of equity in the firm. Product-related businesses tend to compare the basis of return on assets under management, which is used to measure how well management uses the company's resources.

Determining the Economic Value   Once the expense basis is selected, the next action is to develop an economic value of those expenses. One approach is the opportunity cost associated with those expenses. That is, what yield would those expenses earn if they were employed elsewhere, as in the debt market? A key consideration here is to pick an alternative investment opportunity comparable in risk of return to operating a design firm. As an example, it would not be reasonable to choose a government security, such as a Treasury Bill, because of its low risk.

For the purposes of the example, the hypothetical firm chooses to use the equity basis as the expense basis and the prime rate plus 6 percentage points. The addition of 6 percentage points suggests a risk of return of 50 percent higher than a commercial bank would accept from its best customer.

Calculating the Profit Target   The firm's profit target is calculated by multiplying the equity level in the firm, $261,000, by 18 percent (assuming a prime rate of 12 percent). Therefore, the firm's annual profit target is $47,000 before taxes.

In summary, the steps to establishing an annual profit target are

1. Choose expense basis: operating, investment (equity), or asset.

2. Determine opportunity cost of expenses.

3. Multiply expense basis times opportunity costs.

The Annual Business Volume Target

With the profit target established, the next step is to determine the amount of business required to achieve the desired return on expenses, equity, or assets. The volume of business can be measured in different ways. One approach is to determine the amount of net revenue (gross revenues less consultant expenses, reimbursable expenses, project equipment and furnishings, etc.) the firm needs to generate during the year. A second approach is to determine the amount of direct labor hours that need to be billed during the year.

The use of historical information generated from the firm's prior years of operation can facilitate many of the calculations. Two historical figures are needed in combination with the profit target to establish the business volume target. One figure is the amount of profits achieved per direct labor hour charged. The second is the amount of profits achieved per net revenue dollar received.

Historical data from the hypothetical firm are used for the example. The hypothetical firm was able to generate $1.75 in profits on each direct labor hour billed and $4.20 in profits on each $100 in net revenues. Therefore, in order to achieve profits of $47,000, they need to bill 26,900 direct labor hours ($47,000 divided by $1.75) and they need to collect $1,119,000 in net revenues ($47,000 divided by $4.20).

Calculating the Business Volume Target

1. Measure historical level of profits per direct labor hour.

2. Measure historical level of profits per net revenue dollar.

3. Calculate business income requirements.

4. Calculate billable hours.

The Annual Firm Budget

The annual budget can be derived from historical data and the business volume target. The two historical statistics needed are the actual cost per direct labor hour and the ratio of general and administrative expenses to direct labor expenses. The hypothetical firm's historical cost (labor and direct nonreimbursable expenses) per direct labor hour is $15.50. The historical overhead rate (including bonuses and incentive compensation but excluding profits) is 157 percent. Therefore, the firm's annual expense budget should be $417,000 for direct labor (26,900 hours multiplied by $15.50) and $655,000 for the remaining direct and indirect expenses ($417,000 multiplied by 157 percent). The firm's total expense budget is $1,072,000 ($417,000 plus $655,000).

Calculating the Annual Budget

1. Measure historical level of general and administrative expenses (overhead) per direct labor expense.

2. Measure historical level of the cost of a direct labor hour.

3. Calculate direct labor expense and nonreimbursable expenses.

4. Calculate general and administrative expense.

The Compensation Method

Several kinds of compensation methods are used by firms to bill their clients. The more common ones are cost-plus-fee, stipulated sum, percentage of construction cost, and unit cost. The variations between these methods are described briefly:

A *cost-plus-fee* recovers the actual costs incurred in providing a specific set of services plus a provision for profit (these methods include multiple of direct salary expense, multiple of direct personnel expense, professional fee plus expenses, and hourly or daily billing rates).

A *stipulated sum* is a fixed amount of compensation for a specific set of services performed.

A *percentage of construction cost* relates compensation to the cost of constructing the project.

A *unit cost* relates compensation to specific units of the project, such as square feet of construction.

A 1989 survey by the American Institute of Architects illustrates the frequency with which various compensation methods are used.

Compensation method	Frequency of use, %
Cost-plus-fee	37
Stipulated sum	36
Percentage of construction cost	22
Unit cost	4
Other	1

Other Trends Affecting Profits

This profit planning approach is largely quantitative and does not take into account changes to the business environment. The reality of the near future is that the ability of a firm to achieve its profit plan in the current year has much more to do with its business strategy and positioning done in the prior year(s) than in simply putting together an annual plan. The distinction between the annual profit plan and a multiyear business plan is becoming increasingly blurred. A firm's position relative to their market(s) is a stronger determinant of its profit potential than any amount of profit planning or ongoing ratio monitoring and analysis.

Profit planning also should be considered on a multiyear basis. The plan must balance between profit distributions in a current year and reinvestment for future years' growth.

Profits are thought of as surplus cash after all expenses have been met. The concept of profits needs to take on a broader definition that is more closely aligned with the character and values of the firm. For example, an owner might gain a great deal of personal satisfaction from receiving an award. If the owner had to sacrifice some level of profits to attain a design quality that resulted in the award, should not the goodwill and recognition generated by the award fall within a "profit mix"?

Bibliography

The Architect's Handbook of Professional Practice, 11th ed., The American Institute of Architects, Washington, D.C., 1988.

Financial Performance Survey for Design Firms, Birnberg & Associates, Chicago (latest edition).

The 1989 AIA Firm Survey Report, The American Institute of Architects, Washington, D.C., 1989.

How to Write a Business Plan, 2d ed., American Management Association, and Education for Management, Inc., New York, 1986.

11

Project Fee Budgeting

Steve L. Wintner, AIA

A traveler who does not plan his journey
will only end up where he is headed.
—CONFUCIUS

And so it would be for any design professional who would attempt to negotiate a fee proposal or complete a project without a "road map" called the project fee budget.

Primary Aspects of Project Fee Budgeting

1. Development of an estimated fee to be negotiated with the client

2. Defined scope of services

3. Preparation of a detailed fee budget

4. Implementation and monitoring of the project fee budget through each phase of the project

What You Need to Know

Before a project fee budget can be prepared, several important elements must be identified. Without this information the project fee budget can only be an estimate of what it will cost in time and money to complete the project.

Scope of Services

When a client issues a request for proposal (RFP), it usually contains a detailed description of the proposed project. It may not, however, include a detailed definition of the scope of services required to design, produce, and administer the proposed project. If this information is not included in the RFP, it is essential that the design professional request that the client provide it. To attempt to develop a project fee budget in response to an RFP without this information would be as foolhardy as driving without the benefit of a road map to a city you have only heard about and have no idea how to get there. You might be able to start your trip, but you are likely to waste a lot of time and gas driving around trying to find your destination. You will undoubtedly have to stop several times to ask for directions. So why not ask for directions before you embark and save yourself the aggravation, frustration, and cost of getting lost?

Asking clients to identify the specific services they expect you to provide not only will help you develop your fee budget but will also enhance your credibility with your clients. It will show your interest in the project through your request for information that is essential to the submittal of a well-developed proposal. Perhaps a review of AIA Documents B161 and B162—Designated Services* would be an appropriate means for determining the client's needs and the services required.

Included in the designated scope of services should be some indication about the requirements for the appropriate consultant services for the project. Once identified, each of these consultants should be contacted and asked to submit their fee and scope of services proposals for inclusion in your response to the RFP. These consultant fees may or may not be marked up by an appropriate percentage prior to inclusion in your RFP response. These markups range from 5 to 20 percent depending on the services required and prevailing market conditions. It should be noted that if your markup is excessive, you risk having a noncompetitive fee proposal and thereby reduce your chances of being selected for the project. The type of fee negotiated will also be a determinant in whether or not you include a markup of your consultant's fees.

Levels of Compensation

Having a clear understanding of the appropriate level of services required to complete a project must be balanced with an adequate level of compensation to deliver the project. This delicate balance serves the interests of both the client and the design professional. It leads to appropriate, competent professional services and thereby a project which meets the expectations, needs, and return on investment for the client.

To determine an appropriate level of compensation for professional services a number of factors must be considered early in the process of establishing the fee. These factors include:

---

*AIA Documents B161–162 are currently being revised by the AIA for publication in 1992.

- *Profitability goals of the firm:* Unless each project takes this factor into consideration and has achieved its goal at the end of the project, other projects will have to bear the burden of its lower profitability.

- *Cost of providing the services:* The cost to the firm for staffing the project and the required supplies and materials to complete the work must be clearly identified and scheduled before profit margins can be established.

- *Backlog of work:* At times a firm might find it appropriate to adjust the level of compensation for a particular project, based on how badly they need the work (adjust compensation downward) or have a strong backlog and don't particularly need the project (adjust compensation upward).

- *Marketing strategy:* When a firm attempts to enter a new market, the level of compensation is likely to be lower than it would be for a firm with strong qualifications in a specialized market. This sometimes is referred to as a "loss leader" with the goal of gaining a foothold in a new market. In any case, the loss leader fee should never be below your break-even point.

- *Value of the services vs. cost:* It is essential that you understand the perceived value of your services to a client and match this to your cost of delivering the services required. In a market where competition from other firms is keen, your value to the client is reduced, unless your firm has a tangible uniqueness that will result in beneficial return on a client's investment.

Fee Basis Types

Having considered the above factors, the design professional must select the fee basis upon which the contract will be negotiated. This selection will have an impact on the development of your fee proposal. The most common fee types upon which your contract might be based are:

- Stipulated Lump Sum (SLS)
- Fixed Fee, Plus Expenses
- Unit Cost Fee
- Hourly, No Maximum
- Hourly, to a Guaranteed Maximum
- Percentage of Construction Cost

Each of these types of fee has a specific basis for how they are calculated and a respective methodology for how they are billed.

- *Stipulated Lump Sum:* Based on value of services to be performed plus cost of project-related expenses. Billed as a percentage of completed work for each phase or as a stipulated amount for each monthly invoice or divided into a specified number of payments during the course of the project. All project-related expenses are included in the SLS and are not invoiced as reimbursables.

- *Fixed Fee, Plus Expenses:* Based and billed the same as an SLS, plus current reimbursable expenses incurred for the invoice period.

- *Unit Cost Fee:* Based on a quantified unit, such as square feet of constructed area or number of rooms or apartments. Billed on an hourly basis at approved standard hourly rates for staff types or specific staff on project. This fee type will usually have an established maximum.

- *Hourly, No Maximum:* Based on actual time and expenses incurred, without any upward limit. Billed on an hourly basis at either a multiple of direct salary or Direct Personnel Expense (DPE), plus expenses incurred for invoice period. Overhead and profit included in DPE and selected multiple.

- *Hourly, to a Guaranteed Maximum:* Based on actual time and expenses incurred, to a specified upward limit. Billed the same as Hourly, No Maximum, except the invoiced amount, exclusive of incurred expenses, cannot exceed a preagreed maximum amount.

Occasions will arise when your clients will want you to work on an hourly basis up to a guaranteed maximum. This means that you will only be able to bill for the hours you spend and then only up to the maximum amount agreed upon. This is essentially the same kind of fee basis as a fixed fee except that here you are subjected to being penalized for your ability to get the work done quickly and efficiently—i.e., the faster you complete the work, the less money you can earn. This is a no-win situation, and you should avoid this fee basis and negotiate for the Fixed Fee plus Expenses method instead. If you can accurately predetermine your related project expenses, the stipulated Lump Sum Method would also be preferable.

- *Percentage of Construction Cost:* Based on the cost of construction of the project rather than the scope of services to be provided. Billed on a percentage of the completed work through the bidding and negotiations phase, the construction administration phase portion of the fee is billed on a monthly basis equal to the percentage complete indicated by the general contractor on the application for payment request. For example, if the application stipulates the project construction is 18.5 percent complete (including approved stored equipment and materials), the design professional's invoice for that month would be 18.5 percent times the portion of the total fee allocated to the construction administration phase.

   Because this fee basis does not take into consideration the level, duration, and complexity of services required, it is another no-win situation and should be avoided if at all possible. Usually this type of fee basis is used on local, state, and federal government projects and can't be avoided. In this case be sure to negotiate that the construction cost basis for your fee will be fixed at the end of the design development phase and the budgeted figure established and approved by the client at that time. During the construction phase additive change orders should increase your fee by the established contract fee percentage, unless created by errors and omissions related to your services. Usually, deduct change orders will not negatively impact your fee.

The determination of an appropriate fee basis and the method and frequency of invoicing should be included in negotiations with your clients. Even if the RFP requests a specific fee basis, you can sometimes successfully lead clients to a more appropriate fee basis that best meets their needs and is more appropriately suited to the project type and its specific circumstances.

On occasion it might be appropriate to start the project on the basis of one fee type and then shift to another type as the project progresses. This situation might occur if, at the outset of the project, the scope of services cannot be specifically defined. It would be to the design professional's benefit in this instance to start the work on an hourly fee basis until the scope could be defined. At that time, the fee basis could be one of the others listed above, with the expended hourly fee credited against an established maximum.

Other Useful Information

As the quality-based selection (QBS) process becomes more prevalent, an RFP may not require you to submit a fee. If you were the selected firm or are one of a group of "short-listed" firms for such a project, you will have more time to carefully develop your project fee budget. In these instances you should have the benefit of other detailed information, about not only the scope of services but also the anticipated complexity of the project, the extent and nature of governmental approvals for those agencies having jurisdiction over the project, the project schedule, client's construction budget, client level of sophistication and knowledge about what is involved to deliver such a project, and whether the project will be an open bid, closed bid, or negotiated construction contract. In addition, any historical financial data from a similar previously completed project will enhance the firm's ability to develop an appropriate fee budget. Each of the above factors will have an impact on the project fee budget and must be considered carefully.

The basis of your project fee budget will be the key financial factors derived from the Profit Plan, as discussed in Chapter 10. Having a clear understanding of the services you will provide and the estimated number of hours each task and/or phase of work will require to complete leaves only the cost of these hours to be computed. To do so, the key financial factors must be applied. The most important of these factors is the overhead rate. The overhead rate is the total cost of indirect expenses divided by the total cost of direct salaries. Example: The indirect expenses for Penniless and Browbeaten are anticipated to be $350,000 for the year and its direct salaries are projected to be $250,000. This then would result in an overhead rate of 1.40, or 140 percent of direct salaries. Unless you know what your overhead rate is for an hour of labor, you cannot determine the cost of your services. If you don't know what your services cost to deliver, you will never know if your projects are profitable or losing money.

The overhead rate times the hourly cost of labor times the number of hours estimated to do the work plus the hourly cost of labor will calculate your cost of services, otherwise known as your "break-even" cost. This cost, when multiplied by a profit percent factor, will establish the bottom line for your fee negotiations.

Example   Assume an overhead rate of 140 percent (1.4) and an hourly salary of $10. The break-even cost using these assumptions would be

$$\text{Overhead rate} \times \text{hourly rate} \times \text{no. of hours} \times \text{hourly rate,}$$
$$\text{or } 1.4 \times \$10 + 10 = \$24 \text{ per hour}$$

Therefore, for every hour of a staff member earning $10 in salary, the cost to the firm is $24.

For each of your projects you can multiply the cost of each member of the staff working on a project by the number of hours for each staff person to determine your break-even cost. Armed with this data, you will be prepared to negotiate effectively with your client and will know when to back out of the negotiation should your client only agree to a fee that is at or below your break-even cost.

Note: In addition to your general and administrative expenses, the overhead rate includes the customary and mandatory benefit expenses commonly referred to as Direct Personnel Expenses (DPE). You would be wise to avoid reference to this phrase in your negotiations and the development of your hourly rates at some contrived multiple of this factor, e.g., 2.75 times DPE. This only subjects you to your clients' intrusion into your business records and a need to justify each element comprising the Direct Personnel Expense factor.

In developing your fee budget, several elements are almost always overlooked as required project tasks or services. These include:

- *Project management:*   During each phase of a project the project manager will spend a substantial number of hours in carrying out required duties. For this reason it would be wise to initially create a separate category in each phase of the project fee budget to account for these required hours.

- *Principals' administration time:*   Because the project manager cannot control the time spent on a project by the principal-in-charge, it is essential that these hours be identified early for each phase as a contract between the project manager and the principal-in-charge and included in the project fee budget. See Budgeting Techniques and Formats, below.

- *Clerical and word processing:*   More and more professional firms are now charging for the cost of their administrative staff to perform the necessary clerical and word processing duties specifically related to a project. A separate category also might be created to account for these required hours in each phase of the project fee budget.

Budgeting Techniques and Formats

Depending on the fee basis type used, you could apply one of the two methods shown in Fig. 11.1 to allocate the project fee budget.

Top-Down Budgeting   This process begins with an established fee, as might be the case with a percentage of construction cost fee or a unit cost fee. Here the fee is first allocated to each of the non-staff-related expenses to ascertain the net fee. This is then allocated as a percentage to each phase or department and when divided by an average hourly billing rate will define the number of staff hours available.

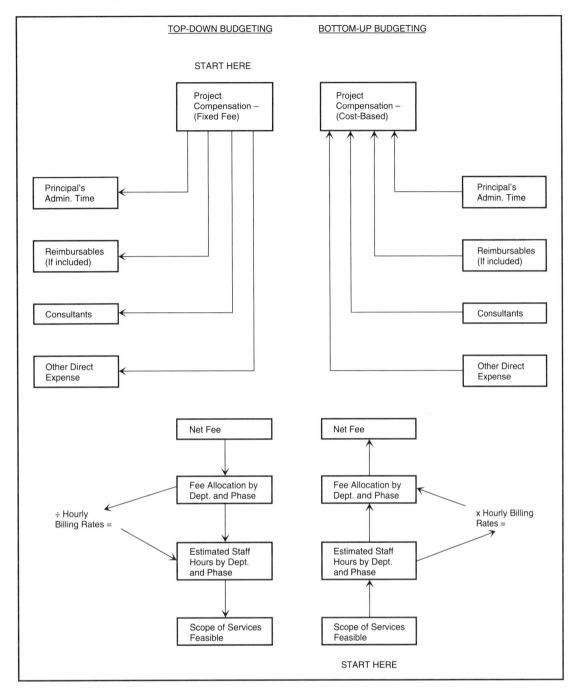

TOP-DOWN BUDGETING   BOTTOM-UP BUDGETING

START HERE

Project Compensation – (Fixed Fee)

Project Compensation – (Cost-Based)

Principal's Admin. Time

Principal's Admin. Time

Reimbursables (If included)

Reimbursables (If included)

Consultants

Consultants

Other Direct Expense

Other Direct Expense

Net Fee

Net Fee

Fee Allocation by Dept. and Phase

Fee Allocation by Dept. and Phase

÷ Hourly Billing Rates =

x Hourly Billing Rates =

Estimated Staff Hours by Dept. and Phase

Estimated Staff Hours by Dept. and Phase

Scope of Services Feasible

Scope of Services Feasible

START HERE

Figure 11.1

These hours then can be matched to the required tasks and services to be provided to see if the fee established is feasible.

Bottom-Up Budgeting or Cost-Based Budgeting   This is just the opposite and obviously a more scientific approach than top-down budgeting. This method could also be used to test the feasibility of a top-down budget. The *AIA Compensation Guidelines for Architectural and Engineering Services** provides an excellent tool for analyzing a budget in this manner.

---

*This publication is in the process of being updated for release in 1992.

Other budgeting techniques that can be used to test a fee include cost per square foot of constructed area or cost per sheet of drawings. Figures 11.2 to 11.5 are different formats that can be used to develop the project fee budget for each phase of the work and allocate costs for principal's time, consultants, reimbursables, and other direct expenses. Each of these formats can be created on Lotus, Symphony, or Excel Spreadsheet software for ease of calculations and necessary revisions.

PROJECT FEE BUDGET

WORKSHEET NO. 1 — METHOD 'A'
STAFF TIME/FEE PROJECTION BY PHASE

Project: _____

Project No.: _____

Date: _____

PHASE	STAFF	HOURS	x BILLING RATE	= FEE
0. General/Start-Up/PM			$ /HR. AVG. $ /HR.	$ SUB-TOTAL: $.
1. Pre-Design			$ /HR. AVG. $ /HR.	$ SUB-TOTAL: $.
2. Schematic Design/ Space Planning			$ /HR. AVG. $ /HR.	$ SUB-TOTAL: $.
3. Design Development			$ /HR. AVG. $ /HR.	$ SUB-TOTAL: $.
4. Construction Documents/Specs			$ /HR. AVG. $ /HR.	$ SUB-TOTAL: $.

Figure 11.2

PHASE	STAFF	HOURS	x BILLING RATE		= FEE	
5. Furnishings Documents/ Furniture Specs			$	/HR.	$	
			AVG. $	/HR.	SUB-TOTAL: $	.
6. Statements of Probable Costs			$	/HR.	$	
			AVG. $	/HR.	SUB-TOTAL: $	.
7. Bidding/Negotiating			$	/HR.	$	
			AVG. $	/HR.	SUB-TOTAL: $	.
8. Contract Administration			$	/HR.	$	
			AVG. $	/HR.	SUB-TOTAL: $	.
9. Close-Out/Move-In			$	/HR.	$	
			AVG. $	/HR.	SUB-TOTAL: $	.

TOTALS: $.
AVG. BILLING RATE/HOUR: $ /HR.

CONSULTANT FEES: $.

CONTINGENCY: _____% x TOTAL ARCH. FEE $.
_____

GRAND TOTAL: $.

Figure 11.2 *(Continued)*

PROJECT FEE BUDGET

<u>WORKSHEET NO. 2 — METHOD 'B'</u>
TASK ASSIGNMENT BY PHASE

Project: _____

Project No.: _____

Date: _____

PHASE	TASK/BY	HOURS	x BILLING RATE	= FEE
0.			$ /HR.	$
General/Start-Up/PM			AVG. $ /HR.	SUB-TOTAL: $.
1.			$ /HR.	$
Pre-Design			AVG. $ /HR.	SUB-TOTAL: $.
2.			$ /HR.	$
Schematic Design/ Space Planning			AVG. $ /HR.	SUB-TOTAL: $.
3.			$ /HR.	$
Design Development			AVG. $ /HR.	SUB-TOTAL: $.
4.			$ /HR.	$
Construction Documents/Specs			AVG. $ /HR.	SUB-TOTAL: $.

Figure 11.3

PHASE	TASK/BY	HOURS	x BILLING RATE	= FEE
5. Furnishings Documents/ Furniture Specs			$ /HR. AVG. $ /HR.	$ SUB-TOTAL: $.
6. Statements of Probable Costs			$ /HR. AVG. $ /HR.	$ SUB-TOTAL: $.
7. Bidding/Negotiating			$ /HR. AVG. $ /HR.	$ SUB-TOTAL: $.
8. Contract Administration			$ /HR. AVG. $ /HR.	$ SUB-TOTAL: $.
9. Close-Out/Move-In			$ /HR. AVG. $ /HR.	$ SUB-TOTAL: $.

TOTALS:
AVG. BILLING RATE/HOUR: $ /HR.

$.

Figure 11.3 *(Continued)*

CONSULTANT FEES:

CONSULTANTS	BASE FEE		FEE x 1.	*
Mechanical	$	.	$	.
Electrical		.		.
Plumbing		.		.
Structural		.		.
Other		.		.
				.

TOTALS: $. $.

CONTINGENCY:

_____% x TOTAL ARCHITECTURAL FEE	$	.

* Indicate Appropriate % of Mark-Up.

Figure 11.3 *(Continued)*

WORKSHEET NO. 3 – METHOD 'C'
FEE ALLOCATION BY %, HOURS/PHASE

Project: _____

Project No.: _____

Date: _____

PHASE	HOURS	x AVG. BILLING RATE	= FEE	% TOTAL
0. General/Start-Up/PM		$. /HR	$.	%
1. Pre-Design		$. /HR	$.	%
2. Schematic Design/Space Planning		$. /HR	$.	%
3. Design Development		$. /HR	$.	%
4. Construction Documents/Specs		$. /HR	$.	%
5. Furnishings Documents/Specs		$. /HR	$.	%
6. Statements of Probable Costs		$. /HR	$.	%
7. Bidding Negotiations		$. /HR	$.	%
8. Contract Administration		$. /HR	$.	%
9. Close-Out/Move-In		$. /HR	$.	%

TOTALS $. /HR $. %

CONSULTANT FEES:

Mechanical	$.	%
Electrical	$.	%
Plumbing	$.	%
Structural	$.	%
Other	$.	%

TOTALS $. %

CONTINGENCY:

_____ % TOTAL ARCHITECTURAL FEE	$.	%

GRAND TOTAL: $. 100%

Figure 11.4

WORKSHEET NO. 3 – METHOD 'D'
PERCENTAGE OF COSTS

Project: _____

Project No.: _____

Date: _____

---

1. **CONSTRUCTION BUDGET:**

   Project Area: _____ SQ.FT. x Construction Cost: $ _____/SQ.FT. (Assumed) =

   a) TOTAL CONSTRUCTION BUDGET: $ _____

2. **FURNITURE BUDGET:**

   Project Area: _____ SQ.FT. x Furniture Cost: $ _____/SQ.FT. (Assumed) =

   a) TOTAL FURNITURE BUDGET: $ _____

   or

   Furniture Cost: $ _____/Person x Number of People _____ =

   b) TOTAL FURNITURE BUDGET: $ _____

3. **ARCHITECT'S FEE (CONSTRUCTION):**

   Construction Budget (1a.) $ _____ x Fee @ _____ % = $ _____

4. **ARCHITECT'S FEE (FURNITURE):**

   Furniture Budget (2a. or 2b) $ _____ x Fee @ _____ % = $ _____

   TOTAL ARCHITECT'S FEE (3 + 4): $ _____

Figure 11.5

Professional service firms traditionally have developed their fees on a time- and cost-based compensation method. This methodology evolved as a result of the elimination of the AIA fee curves by agreement with the U.S. Department of Justice in the mid-1970s. The AIA has since developed several publications on compensation guidelines and management that eventually became the basis for AIA Documents B161 and B162, Standard Form of Agreement between Architect and Owner for Designated Services (AIA, 1977).

Design professionals for years have been looking for new ways to justify their fees and hourly rates to their clients. It may just be that this "justification posture" is the obstacle to achieving higher compensation levels. Instead, more energy could be expended in developing our service to the client. This could include improving our presentation skills, learning to listen better, taking time to understand the client's needs and concerns, and educating clients about the value-added aspect of working with your firm.

David Maister, in his article "Quality Work Doesn't Mean Quality Service" (Maister, 1982), wrote that the key to client satisfaction is the client's perception and expectations in the area of the service they receive and not the services we perform. Maister offers the following formula for client satisfaction:

$$Satisfaction = perception - expectation$$

When a client *perceives* the service we render at a certain level, but *expected* something more or different, the level of *satisfaction* is diminished.

To graphically describe the distinction between service and services and their relative impact on value-based vs. cost-based compensation, consider the following:

> *Services* (tangible product, client expected)
>> = *time-sensitive tasks* (time card hours)
>> = *$ per time fee or cost-based compensation*

Client has a low level of appreciation and understanding of the complexity of these *services*.

> *Service* (nontangible product, not expected by client)
>> = *non-time-sensitive action* (listening, responsive, communicative, collaborative, concerned, etc.)
>> = *$ per value fee or value-based compensation*

Client has a high level of appreciation and understanding of these aspects of *service*.

Most of our clients are able to perceive and appreciate the value of the soft items included in the project delivery process, called service, more easily than the subtleties of the services included in the design process and the technology of the documentation and construction processes. Understanding this distinction then allows for the inclusion of a value-added factor in the development and negotiation of the fees we propose.

"Appropriate compensation comes from negotiating an arrangement, not a fee. We need to educate our clients on the interdependence of quality, time, budget and compensation."*

Consider the impact of the design professional on any project. Creativity, problem solving, concern for health, safety, and welfare of the public, functionality and environmental sensitivity are but a few of the value-added aspects of the design professional's role on any project. The impact of these greatly defines the success of the project, and yet the dollars spent on the design professional's fee are the smallest percentage of all the component financial aspects of a project pro forma.

The relative amount spent for the various aspects of a project might be graphically illustrated as follows:

$	$	$	$
Acquisition and financing of property	Design professional fees	Construction and furnishings	Operations and maintenance

This is how it is, not necessarily how it should be, as far as the design professional is concerned. This situation can be altered to provide for more appropriate compensation for the design professional when the shift to value-based compensation is embraced and practiced.

Project Fee Budget Contingencies

The development of the project fee is contingent upon several factors. These items may or may not require the fee to be increased. The nature and the amount of the increase, if any, will depend on the circumstances involved for each project.

Salary Increases

Depending on the duration of the project, you may have to anticipate increases in staff salaries that will occur during the course of the project. At the same time it's important to maintain a competitive edge with your hourly billing rates. This means that you may have to consider other forms of compensation in lieu of salary increases for your higher-salaried staff members. These types of compensation will also have an impact on the hourly billing rates. Your key financial factors will define the extent of that impact. It would be wise to look at both methods of increased compensation to determine which approach would be more cost-effective.

When your fee basis allows you to bill hourly, you might find that using a schedule of flat fees will cancel the need to negotiate salary

---

*Paul Segal, FAIA—N.Y., architect at New York AIA Convention, 1986.

increases and the discussion of what is included in the direct personal expense (DPE) factor, as previously suggested. In developing your flat hourly rates, the knowledge of several key elements is critical and will help you to calculate the appropriate rates. These include hourly wages, factored for any potential increases for projects of a duration bracketing one or more salary reviews, the overhead rate as previously discussed and the multiple for profit. For each staff member or category of staff an appropriate multiple can be assigned. For staff who will charge more hours to the project and are at a lower salary level, you might use a higher multiple than the one assigned to staff with higher salary rates who will spend less time on the project. This allows you the opportunity to maximize your profit margin for lower-salaried, higher-hour-intensive staff and keep the rates for your higher-salaried, lower-hour-intensive staff at an attractive, competitive market rate.

As an experiment you might consider negotiating for a single hourly flat rate for all team members engaged in the project. This is very seductive to a client who now has to deal with only one hourly rate and yet can still have the most experienced staff and officers of the firm on their project at this "lower" rate. Caution!! This rate must be calculated carefully to include the percentage of time each staff member will be involved, especially the higher-paid members of the team. If you do not have a specific scope of service, you should not consider this alternative approach.

Client Sophistication

This one is difficult to factor into the fee calculation process. The level of sophistication, or rather unsophistication, of your clients could lead to an unexpected expenditure of time. Therefore, your assessment of your client in this regard is very important. If you're wrong, it could be costly to your firm and erode some, if not all, of the project profit margin. If you're going to "hold your client's hand" through the project, you better make allowances to get paid for the service.

Risk Management

The magnitude of exposure to risk will vary from project to project. Regardless of the magnitude, risk management must be a part of your compensation development process. To the extent that you are successful in getting your clients to share your risk, or at least pay for your acceptance of it, you will be that much ahead.

Among the risks to be carefully considered and managed are

Professional liability

Personal liability

Loss of compensation

Loss of profit margin

Be sure to include your professional liability insurance representative in your decisions regarding the management of these risks and their impact on your insurance coverage and premium.

Governmental Jurisdictional Approvals

Some projects are subject to greater governmental review and approval processes than others. It is essential that the extent of governmental reviews and approvals be identified before you establish your final fee. You need to determine the number, type, and submittal requirements for each governmental agency that has jurisdiction over your projects. Allow adequate hours for members of the team to prepare for these reviews, presentations, and approvals.

Miscellaneous

Some unforeseen activity will always arise during the course of any project. These activities might include extra meetings or approval presentations beyond those agreed upon, responses to the contractor for clarifications to the documents, requests from governmental agencies, the need to prepare supplemental drawings or details, etc. This list can be extensive, and yet you don't want to nickel and dime your client for every little additional item as a request for additional fee. Instead, allow a 5 to 15 percent contingency to the number of hours in each phase to cover these circumstances. You may not choose to make this contingency visible in your fee proposal. Let your professional judgment determine how this is handled.

Implementing and Monitoring the Project Fee Budget

Once the project is underway the implementation and monitoring of the project fee budget typically becomes the responsibility of the project manager. Implementation includes the development of a work plan and schedule which incorporates the allocation of hours and fee to specific tasks in every phase of the project. For those firms who have automated the job-costing process, it will also include data entry of the budgeted hours and fee dollars per phase. These computerized financial management systems will greatly enhance the accuracy of tracking hours and fees spent, making the monitoring of the project a more efficient process.

Each project team member should be given a comprehensive description of their respective duties and responsibilities for each phase of the project and the related hours required to fully perform and complete their tasks. The key to successful monitoring of the project fee budget is to do so on a regular basis. This periodic review process is generally aligned with each time sheet submittal period. At the end of each project phase it is essential for the project manager to review the hours and fees spent. He should revise the project fee budget accordingly to be sure adequate hours and fees are available for the remaining phases of work. Obviously, the more frequent the review of project status, the better the chances are of determining if any phase of the project is off schedule, and providing the necessary adjustments.

During the course of the project the manager will need to be sensitive to any client-requested changes to the contract scope. These changes could erode the profitability of the project and offset planned milestones and phase completion dates. If the requested changes significantly revise the scope of services, an adjustment to the project fee needs to be discussed with the client. Any such approved adjustments will require reallocation of hours and dollars of the project fee budget for the remaining portions of the project phases.

When properly performed, the implementation and monitoring processes can ensure the achievement of the firm's project profitability objectives. At the same time, these functions can be a key factor in enhancing the quality of the services rendered and lead to opportunities for future projects with the client.

Bibliography

The Architect's Handbook of Professional Practice, 11th edition, vol. 1, chap. 1.11, "Financial Management" by Lowell Getz, chap. 1.12, "Project Management" by Frank A. Stasiowski, AIA, The American Institute of Architects, Washington, D.C., 1988.

AIA Documents B161–162, The American Institute of Architects, Washington, D.C., 1977 edition.

Birnberg, Howard, *Project Management for Small Design Firms,* Birnberg & Associates, Chicago, 1986.

Coxe, Weld, *Managing Architectural and Engineering Practice,* Wiley, New York, 1980.

Getz, Lowell, and Frank A. Stasiowski, AIA, *Financial Management for the Design Professional,* Whitney, New York, 1984.

Gutman, Robert, *Architectural Practice: A Critical View,* Princeton Architectural Press, New York, 1988.

Haviland, David S., *Managing Architectural Projects: The Effective Project Manager,* AIA Press, Washington, D.C., 1981.

Haviland, David S., *Managing Architectural Projects: The Process,* AIA Press, Washington, D.C., 1981.

Haviland, David S., *Managing Architectural Projects: Three Case Studies,* AIA Press, Washington, D.C., 1981.

Kliment, Stephen A., FAIA, *Compensation Guidelines for Architectural and Engineering Services,* 2d ed., The American Institute of Architects, Washington, D.C., 1978.

Maddox, Robert, FAIA, *Financial Management for Architects,* American Institute of Architects, Washington, D.C., 1980.

Maister, David A., "Quality Work Doesn't Mean Quality Service," 1982.

Piven, Peter, FAIA, *Compensation Management, A Guide for Small Firms,* American Institute of Architects, Washington, D.C., 1982.

12

Project Status Reporting

David Haviland

Periodic project status reporting tells architects or engineers where their projects stand relative to goals and plans. More importantly, status reports provide a basis for estimating how projects are likely to turn out and what must be done to keep them on track. In the hands of capable project managers, these reports are powerful tools for helping to reach project goals.

Why Status Reports?

Architects and engineers seek status reports because they want to know how their projects are performing relative to the objectives set for them. These questions are on the table:

- Is the project *scope* holding as planned or has it changed—most likely, grown—as the project has progressed?
- Are the architectural and engineering *services* being provided as planned in the agreement for professional services?
- Is the work on *schedule,* meeting its deadlines?
- Is the work on *budget,* consuming staff time and other resources as planned?
- Is the firm receiving the planned *compensation* for services, and is it being paid on time?

These five aspects of project control are interrelated. Schedule slippage or budget overage may signal that scope or services are out of control. Delays in compensation may suggest that the client is having difficulties with the project or the services being provided. Any of these variations can reveal problems. All require attention.

The Project Control Cycle

A key idea is that of *control*. The principal reason for investing time and effort in project status reporting is to provide some measure of control of scope, services, schedule, budget, and compensation. Four requisites for effective control are:

- *Yardsticks:* By what standards will we measure project progress and determine that it is or is not acceptable?

- *Pulse taking:* What information do we need to capture in order to measure project progress?

- *Comparisons and projections:* How does progress to date compare with plans? Where will we be at key milestones or at the end of the project?

- *Willingness to act:* All the information in the world is of little value if the architect or engineer cannot or will not take action—either to bring the project back into the plan or to revise plans.

These building blocks produce the project reporting and control cycle shown in Fig. 12.1. Yardsticks are set, information is collected, progress is compared with goals, projections are made, variations are uncovered, and action is taken.

In planning their approach to project status reporting and control, firms must address these key questions:

- How frequently should the cycle be repeated? How often should project managers (PMs) have the opportunity to review progress and take corrective action? Cycles are related to the aspect being controlled: For many projects it makes sense to review schedule and budget weekly (especially when the project is active), compensation according to the billing cycle (monthly, quarterly, or by phase), and scope and services at least at key project milestone dates (while the work itself is being reviewed within the firm). The best advice is to conduct these reviews as frequently as possible when projects are active. Most architectural and engineering projects proceed quickly and intensely when they are moving. During these periods, it is easy to veer out of control and, if corrective action is not taken quickly, to find that the easy routes for making corrections are closed.

- Who should be responsible for reviewing information, making projections, and taking corrective action? Here the answer is less complicated; this responsibility should be given to the project manager—the professional within the firm who is charged with meeting the project's quality, time, and cost objectives.

- How much detail should be provided? The golden rule is only as much as necessary. Periodically it is useful for project managers to review the status reports they receive and to identify information they are *not* using with an eye to eliminating it from the report.

- If the project manager is not managing the firm, what information should be provided to others—department heads and the firm's top management? Department heads are usually interested in where and how well staff spend their time. Top management is typically interested in major departures from plans, actions that require client approval, and overall project profitability.

Firms also should decide whether to use an identical control approach for all projects. While standardization has several advantages, most design firms have a large number of different kinds of projects on their books. Depending on firm size, orientation, and range of project types, clients, and sizes, it may make sense to vary the level of detail used for planning and control. Smaller projects or small scope extensions of larger projects may be planned and controlled by deliverables—the products the firm is to produce (reports, surveys, drawings, etc.). Similarly, the firm may vary its approach to inactive projects; a summary report that flags changes only may be sufficient.

Exempting whole projects, however, from the discipline established for status reporting and project control is not wise. Even though very small projects (where expected fees are less than

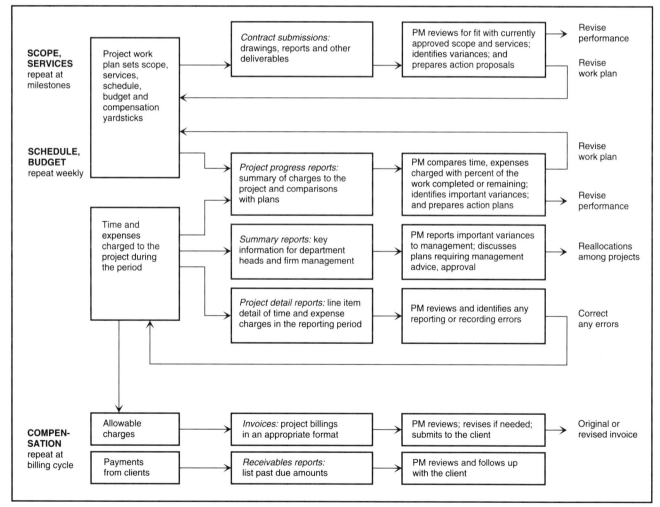

Figure 12.1 Project reporting and control cycle.

$10,000) may not produce a great deal of data or many reports, they tend to be intense in those weeks or months when they are active; at these times, they require as much attention relative to their size as do larger projects. For small projects, however, the firm may elect to give the project manager strong or even unilateral discretion on actions to be taken to meet project objectives. With these decisions in hand, it is possible to develop a firmwide approach to project control and status reporting.

Establishing Yardsticks

The project work plan provides the yardsticks. Project planning, addressed in Chaps. 11 and 19, must be sufficiently comprehensive and specific to provide the targets needed for project control. Information on these targets, summarized in Fig. 12.2, is then loaded into the firm's project status reporting and control system.

Planning and control, including project status reporting, must operate at a *consistent* level of detail. For example, planning the work by breaking it into phases and tasks (using, for instance, the breakdown of project tasks in the AIA's owner-architect agreement using designated services, AIA Document B161/162) and then collecting time and expense data only by project makes little sense. Moreover, yardsticks must be coordinated with the project reporting and control cycle. If project costs are assessed monthly, it is valuable to express the budget in monthly terms. This will enable an apples-to-apples comparison when the project status report is analyzed.

Taking the Pulse

Taking the project's pulse as the work progresses is necessary to determine if the project is meeting its goals. Pulse taking occurs in several ways. As outlined in Fig. 12.3, the key information comes from records of time and expenses charged to the project as well as from agreed changes in scope, services, schedule, and compensation.

Scope and Services Changes Changes in project scope or services should be formally documented, acknowledged by the client, and reported to the project manager. Most firms use a form designed for this purpose and keep a careful log of submitted (pending) and approved changes to project scope and services, along with concomitant changes to project schedules, budget, and compensation.

Time Reports Because a very large portion of project expenses arises from professional, technical, and support staff working on the project, employee time records are crucial to pulse taking. All members of the firm, including principals, should keep and submit time records.

Time charged to projects should be recorded at the level of detail established in the work plan. This may be by project, by project and phase (e.g., phase 7, construction contract administration), by deliverable (e.g., final site selection report), or by project, phase, and task (e.g., update preliminary estimate of construction cost). Some firms set individual schedule and budget targets for parts of contract deliv-

Initial Information for Project Control	
Element of the work plan	Key information (yardsticks) for project control
Client project objectives	Relative importance of meeting quality, cost, and time goals
Firm project objectives	Project priority Profitability objective
Project scope	Description of project scope Record of approved scope revisions
Services	If AIA Document B141 (C141 for consultants) is used: • Basic services provided under the agreement • Record of contingent additional services added during the project • Record of optional additional services added or subtracted during the project If AIA Document B161/162 (C161 for consultants) is used: • Designated services provided under the agreement • Record of designated services added or subtracted during the project
Schedule	Milestone dates • By phase or deliverable • By task within phase (optional) • Key interim milestones (optional) Record of approved schedule revisions • Tied to scope or services changes • Internal schedule adjustments
Budgets controlled by project manager	Hours and salary budgets by project, phase, or deliverable • By task within phase (optional) • By staff member or category • By department (optional) • By time period: weekly, monthly, quarterly (optional) Other direct expenses • Consultant expenses • Other direct expenses Allowable reimbursable expenses Record of approved budget revisions • Tied to scope or services changes • Internal budget adjustments
Other budget targets	Other project budgets • Overhead rate, multiple, or other indirect expense measure • Profit target Record of approved budget revisions
Billing information	Method of compensation for services Billing schedule (and invoice amounts if already established) Interest rate for past due invoices Record of approved revisions to compensation or billing

Figure 12.2 Initial information for project control.

Updated Information for Project Control	
Yardstick	Required information

Scope and Services Information	
Scope	Scope changes since the last status report ■ Approved by the client ■ Pending client approval
Services	Services changes since the last status report ■ Contingent additional services added (and client notified) ■ Changes approved by the client ■ Changes pending client approval

Schedule Information	
Schedule	Time elapsed since start of ■ Current phase or deliverable ■ Tasks within current phase (optional) ■ Key interim milestones (optional) Changes in phase or deliverable, task, or other milestone dates since the last status report ■ Approved by the client ■ Pending client approval ■ Internal schedule; client approval not required

Budget Information	
Project budgets	Budget changes since the last status report ■ Approved by the client ■ Pending client approval ■ Internal schedule; client approval not required
Time and expenses charged to the project	All time and expenses should include: ■ Detail for the period covered by the status report (for PM review and verification) ■ Any PM-approved revisions of charges on the previous status report ■ Total for the period ■ Total for the project to date
Staff time	Personnel hours and dollars spent on the project, by phase or deliverable and possibly by task, department, staff member, or category, as recorded in approved time reports
Expenses	Expenses charged to the project, by phase or deliverable, and possibly by task or department, as recorded in approved invoices and expense reports
Consultants	Expenses charged to the project, by phase or deliverable, and possibly by task, as recorded in approved consultant invoices or as set out in an agreed consultant payment schedule
Reimbursable expenses	Reimbursable expenses charged to the project, by phase or deliverable, and possibly by task, as recorded in approved invoices and expense reports (these should be related to the expense types or accounts approved as reimbursable by this project)

Compensation Information	
Billing guidelines	Any approved changes in compensation type, amount, or schedule of billings
Receivables	Information on client invoices submitted and due but not yet paid

Figure 12.3 Updated information for project control.

erables, most commonly individual drawings (e.g., drawing A7: exterior details). Where this is done, time and expenses should be recorded at this level of detail.

Staff time should be recorded and submitted frequently, at a minimum of once a week. This also needs to be tied to the firm's cycle of project status reporting; if project managers are to have weekly reports and weekly opportunities to make adjustments, time must be reported weekly. If time is to be reported at a very detailed level (such as by task), daily reporting is better.

Time records also must include time that is not being billed to active projects, that is, time charged to marketing, professional development, firm management, and other overhead items as well as vacation, sick, and personal leave and other purposes.

Some firms require project managers to sign off on time sheets. If the PM is receiving a weekly status report (and all time up to the end of the previous week is reflected in this report), this extra step may not be necessary. In any event, PM approval of overtime charges is a wise move.

Expense Reports   Nonsalary expenses should be tagged with project numbers (and, as appropriate, phase, deliverable, or task designations) and recorded frequently enough to appear on the project status report. Distinctions between reimbursable and nonreimbursable expenses, which will vary according to project agreement, should be recorded as well.

Consultant Expenses   Most firms require the project manager to approve consultant invoices before they are recorded. The amounts of these invoices and any markups should be included in the project status report.

Indirect Expenses   By their very nature, indirect expenses are not charged to projects and lie outside the project manager's purview. These expenses are reflected in multipliers, overhead rates, or hourly charges recorded on client invoices or, in the case of lump-sum contracts, on the firm's profit and loss statement for each project.

Periodic Status Reports

Project status reports are issued at the appropriate times in the project cycle, often weekly. These reports address principally schedule and budget progress; they may record changes in scope, services, and compensation as well. In their simplest form, these reports:

- Record time and expenses charged to the project during the period covered by the report
- Total these charges for the project to date
- Compare the totals to date with the relevant targets or yardsticks presented in the project work plan
- Allow the project manager to review and verify the accuracy of charges to the project

- Require the project manager to estimate the amount or fraction of work actually completed (or, conversely, yet required to complete) for the project, phase, deliverable, or task

- Help the PM identify key variations between planned and actual progress to date

- Provide summary and exception information for department heads and the firm's top management

Report Forms The specific forms of project status reports will most likely depend on the financial management system used by the firm. Reports generally are produced at three different levels of detail:

- *Project progress reports* summarize progress for the reporting period and for the project as a whole. They are the project manager's principal review and analysis documents.

- *Project detail reports* list individual time and expense entries for the reporting period. These reports allow project managers to verify

```
                        Apple and Bartlett                        Page    1
                                                                  03/31/88
                        Project Progress Report                   PROJPG7C
                    For the period 03/01/88 - 03/31/88

Number:08005.00              Principal: Apple        Client:          COC
Name:  City Hall             Proj. Mgr: Gray         Type of Work: Govt
                             Fee:    350,000         255/254:        101-4
```

Description	Current Hrs	Current Amt	Proj-to-Date Hrs	Proj-to-Date Amt	Budget Hrs	Budget Amt	% Exp	% Rpt	Balance Hrs	Balance Amt
A Architectural										
1 Predesign			8	120						
2 Site Analysi			16	224						
3 Schematic De	2	40	634	8852	600	8300	107	100	34-	552-
4 Design Devel	14	280	223	3145	1100	10000	31	30	877	6855
5 Construction	23	344	1143	9906	3500	32000	31	25	2357	22094
Total	39	664	2024	22247	5200	50300	44	38	3176	28053
I Interiors										
3 Schematic De	27	335	239	3885	300	4000	97	75	61	115
5 Construction					2000	16000		5	2000	16000
Total	27	335	239	3885	2300	20000	19	19	2061	16115
Total Labor	66	999	2263	26132	7500	70300	37	33	5237	44168
Overhead Alloc.		3344		39387		112480	35	33		73093
- -										
Direct Expenses										
611.00 Structural Con		300		10000		36000	28	25		26000
612.00 Mechanical.Con		2000		10875		64000	17	25		53125
621.00 Travel,Meals &						4250		5		4250
622.00 Reproductions				3						
Total Directs		2300		20878		104250	20	24		83373
Total Lab-OH-Dir	66	6643	2263	86397	7500	287030	30	30	5237	200633
- -										
Reimbursable Expenses										
511.00 Structural Con		250		250						
521.00 Travel,Meals &		251		1304		4000	33	50		2696
522.00 Reproductions		25		198		6000	3	10		5803
523.00 Models/Renderi						8000		95		8000
524.00 Long Distance				25						
Total Reimbs.		526		1776		18000	10	57		16224
Project Totals	66	7169	2263	88173	7500	305030	29	31	5237	216857

Figure 12.4 Example Project Progress Report. (*Source: Harper & Shuman, Computer-Based Financial Management System, as reported in David Haviland, ed., The Architect's Handbook of Professional Practice, The American Institute of Architects, 1988. Used by permission.*)

charges made against their projects and to correct any resulting errors.

- *Summary reports* provide department heads and the firm's management with critical information on all projects.

Figures 12.4, 12.5, and 12.6 provide examples of these three levels of detail.

Report Design When first designing a status report or in reviewing potential financial management systems that produce them, these guidelines may be helpful:

- Keep the format as simple and straightforward as possible. Make sure that yardsticks read loud and clear. Both schedule (milestones) and budget (planned expenditures) for each phase, deliverable, or task should be apparent.
- Show both hours of time charged and associated dollars expended.

```
                            Apple and Bartlett                      Page   1
                                                                    03/31/88
                          Project Progress Report                   PROJPG70
                        Project-to-date thru 03/31/88

    Number:08005.00               Principal: Apple        Client:        COC
    Name:  City Hall              Proj. Mgr: Gray          Type of Work: Govt
                                  Fee:    350,000          255/254:       101-4

                    --Current--  Proj-to-Date  ---Budget---  %   %   --Balance---
    Description     Hrs    Amt    Hrs    Amt    Hrs    Amt  Exp Rpt  Hrs    Amt

    A Architectural
      1 Predesign
        Gray        01/88           8    120
          Subtotal                  8    120
      2 Site Analysis
        Apple       01/88           8    160
        Spencer     02/88           8     64
          Subtotal                 16    224
      3 Schematic Design
        Apple       01/88           8    160
        Apple        2     40       2     40
        Bartlett    02/88          16    320
        Gray        02/88           8    120
          Subtotal   2     40     634   8852   600   8300  107 100   34-    552-
      4 Design Developmt
        Apple       14    280      14    280
        Bartlett    02/88           8    160
          Subtotal  14    280     223   3145  1100  10000   31  30   877   6855
      5 Construction Doc
        Bartlett    12    240      12    240
        Lambert      8     80       8     80
        Spencer      3     24       3     24
          Subtotal  23    344    1143   9906  3500  32000   31  25  2357  22094
    Total           39    664    2024  22247  5200  50300   44  38  3176  28053

    I Interiors
    ..3 Schematic Design
        Gray        17    255      17    255
        Spencer     10     80      10     80
          Subtotal  27    335     239   3885   300   4000   97  75    61    115
      5 Construction                            2000  16000        5  2000  16000
    Total           27    335     239   3885  2300  20000   19  19  2061  16115

    Total Labor     66    999    2263  26132  7500  70300   37  33  5237  44168

    Project Totals  66    999    2263  26132  7500  70300   37  33  5237  44168
```

Figure 12.5 Example Project Detail Report. (Source: Harper & Shuman, Computer-Based Financial Management System, as reported in David Haviland, ed., The Architect's Handbook of Professional Practice, The American Institute of Architects, 1988. Used by permission.)

Hours may be easier to comprehend but differences in the cost of staff, and in the cost of straight time and overtime, can be significant. Tracking projects using only hours is likely to result in dollar amounts that are at variance with budgets.

- Identify the total elapsed time and dollars spent on each phase, deliverable, or task during the report period and, in the project detail report, provide a line item listing documenting each time and expense charge.

- Display the total elapsed time and dollars spent to date on each phase, deliverable, or task and calculate the percentage of planned resources used to date (or, conversely, those available to complete the work).

- Provide room to allow the project manager to enter her or his estimate of the fraction of the work actually completed (or remaining to be completed) for each phase, deliverable, or task.

```
                        Apple and Bartlett                      Page   2
                                                                03/31/88
                     Project Summary Report                     PRJSUM70
                For the period 03/01/88 - 03/31/88

                     --Current--    Proj-to-date   ---Budget---    %    %
                     Hrs    Amt     Hrs    Amt      Hrs    Amt    Exp  Rpt


08005.00 City Hall
         Labor        66    999    2263   26132    7500  70300    37   33
         Overhead           3344          39387          112480   35   33
         Directs            2300          20878          104250   20   24
         Reimbs.            526           1776            18000    10   57
         Total         66   7169   2263   88173    7500  305030   29   31

08015.00 Balboa
         Labor                     6789   88532
         Overhead          2550          132942
         Directs           3000          3000
         Reimbs.           200           589
         Total             5750   6789   225063

08101.00 University Library
         Labor         32    256    879   11990
         Overhead           3142          18163
         Directs                         134
         Reimbs.                         314
         Total         32   3398    879   30600

08102.00 Government Center
         Labor         22    344    654   50973
         Overhead           1984          76572
         Directs            20            20
         Reimbs.            99            1516
         Total         22   2447    654   129081

08102.01 Govt Center Revisions
         Labor         45    604    227   4732
         Overhead           1545          7185
         Reimbs.                          12
         Total         45   2149    227   11929

08102.02 Govt Center Fountain
         Labor                     59    880
         Overhead           827           1367
         Directs            2000          2000
         Reimbs.                          15
         Total             2827    59    4262
```

Figure 12.6 Example Summary Report. (*Source: Harper & Shuman, Computer-Based Financial Management System, as reported in David Haviland, ed., The Architect's Handbook of Professional Practice, The American Institute of Architects, 1988. Used by permission.*)

Related Reports It may be desirable to produce other forms of progress reports for the project manager (for example, tracking progress by individual drawing or deliverable as shown in Fig. 12.7) or for others in the firm (for example, reports on staff existing and projected utilization for department heads and reports on cash flow, profitability, or planning and operating ratios for the firm's managing partner).

Verification The reports should allow the PM to review each of the individual time and expense charges made against the project during the period covered by the report. Because errors can be introduced in the reporting and recording process, project managers should have opportunities to review and correct entries even if they have been specifically approved. On finding an error, the PM should be able to mark the status report and return it for correction, keeping a copy to verify that the correction appears on the next edition of the report.

Projection Now, the moment of truth. How does actual progress, as documented in the report, compare with project plans? To do this, the

```
CONTRACT MONITOR DETAIL REPORT  05/14/80
```

Sheet No.	Overplay No.	Base No.	Sheet Name	Antic. Start date	Date Started	& Total	% Complete	% Complete Total
			GENERAL..............JOHN GROSS					
1.1			Cover Sheet	3/18/80	4/02/80	100%	95%	95%
1.2			Symbols	3/19/80	4/02/80	100%	100%	100%
1.3			Equipment Listing	4/15/80	5/10/80	100%	95%	95%
			SITEWORK............BRIAN GUTHEINZ					
2.1	2.1	AA	Existing Site Plan (demo., clearance)	4/5/80	4/12/80	25%	95%	
			Existing Site Conditions to Remain	3/20/80	4/12/80	75%	95%	95%
2.2	2.2	AA	New Site Plan	4/15/80	4/12/80	25%	95%	
			Existing Site Conditions to Remain	3/29/80	4/12/80	75%	95%	95%
2.3	2.3	AA	Utilities Site Plan	5/03/80	5/06/80	70%	75%	
			Existing Site Consitions to Remain	3/29/80	4/12/80	30%	95%	92%
2.4	2.4		Site Details	4/1280	4/12/80	100%	95%	95%
			STRUCTURAL............MAC EPPERSON					
3.1	3.1		Basement Floor Plan (Dimen., notes)	4/15/80	4/08/80	40%	95%	
		AB	Existing Plan Basement	3/18/80	4/02/80	25%	95%	
		AC	New Plan, Basement	3/20/80	3/20/80	35%	95%	95%
3.2			Tunnel Connection Details	4/19/80	5/06/80	100%	80%	80%
3.3	3.3		First Floor Plan (Dimen., notes)	4/15/80	4/09/80	40%	95%	
		AD	Existing Plan, First Floor	3/21/80	4/01/80	25%	95%	
		AE	New Plan, First Floor	3/21/80	4/01/80	35%	95%	95%
3.4	3.4		Second Floor Plan (Dimen., notes)	4/15/80	4/10/80	40%	95%	
		AF	Existing Plan, Second Floor	3/22/80	4/02/80	25%	95%	
		AG	New Plan, Second Floor	3/22/80	4/02/80	35%	95%	95%
3.5	3.5	AH	Third Floor & Roof Plan (Dimen., notes)	4/15/80	4/11/80	40%	95%	
			Existing Plan, Third Floor	3/25/80	4/03/80	25%	95%	

Figure 12.7 Example Deliverables Progress Report. (*Source: Hansen Lind Meyer Architects, as reported in David Haviland, Managing Architectural Projects: Case Studies 2, The American Institute of Architects, 1981. Used by permission.*)

PM should look at each project phase, deliverable, or task and estimate the percentage of the total work actually completed (or, alternatively, yet to be completed). Some keys to effective projections:

- Focus on what remains to be done. Looking to the future orients the project manager to forward planning and mitigates the tendency to extrapolate based on the past. For example, even though only 25 percent of the time or budget may have been used, only 60 percent more of the original schedule or budget may be needed to complete the work.

- Decouple schedule and budget. They do not always track each other, so project them independently.

- Be critical in making projections. This step calls architects and engineers to replace undue optimism or pessimism with healthy skepticism.

- Consider the impacts of any changes in scope or services when making projections.

Variances The next step is to calculate the gap, if any, between remaining available schedule or budget and the project manager's assessment of what is needed to accomplish each task or deliverable. Assuming that both measures are expressed in common terms (schedule in days, weeks, or months; budget in dollars), the calculation of variances is a mechanical act. If the project status report is presented in an interactive computer format, the PM can enter percentages on the screen and the system can calculate the variances. If the status report comes only in hard copy, then the PM does the calculation by hand. Either way, the art is not in the mechanism but in the realistic assessment of what needs to be done.

Analysis and Action

Not all variances between planned and actual performance are significant. Project managers should review them and place each variance into one of three groups:

- *Green list:* These variances are small, perhaps within the noise of the data and estimates, and are of no real consequence.

- *Yellow list:* These variations bear watching. They may suggest a wide range of possibilities, including errors to be corrected, corrective actions already taken but not yet reflected, small effects that will likely work themselves out, or most important, the seeds of a growing problem. This warning list should be reviewed each week (if that is the firm's review cycle) and its items moved to the red or green lists as quickly as possible.

- *Red list:* Action is required, and it is required now.

Variances can be color-coded directly on the project status report; a separate log of red-list variances (together with a record of corrective actions taken) is a good idea. This log should be evaluated in the light of the progress information on a weekly basis.

Coding variances requires careful judgment and analysis by the PM:

What is really happening here? Is there a trend? What is causing the variance? Are there problems with the project staff or consultant assignments, performance, or management? Is the project not getting the attention or priority it deserves within the firm? Is the client providing required information or decisions? Are shifts in scope or services underway?

Corrective actions fall into two categories: those that adjust performance to the plan, and those that require revision of the plan. The first group includes:

- Shifts in staffing levels and assignments
- Authorization of overtime
- Shifts in supporting resources
- Interventions in staff supervision
- Revisions in the logic used to get the job done

The limit of the project manager's authority in making these decisions must be established within the firm's overall system of responsibility and authority. However changes are made, they should involve those who will be responsible for abiding by them.

A less common, but sometimes necessary, alternative is to replan the project, revising the work plan to respond to changing circumstances. If the PM is not also managing the firm, revisions will have to be resolved with the firm's leaders. Project consultants and perhaps the client must be involved if these revisions affect them or their agreements with each other.

Compensation Review

Project agreements include arrangements for compensation of architects and engineers for their services. The specified methods and amounts of compensation as well as information on billing cycles, retainers, interest rates on unpaid invoices, and related items will set the terms for client invoicing. Following these rules, the firm's financial management system keeps track of amounts earned, billed, and received; produces invoices; and summarizes accounts receivable—amounts invoiced but not yet paid.

As suggested in Fig. 12.1, the project manager plays important roles in this area, reviewing and approving invoices before they are sent to the client, and then following up on any past due accounts. In the first instance, client invoices must be accurate, reflecting both the terms of the project agreement and the client's understanding of the status of the work. Where there has been little contact, a brief report of what has been done during the period covered by the invoice may be appropriate.

Delays in receiving compensation are of particular concern because they may reflect problems within the client's purview (for example, availability of funds, concerns about the marketability of the project, or delays in securing necessary approvals) or dissatisfaction with the firm, the services being performed, or the design work itself. All are causes for concern and require follow-up.

Scope and Services Review

The final aspect of project status reporting and control relates to scope of the project and the services being performed. Effective architects and engineers informally assess scope and services constantly, adjusting the work to respond to the terms of the project agreements or, when necessary, seeking scope or services modifications.

Most firms profit from *formal* reviews of project scope and services. These can be done on two cycles:

- As part of the project manager's weekly progress assessment; schedule, budget, or compensation variances may, in fact, reflect developing scope or service problems.
- As part of the internal review of client submissions; most firms establish some sort of formal discipline to assure that drawings, specifications, schedules, construction cost estimates, and other deliverables meet both the client's objectives and the firm's standards.

Revisions to project scope or services usually require modifications to project agreements between owner and architect or engineer, and perhaps to consultant subcontracts as well. As suggested in Fig. 12.8, agreement modifications should be approved within the firm, formally proposed, acknowledged by the client, and carefully logged. Finally, the work plan and the targets used in the project status reports should be updated to reflect approved changes.

Directions

Architects and engineers are under constant pressure to provide quality services within tight project schedules and carefully negotiated fees. As a result, there is little room for error. As services are provided, it is in the firm's best interest to maintain careful control of project scope, services, schedule, budget, and compensation.

Project management, control, and reporting systems must be carefully selected or designed. While they provide important accounting and financial management data, they are most effective in the hands of project managers who are design professionals and not financial managers. These systems are means to important ends—quality service and continuity of the firm—but not ends in themselves. Computers offer attractive possibilities, particularly as financial management programs move away from "batch" systems that require and disgorge vast amounts of data on an infrequent basis to more interactive systems that accommodate continuous data entry, review, and analysis. Interactive systems allow design firms to shorten project review cycles (from monthly or semimonthly to weekly or even daily) and project managers to review progress, correct errors, and project variances on a continuing basis. The net result is that the firm and the PM can establish a discipline of project status reporting and review that is most appropriate to their needs, perhaps varying it from project to project or even from time to time within the course of a specific project.

Professional Services
Scope Change ___

hlm

Hansen Lind Meyer, P.C.

Project _____ Project No. _____

_____ Date _____

Please be advised that we anticipate the below described change(s) in scope of professional services from that upon which our fees were based in our agreement dated _____.

Notes to person completing draft copy of this form:

1. *This copy is to be used to prepare the draft for typing. Remove it from the set before completing.*
2. *Consider when completing this form:*
   a. *Is it appropriate to mention any normal or unusual reimbursable expenses related to this scope change?*
   b. *Is there anything about this service which is contrary to the agreement which should be identified? If so, explain on this form.*
3. *Transmit this form to the owner for signature with a cover letter.*
4. *The typed draft of this form is to be reviewed by the director of finance and the principal in charge prior to signature and forwarding to the owner.*

Requested fee this scope change _____
Original fee _____
Total previous scope change(s) _____
Total fees to date _____

Please acknowlege your acceptance by signing in the space provided. Retain the original and one copy. Return the remainder to our office.

Owner or Agent _____ Hansen Lind Meyer, P.C. _____

Figure 12.8 Example Scope and Services Changes. (*Source: Hansen Lind Meyer Architects, as reported in David Haviland, Managing Architectural Projects: Case Studies 2, The American Institute of Architects, 1981. Used by permission.*)

Appendix A. Computer Systems for Project Status Reporting and Control

Consider project status reporting within the framework of the firm's overall financial management system for maintaining a general ledger and handling billings, receivables, payables, and possibly payroll. Much of the data required to produce status reports, especially time and expenses charged to the project, are generated and used for a variety of purposes within the financial management system.

In reviewing candidate financial management systems, ask your project managers to look carefully at the project status reporting features. Most systems are developed by and for accountants and not the architects and engineers who are charged with attaining project quality, time, and cost goals. These guidelines may be helpful:

- Look for systems that offer simplicity, speed, fill-in-the-form approaches, and interactive computing. Interactive systems allow project managers to work with up-to-date information at their desks. To be effective, these systems must present easy-to-use screens, straightforward editing, appropriate protection of data, and extensive back-and-forth movement between the various input and analysis screens.

- Select systems that require the user to enter a single piece of data once (for example, a consultant's name, address, and billing requirements) and then automatically retrieve the information each time it is used (in this case, to provide targets for project progress reports, prepare client invoices, update accounts payable, and record checks written to consultants). Such systems allow users to focus on the project itself and not on record keeping.

- Find systems capable of breaking project services into varying levels of detail ranging from considering the project as a single entity to breaking it into phases, deliverables, or tasks within phases, contract extensions, and (if relevant to the firm) departments or disciplines.

- Look for systems that allow the project manager to specify the particular reimbursable expense categories allowed for each project.

- Obtain a system that automatically produces invoices for client billing, handles the range of compensation methods and billing cycles encountered in practice and, where appropriate, provides the necessary backup information for these invoices.

- Select systems that can summarize project budget and schedule performance in formats that facilitate future project planning and estimating.

For further guidance, see Lowell Getz, "Computerized Financial Systems" (1988).

The sample computer screens shown in Fig. 12.9 were produced by the Project Accounting and Control System (PACS), developed by Dimension 4, O'Connor and Marsh Architects, Albany, N.Y. Because it is developed by architects, PACS focuses on the project control aspects of managing small architecture practices. Other necessary financial management transactions and reports are handled as well.

Shown are some of the screens used to enter, check, and update project scope, services, schedule, budget, and billing information as well as time and other project expenses. Other screens capture information about clients, consultants, and vendors; payroll adjustments; and receipts. Like other financial management systems designed for firms whose work consists largely of projects, PACS produces a variety of project reports (e.g., time verification, payables posting, phase percent of completion, project progress, projects summary, project invoice generation, invoices, billing summaries, and outstanding receivables reports), analyses of department and firm performance, and other accounting documents (accounts listings, trial balance, income statements, and balance sheets). These example screens are used by permission.

```
PROJECT SCHEDULE
----------------------------------------------------------------
Proj#:   100101    Name: Unicorn Home Office              Page 1 of 1

                          Appvd       %    Start       Compl.
Ex  Ph  Name               by       Comp   Date        Date

00  01  Program            MOC      100%   02/15/1990  03/01/1990
    03  Schematic Design   ADF       14%   03/15/1990  04/21/1990
    04  Design Development FAS       27%   04/28/1990  06/15/1990
    05  Contract Documents MOC        9%   07/01/1990  09/15/1990
    06  Bid/Negotiate      MOC             10/15/1990  11/21/1990
    07  Construction Admin MOC             01/01/1991  01/15/1992
01  03  Board Room         MOC             03/15/1990  04/07/1990

----------------------------------------------------------------
E dit    A dd    X extension add    F ind    D elete        F1 EXIT




DEPARTMENT BUDGET
----------------------------------------------------------------
Proj#:   100101    Name: Unicorn Home Office    Code: A    Dept 1 of 2
                                                Dept: Architectural
                                                Page 1 of 1

                          %               Avg              In-house
Ex  Ph  Name             Comp    Hrs     Rate    Total      Comp

00  01  Program          100%    104    21.75    2262      10500
    03  Schematic Design   5%    222    19.05    4229      21000
    04  Design Development 20%   509    17.70    9009      42000
    05  Contract Documents      1066    16.35   17429      84000
    06  Bid/Negotiate            104    21.75    2262      10500
    07  Construction Admin       509    17.58    8948      42000
01  03  Board Room                60    28.50    1710       7500

----------------------------------------------------------------
E dit    A dd    F ind    D elete                          F1 EXIT




IN-HOUSE PROJECT BUDGET
----------------------------------------------------------------
Proj#:   100101    Name: Unicorn Home Office              Page 1 of 1

         %               Avg             Other  In-house     Est
Ex  Ph  Tot   Hours     Rate    Total     Dir    Comp       Reimb

00  01    5    200     21.75     4350     250    15000       375
    03   10    246     19.05     4686     468    24750       285
    04   20    565     17.70    10000     999    48750       750
    05   40   1184     16.35    19358    1935    96750       900
    06    5    115     21.75     2501     250    12750      1800
    07   20    565     17.58     9933     999    48750      1050
01  03         60      28.50     1710     188     7500        75

----------------------------------------------------------------
E dit    F ind                                             F1 EXIT
```

Figure 12.9   Sample screens.

```
C O N S U L T A N T   B U D G E T
------------------------------------------------------------------------
Proj#:   100101     Name: Unicorn Home Office              Page 1 of 1

Ex   Ph    Struc    HVAC     San  FrProt  Elect  Civil   Land  Estim  Other

00   01    1125      900     300    225   1125    200    190
     03    2250     1800     600    450   2250    405    375    750
     04    4500     3600    1200    900   4500    810    750
     05    9000     7200    2400   1800   9000   1620   1500   1500
     06    1125      900     300    225   1125    205    190
     07    4500     3600    1200    900   4500    810    750
01   03     750      300


------------------------------------------------------------------------
E dit     F ind                                             F1 EXIT




P O S S I B L E   R E I M B U R S A B L E   A C C O U N T S
------------------------------------------------------------------------
Proj#:   100101     Name: Unicorn Home Office        Ext: 01  Phase: 03


5220    Outside Printing

------------------------------------------------------------------------
A dd     F ind      D elete                                 F1 EXIT




P R O J E C T   B I L L I N G
------------------------------------------------------------------------
Proj#:   100101     Name: Unicorn Home Office              Page 1 of 1

          Bill     Sal     Per    Lump                Constr   Reimb  Consul
Ex   Ph   Type     Mult    Mult    Sum       %          Est     Mult   Mult

00   01    A       2.50                               5550000   1.10   1.10
     03    D                               6.00       5550000   1.10   1.10
     04    D                               6.00       5550000   1.10   1.10
     05    A       2.50                               5550000   1.10   1.10
     06    A       2.50                               5550000   1.10   1.10
     07    A       2.50                               5550000   1.10   1.10
01   03    E                       5000               5550000   1.10   1.10

------------------------------------------------------------------------
E dit     F ind                                             F1 EXIT
```

Figure 12.9 Sample screens *(Continued)*.

```
PLANNED PROJECT COMPENSATION
---------------------------------------------------------------
Proj#:   100101    Name: Unicorn Home Office          Page 1 of 1
                                          Project Total    353248

                Comp for      Comp for      Comp for       Total
Ex   Ph         In-house      Consult       Reimb          Comp

00   01            15000         4471           413        19740
     03            24750         9763           314        34827
     04            48750        17886           825        67461
     05            96750        37422           990       135162
     06            12750         4472          1980        19202
     07            48750        17886          1155        67971
01   03             7500         1155            83         8738

---------------------------------------------------------------
F ind                                                     F1 EXIT



EMPLOYEE TIME ENTRY
---------------------------------------------------------------
Employee name:  Ahrens, William H          Total hours:     80.0

Earning           0 : Direct      3 : Promotion    6 : Vacation
categories:       1 : OT Direct   4 : OT Admin     7 : Sick
                  2 : Admin       5 : Holiday      8 : Other

Proj#       Dept       Ex  Ph    Serv    Cat    Class       Hours

100001        A        00  01     13      0      B           40.0
100101        A        00  03     14      0      B           40.0

---------------------------------------------------------------
F ind    A dd    R emove page    E dit                    F1 EXIT
Left and Right Arrows (Page Control)



INVOICE ENTRY
---------------------------------------------------------------
                                 Owner type..  Vendor
Reference          40            Date........  03/16/1990
Pay to...          Fred Sheldon  Balance.....      300.00
                                 Next payment


Proj#   Ex  Ph   Acct#   Acct#   Name                    Amount

100001  00  01   6140    2160    Uninvoiced A/P Consultant 225.00
100101  00  01           6140    Fire Prot. Consultant      75.00

---------------------------------------------------------------
E dit    A dd    D elete    F ind    H old               F1 EXIT
S et Payment    O wner Select    M ake Adjustment    R elease
```

Figure 12.9 Sample screens *(Continued).*

```
┌──────────────────────────────────────────────────────────────────────┐
│                                                                        │
│  E D I T   P R O J E C T   B I L L I N G      Billing Type    D        │
│                                               Invoice Date  03/30/1990 │
│  Client Name..  Mark of the Unicorn, Inc.     Invoice Amt    50856.63  │
│  Project......  100101  Unicorn Home Office   Invoice Bal    48921.74  │
│  --------------------------------------------------------------------  │
│  Ref. No. 8     Extension.. 00  Phase.. 03    Created..     03/30/1990 │
│                                                                        │
│                 Comment:                Acct#                  Amount  │
│                                                                        │
│  Basic Services From 5 to 100% Complete 4010  Invoiced Revenue 28305.00│
│  Reimbursables  In March                4210  Invoiced Reimb    742.50 │
│  Service Charge                         4110  Misc Revenue        0.00 │
│  Misc Charges                                                     0.00 │
│  Misc Charges                                                     0.00 │
│  Misc Credits   Overpayment Check 654   2520  Overpayments     1934.90 │
│  Misc Credits                                                     0.00 │
│                                               Phase Total     29047.50 │
│                                                                        │
│  Plan Deps   0.00    Retainage  0.00    Over 1934.90    Bal   27112.60 │
│                                                                        │
│  --------------------------------------------------------------------  │
│  F ind    E dit    H old    R elease                          F1 EXIT  │
│  N ext Phase    P revious Phase                                        │
│                                                                        │
│                                                                        │
│  ======================================================================│
│                                                                        │
└──────────────────────────────────────────────────────────────────────┘
```

Figure 12.9 Sample screens *(Continued).*

Bibliography

Birnberg, Howard, *Financial Management for Small Design Firms,* Birnberg & Associates, Chicago, 1985.

Burstein, David, and Frank Stasiowski, *Project Management for the Design Professional,* Watson-Guptill, New York, 1982.

Getz, Lowell, "Computerized Financial Systems," in *The Architect's Handbook of Professional Practice* (an appendix to Chap. 1.11, Financial Management), The American Institute of Architects, Washington, D.C., 1988.

Getz, Lowell, and Frank Stasiowski, *Financial Management for the Design Professional,* Whitney Library of Design, New York, 1984.

Haviland, David, ed., *The Architect's Handbook of Professional Practice,* 11th edition, The AIA Press, Washington, D.C., 1988. See especially chap. 1.11, "Financial Management," and chap. 1.12, "Project Management."

Haviland, David, *Managing Architectural Projects: The Process,* The AIA Press, Washington, D.C., 1981.

Haviland, David, *Managing Architectural Projects: Case Studies* (3 vols.), The AIA Press, Washington, D.C., 1981.

Mattox, Robert, *Financial Management for Architects,* The AIA Press, Washington, D.C., 1980.

13

Cash Management and Collection

Howard Birnberg

Handling cash flow is one of the most distressing aspects of design firm management. The cause of this problem is often a poor billing and collection system. Few firms have adequate procedures to effectively manage this process. Although many of the key billing and payment terms are outlined in the owner and designer contract, it is important to clarify and expand some of these terms. The time to do this is before the first invoice is sent.

It is important to bill regularly. Establish internal procedures to expedite this process. The primary reason for delayed billing is usually a lack of information by those responsible for invoicing.

Clients often are slow to pay an invoice simply because they are not provided essential information. As a result, they are unable to properly review and process the design firm's invoice. Some clients use the lack of information or backup as an excuse for slow payment. Anything the design firm can do to speed up payment is critical.

The three major aspects of cash management in a design firm are: (1) collecting receivables, (2) monitoring needs, and (3) planning cash flow.

Collecting Receivables

This process begins during contract negotiations with the client. When should a bill be submitted, how and when payment is to be made, what is the required billing format, when can interest be added (and how much) are all issues to be addressed before work begins. Do not be afraid to address financial issues. Act in a businesslike manner and clients will generally understand that timely payments are required.

Collecting accounts receivable remains a significant problem for most design firms. According to the "Financial Performance Surveys for Design Firms" conducted by Birnberg & Associates, the average collection period stood at 69 days in 1991. Table 13.1 shows the average collection period for recent years.

There are several other measures of the efficiency of a firm's billing and collection process. The completion to collection period measures the time from when a firm's accounting system recognizes completion of a billable activity to the time the invoice for that work is paid. Table 13.2 shows this figure for recent years.

In addition, the completion to billing period measures how long it takes to invoice once work is completed. Table 13.3 offers this figure for recent years.

Payment cannot be made if invoices are not submitted. Invoice as soon as possible on a regular schedule that recognizes when your clients issue checks (often the first and the fifteenth). It is not neces-

TABLE 13.1   Average Collection Period

Year	Days
1991	69
1990	67
1989	69
1988	77
1987	76
1986	72
1985	60
1984	64

TABLE 13.2   Completion to Collection Period

Year	Days
1991	93
1990	90
1989	91
1988	101
1987	106
1986	93

TABLE 13.3   Completion to Billing Period

Year	Days
1991	20
1990	18
1989	21
1988	19
1987	24
1986	25

CALCULATING BILLING AND
COLLECTION RATIOS

1. *Average Collection Period*

Step 1: $\dfrac{\text{Annual total revenues}}{\text{365 days}}$ = Revenues per day

Step 2: $\dfrac{\text{Average accounts receivable for past 12 months*}}{\text{Revenues per day}}$

*Take your highest accounts receivable each month, total them, divide by 12.

Example:

Step 1: $\dfrac{\$730,000}{\text{365 days}}$ = \$2000

Step 2: $\dfrac{\$120,000}{\$2000}$ = 60 days

2. *Completion to Billing Period*

Step 1: $\dfrac{\text{Annual total revenues}}{\text{365 days}}$ = Revenues per day

Step 2: $\dfrac{\text{Average work-in-process for past 12 months*}}{\text{Revenues per day}}$

*From your financial statement calculate the average, the same as for average accounts receivable.

3. *Completion to Collection Period*

Step 1: $\dfrac{\text{Annual total revenues}}{\text{365 days}}$ = Revenues per day

Step 2: $\dfrac{\text{Average accounts receivable plus average work-in-process}}{\text{Revenues per day}}$

Example:

Step 1: $\dfrac{\$730,000}{\text{365 days}}$ = \$2000

Step 2: $\dfrac{\$120,000 + \$60,000}{\$2000}$ = 90 days

sary to bill only at the end of the month. Many cash-smart firms invoice twice a month or bill half their clients on the fifteenth and half on the thirtieth to speed up the billing process. Do not wait until your cash balance is low to bill. Invoice regularly!

Some other tips on collecting receivables include:

1. Develop a regular procedure for following up on invoices. This should include a contact by you or your project manager to the client's counterpart at the 2-week point to see if the bill has been processed or if there are any questions. At the 1-month mark, a second notice (clearly identified as such) should be sent. At 5 weeks, the senior member of the firm should call (and follow up in writing) the client's senior person. As a last resort, if payment is not forthcoming within 2 weeks after the senior member's call, consider turning the matter over to your attorney where appropriate.

2. Adjust this process to the situation and evaluate the client. Remember, the client who does not pay is worth very little.

3. Firms often charge interest on unpaid accounts (often when the invoice is over 30 or 60 days). The firm's attorney should research the allowable limits (if any) in your state. Typically, designers charge 1.5 percent per month starting after 30 days.

4. Many firms (particularly when working with developer clients) require a retainer (often 10 to 25 percent) before they begin work.

5. Develop and maintain an aged accounts receivable report, listing invoices current, 30 days from billing, 60 days from billing, etc. This report will keep you up to date on action required to collect delinquent receivables.

Numerous examples can be cited of firms that were seemingly growing and profitable but went bankrupt because of cash flow difficulties. This is particularly true when new projects (and their heavy early cash flow) are not coming in to carry those older projects that generate a lower cash flow. Given the nature of the design business, few firms have adequate lines of credit to carry them over those periods.

Other Actions

If all else fails and you cannot collect, other options are still open. Obviously, legal action is always a possibility. Unfortunately, it is the least desirable option. Legal fees will often cost more than the amount outstanding.

Many firms negotiate arbitration clauses to resolve disputes. Often, these disputes lead to a hold or delay in paying your invoices. The use of an arbitration clause will allow you a quicker method to resolve disputes and free your invoice for payment.

Some designers attempt to discontinue services when payment of invoices is seriously delayed. This is an extreme position that slows payment on your regular monthly billings. There are situations in which suspension of services is warranted, but they are rare.

The use of collection services is another option. Many designers avoid the use of collection agencies because of their perceived unprofessionalism. But if a design firm's own efforts have failed to collect a delinquent receivable, few choices remain.

Collection agencies can be helpful. Most work for a percentage of any amount collected. The most widely known agency is Dun & Bradstreet (D & B). The major threat to a debtor is the inclusion of the poor payment information in their D & B credit file. Many lenders and other businesses consult D & B files.

Other collection agencies should be considered by designers. These services can help design firms collect delinquent accounts receivable. Agencies charge on a sliding scale based on the amount and age of the outstanding balance. For example, the typical charge on a $10,000 balance that is 90 days overdue is 20 percent of the collected balance.

Collection agencies may get results for you. It is important to select an agency that has experience working with design firms and in the construction industry.

The Billing Checklist

Well-managed design firms do not rely on general contract terms or on verbal discussions to guide the billing and collection process. A billing checklist is a summary of all terms and conditions for billing and client payment. It can serve as a supplement to the base contractual terms.

Key components of the billing checklist (Fig. 13.1) include:

1. *General project data:* This includes information on the project name and number. If the checklist covers a change order or out-of-scope item, that number and name should appear. The client's name and address also should be included.

2. *Key contacts:* Owner and designer contracts rarely include this vital information. As a result, it is important to indicate clearly who the designer can contact in the event of billing or collection questions. Conversely, an individual in the design firm must be listed in the event the client has any questions. Usually, the project manager is the key contact person.

3. *Who should receive invoices?* It is not unusual for several parties in the client's office to require copies of the designer's invoice. Failure to provide these copies often will result in delays in processing and paying an invoice. As a result, it is important to identify these individuals before the first invoice is sent.

4. *Does the client have its own billing form?* A surprising number of clients have their own form for submitting invoices. Many also require the inclusion of a purchase order number on each invoice. It is important to use their forms and include all the information they request or your invoice may be returned or delayed.

5. *Required backup information:* Many clients require copies of all vendor and consultant bills. Some require copies of employee timesheets. Failure to provide this backup will delay your invoice. It is not unusual for a client to simply wait for you to call about an overdue invoice before informing you of the need for backup. Do not rely on your clients to tell you they need more information.

6. *Is an audit required?* Some clients may wish to come to your office and audit your records before authorizing payment of an invoice. Providing copies of timesheets and vendor bills for these clients is often insufficient.

7. *The client's normal invoice processing date:* It is important to catch your client's billing cycle. Otherwise, your invoice could be held nearly a month until the next processing date.

8. *Specific information concerning the fee basis and dollar amount must be listed:* It is valuable to restate several of the key contract terms concerning billing and collection. These should include:
   - *The fee basis for this project or change order:* The fee basis for a change order often is different from that of the base project and must be noted to avoid misunderstandings or delays.

DATE PREPARED:

PROJECT NO.:   OR CHANGE ORDER NO.:

PROJECT NAME:

CLIENT NAME AND ADDRESS:

CLIENT CONTACT FOR BILLING QUESTIONS:

PROFESSIONAL CONTACT FOR BILLING QUESTIONS:

SEND INVOICES TO (INCLUDE NAME AND ADDRESS):

OTHERS TO RECEIVE COPIES OF INVOICES
    (INCLUDE NAME AND ADDRESS):

GENERAL QUESTIONS:

1. Client billing form required? ☐Yes ☐No (if yes, attach copy)

2. Backup required
    ▪ All vendor and consultant invoices? ☐Yes ☐No
    ▪ Vendors only? ☐Yes ☐No
    ▪ Consultants only? ☐Yes ☐No
    ▪ Other:

3. Timesheet copies required? ☐Yes ☐No

4. Audit required? ☐Yes ☐No

5. Normal client invoice processing date(s):

6. Other:

SPECIFIC QUESTIONS:

1. Fee basis:
    ▪ Multiple of direct salary expense
    ▪ Multiple of direct personal expense
    ▪ Professional fee plus expense
    ▪ Percentage of construction cost
    ▪ Fixed amount
    ▪ Hourly billing rates
    ▪ Other (explain):

2. Maximum fee: $

3. Reimbursable maximum (if any): $

4. CADD billing method:
    ▪ Hourly CADD billing rate: $

5. Errors and omissions project insurance amount to be
        invoiced: $

6. Reimbursable markup percentages: %
    a. All items equal?   Yes   No
    b. If different percentages to be used, list and include
        percentages used

7. Interest on delinquent receivables:
    a. Percentage per month: %
    b. After how many days from the invoice date?   days

APPROVED: APPROVED:

DATE: DATE:

Figure 13.1 Billing checklist.

- *The reimbursable maximum:* Increasingly, clients require an upside limit on reimbursables. This limit must be noted and monitored.
- *The CADD billing method to be used:* If an hourly billing rate is to be used, the amount must be clearly indicated.
- *Errors and omissions project insurance coverage:* Some clients wish to purchase project insurance for all members of the design and construction team. If this is the case, designers will owe the client for their portion of this coverage.
- *Markups on reimbursables:* According to recent surveys, about half of all design firms now mark up reimbursables typically 10 percent. This percentage must be noted in the contract and on the billing checklist. If different items carry varying markups, these must be noted.
- *Interest charges on delinquent receivables must be negotiated and noted:* Surprisingly, only about one-third of design firms negotiate and charge interest on delinquent receivables. While you are not in the banking business, it is important to at least have an interest percentage noted, even if it is never collected, in the event of arbitration or legal action.

Much of this material is already contained in the project contract. Unfortunately, most owner and designer contracts are lengthy and very detailed. As a result, a great deal of important billing and collection information is lost in the fine print. The billing checklist form is intended to highlight significant terms for the benefit of both the design firm and the client.

The billing checklist is an invaluable tool for improving the billing and collection process. It should become part of your contract documents and include space for the date and signatures for you and your client.

Monitoring System

In addition to calculating the status of billing and collection in your firm, you need an effective accounts receivable monitoring system. There are several elements to this system. All project managers must regularly receive accounts receivable status reports on their projects. This listing must include the invoice number, date of billing, amount outstanding, and any other pertinent information.

An accounts receivable aging report is also very useful. It summarizes all outstanding receivables by the length of time since billing. Figure 13.2 provides an example. This report should be distributed to all project managers. By sharing this information among all managers, they may be able to assist one another in the collection of a delinquent account.

Planning Cash Flow

Avoid checkbook management by investing effort in preparing a cash flow plan. This generally takes the form of a monthly cash flow pro-

Project No.	Name	Total	Current	30	60	90	120	150	Over 150
02791	City Hall	$1000	$500	$200	$200	$100	---	---	---
02891	Clinic	500	---	---	---	---	$500	---	---
02991	Townhouse	700	---	400	---	200	---	$100	---
Total		$2200	$500	$600	$200	$300	$500	$100	---

Figure 13.2 Accounts receivable report.

jection of expected income and expenses. At first, your ability to accurately project cash flow may be poor, but with some experience and improved record keeping, these projections will be of great help.

Separate forms can be developed to collect information that is expressed in summary in Fig. 13.3. All of these may be as simple or as complex as necessary. The main goal is to obtain useful projections.

The percentages used for weighting collections should be based on your own experience. *Anticipated collections* are those that have a high level of certainty of being received. *Probable collections* would be on those projects where the client is generally slow in paying or where potential problems may be developing. *Possible collections* are those where there is a dispute or other delay but collection is anticipated. It is always better to plan based on understated revenues and overstated disbursements. Without generating new work or borrowing money, the firm illustrated in Fig. 13.3 will have serious cash shortage in month 6. A 6-month time frame is about all that can be accurately projected.

	1	2	3	4	5	6
Cash Receipts						
Anticipated Collections	$1000	$1000	$ 800	$ 600	$ 400	$ 300
Probable Collections × 50%	500	250	200	---	150	50
Possible Collections × 25%	200	100	---	300	50	---
Total	$1700	$1350	$1000	$ 900	$ 600	$ 350
Cash Disbursements						
Project Costs	$ 600	$ 600	$ 600	$ 500	$ 500	$ 450
Overhead Costs	700	700	700	700	600	500
Other Costs	100	---	50	100	---	---
Total	$1400	$1300	$1350	$1300	$1100	$ 950
Opening Cash Balance	$1000	$1300	$1350	$1000	$ 600	$ 100
Net Gain (Loss)	300	50	(350)	(400)	(500)	(600)
Closing Cash Balance	$1300	$1350	$1000	$ 600	$ 100	$(500)

Figure 13.3 Cash flow projection. (Figures and percentages are for illustration only.)

	Month			Year to date		
	Projected	Actual	Variance	Projected	Actual	Variance
Cash Receipts						
Project 1	$ 500	$ 500	- - -	$ 5000	$ 5000	- - -
Project 2	600	400	(200)	5000	4000	(1000)
Project 3	500	550	50	6000	5000	(1000)
Miscellaneous	100	50	(50)	1000	1000	- - -
Total	$1700	$1500	(200)	$17,000	$15,000	(2000)
Cash Disbursements						
Project Costs						
Salaries (raw labor)	$ 500	$ 550	50	$ 5000	$ 4000	(1000)
Other Direct Costs	100	150	50	1000	1500	500
Overhead Costs						
Salaries (raw labor)	500	600	100	6000	6500	500
Other Overhead	300	300	- - -	2000	4000	2000
Other Costs	100	100	- - -	1000	1000	- - -
Total	$1500	$1700	200	$15,000	$17,000	2000
Cash + or −	$ 200	$ (200)	(400)	$ 2000	$ (2000)	(4000)

Figure 13.4   Cash flow variance analysis.

To do an effective job of cash flow control, examine backlog, cash sources, cash needs, and where cash can be conserved when necessary by reducing staff, overhead, or other cash drain.

Figure 13.4 shows a cash flow variance analysis format that compares actual cash revenue and expenditures with projections. Actual revenues that were less than projections are shown in brackets. Disbursements less than projections are also shown in brackets.

Resources

Books

Class, Robert Allan, and Robert E. Koehler. *Current Techniques in Architectural Practice.* Washington, D.C., The American Institute of Architects, 1976 (out of print).

Getz, Lowell. *Financial Management for the Design Professional.* New York, Whitney Library of Design, 1984.

Jones, Reginald, and George Trentin. *Management Control for Professional Firms.* New York, American Management Association, 1968 (out of print).

Reports and Manuals

American Consulting Engineers Council. *Uniform Cost Accounting Manual.* Washington, D.C., 1977.

American Consulting Engineers Council. *Financial Management and Project Control for Consulting Engineers.* Washington, D.C., 1978.

American Institute of Architects. *Standardized Accounting for Architects.* Washington, D.C., 1978.

American Institute of Architects. *Compensation Guidelines for Architectural and Engineering Services (and Supplement),* 2d ed., Washington, D.C. 1978.

American Institute of Architects. *Architects Handbook of Professional Practice.* Washington, D.C., 1989.

American Institute of Architects. *Financial Management for Architects* (by Robert F. Mattox). Washington, D.C., 1980.

Bevis, Douglas. *Profit: Planning for It, Making It and Keeping It.* Seattle, Wash., Naramore Bain Brady & Johanson, 1976.

Birnberg & Associates. *Financial Performance Survey for Design Firms* (latest edition).

Birnberg, Howard. *Financial Management for Small Design Firms.* Chicago, Ill., Birnberg & Associates, 1984.

Reece, James S. *A Survey of Management Control Practices in Large Architectural/Engineering Firms.* Cambridge, Harvard Business School, 1975.

Other Resources

Guidelines Publications, various newsletters and publications, P.O. Box 456, Orinda, Calif. 94563. (415) 254-0639.

The Profit Center, monthly newsletter and other publications, 1227 W. Wrightwood Ave., Chicago, Ill. 60614. (312) 664-2300.

14

Project Organization and Management

Kenneth Gibble

Successful firms of the future will be those that have developed and rewarded the leaders of the complex process of doing projects. The title may vary, but the role will be as defined below. This is the person who makes it work, whatever that entails. This is the individual with primary responsibility for assuring client satisfaction through control of schedule, budget, and quality on that project. See Fig. 14.1.

The second ingredient of a successful project is the project organization. This includes putting the right project team together within workable organizational structure. Since every project is different, the organization must be different. The final ingredients are planning and executing the project.

The Project Manager

The role of project manager is frequently diverse, but the goal is to achieve project success. Often this means being the chief negotiator between opposing forces. In Fig. 14.2, the project manager is shown as the focal point of four groups that must be served. The word "served" was intentionally used to suggest that project managers need to operate more like servant leaders than bosses (Greenleaf, 1977). Project managers must fill a role that is partly stated and partly implied. The implied element is frequently misunderstood by the inexperienced project manager who does not understand that the human project manager is expected to achieve superhuman tasks.

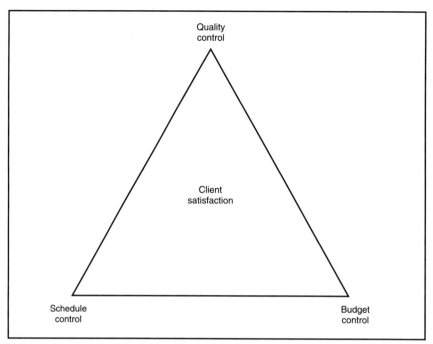

Figure 14.1   Responsibilities of project manager.

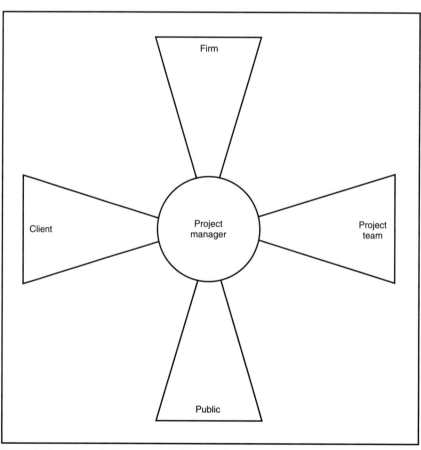

Figure 14.2   The project manager is the focal point of groups served.

To this point, the project manager has been referred to as an individual, but is this necessarily true? In a single-person design firm, the answer is obvious. In small firms, one of the principals normally functions in this role. As the firm grows, this role generally shifts to a key person who may not be a principal. In megaprojects, an entire firm may be designated as project manager. In these very large projects, the duties may be divided among several people, but still, someone must be the leader of that project management effort.

Is the role of project manager filled by a technical person or a management person? The degree of each depends upon the specific case. For example, in the investigation of a roofing failure, the technically skilled roofing expert may individually conduct the investigation and also perform incidental project manager tasks. In contrast, very large projects require the attention of a full-time manager who has an architectural or engineering background. On smaller projects, the project manager will perform both technical and managerial functions.

"Project managers are in a position of trust. They are not only the focal points for their projects, they are also the stewards of all the talent and resources committed to the projects. They have a noble responsibility."* The role of project manager is as diverse as the many different projects and design firms. Each situation is unique. Design firms must be flexible in defining, selecting, and utilizing project managers.

The responsibilities of the project manager are:

1. Planning the who, how, when of the project

2. Implementing the project, which involves initiating, communicating, and resolving conflict

3. Controlling the project within the established budget, schedule, and quality standards

4. Assuring client satisfaction while accomplishing the above responsibilities

In addition to the stated responsibilities, other responsibilities are implied. Ruskin and Estes (1982, pp. 25–30) refer to these as "inherent duties of the project manager." Some of these are as follows:

1. Interpreting the statement of work so that everyone on the team has a common understanding of objectives and constraints

2. Defining, negotiating, and securing commitments for personnel and services for the project

3. Managing and coordinating the interfaces between consultants so that they provide required information at the correct time and moderate their position if they are projecting their own needs above the needs of the project

4. Developing personnel working on the project to become more proficient

---

*From Ruskin and Estes (1982, p. 148).

Why would anyone want to accept a position that is so demanding? For the deep satisfaction of knowing you have achieved the project objectives despite the many obstacles in the way, for financial rewards, and for future rewards. Kerzner (1979, pp. 95–96) said, "If these responsibilities were applied to the total organization, they might reflect the job description of the general manager. This analogy between project and general managers is one of the reasons why future general managers will be developed from the project management ranks."

The qualifications to be a successful project manager are extensive and diverse. Obviously, a small, single-discipline project requires less proficiency than a megaproject, but to some degree the same skills are needed. These skills are shown in Fig. 14.3, with effective communications at the center. Without this, all the other skills will be underutilized.

The project manager is faced with many interpersonal transactions. To be effective, it is important to size up the situation and the stance of the other person. The project manager then needs to respond with the appropriate style. This may be confronting or coaching; it may be delegating or deciding.

The project manager must have a clear picture where he or she fits within the firm. While project managers always strive to meet project objectives, they frequently lose sight of firm objectives. This has been referred to as "projectitis" (Burstein and Stasiowski, 1982, p. 19). When resources such as staff are limited and many project managers

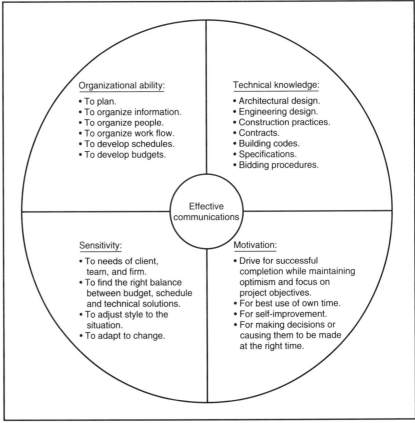

Figure 14.3 Qualifications of a project manager.

are competing for staff, some projects must suffer. Project managers must learn to accept that the higher needs of the firm will prevail.

What is the project manager's relationship with the client and the firm? The project manager is usually the firm's agent in direct day-to-day dealing with the client. In many cases, there is a principal or partner in charge of the project who represents the firm's reputation and loyalty to the client. The project manager must keep the principal informed of all significant issues. The ultimate responsibility for the project and the client lies with the principal. The principal can intervene or replace the project manager if absolutely necessary.

What is the source of the project manager's authority? The source of authority is generally divided into position authority and personal authority. Both are important to project managers.

Position Authority

- Legitimate power based on position within firm and project
- Coercive authority based on the power to punish
- Reward authority based on the power to reward

Personal Authority

- Expert authority based on knowledge or skill of project manager
- Referent authority based on follower's desire to build a relationship with the project manager

Position authority is given by the firm, and just as quickly can be taken back. Frequently, the extent of authority is not precisely defined. Therefore, it is up to the project manager's skill at creating the perception of power and using it wisely.

Personal authority comes from the project manager's building confidence and trust. It comes from the followers only when they accept the expertise or value the relationship. The project manager must work at earning this authority.

The Project Team

Assembling the project team can take a multitude of forms depending on the project and the firms involved. In a multidiscipline architectural engineering firm or an engineering architectural firm, the entire team may come from one organization. Normally, the team is assembled for one project. On many projects the team members will not be working full time on only one project and therefore may concurrently serve on a number of teams. Very large projects would be the exception. Obviously, for many different technical specialists to be serving on more than one team, organizational problems are common.

Many multidiscipline firms have established a matrix organization with varying degrees of success. See Fig. 14.4. In a matrix organization, each staff person is reporting simultaneously to a project manager or managers and a technical department head. It requires excellent communications.

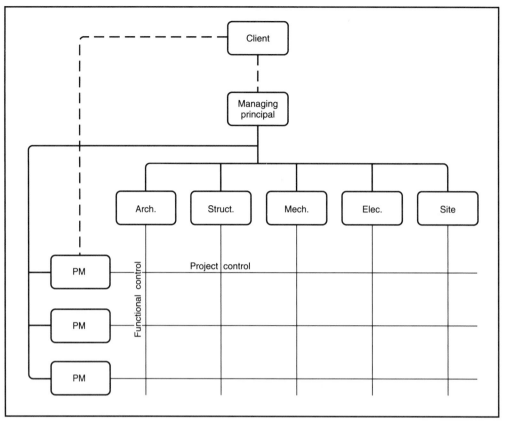

Figure 14.4 Matrix organization.

In contrast, an architectural firm or an engineering firm of a single discipline may be the prime design professional for a project. Expertise in other areas is provided by consulting or subcontracting firms. The majority of architectural projects in the United States are handled this way.

Teams of staff members of several firms are assembled for one project. Since these people usually continue to reside at their parent firm, the project manager has an added challenge of communicating project objectives, progress, data, and charges to a remote team. Poor communications can result in contractual disputes between firms.

Clients often think that forming a team comprising several different firms is too complicated to be workable. Actually, most of these teams function remarkably well. To function best, each team needs:

1. A competent project manager

2. Early assembly of the team

3. Competent team members

4. Good definition of the scope of work for each firm

5. Sufficient fee for each firm

6. Prompt payments

7. Continuous, good communications

Often, each team is formed and activated during the pursuit of the project. The value of separate specialty firms is marketed to clients as an advantage.

The best approach is for each team member to collectively define their scope of services and fees before the prime design professional negotiates a contract with the client. This is true whether it is an architectural engineering firm or an architect and separate consultants.

A somewhat newer trend is forming a multiprime team where each specialty firm has a direct contract with the client. This has the advantage of relieving liability and reducing professional liability premiums for the prime design professional firm. It also provides the client with direct input from all specialists. To an experienced client this may be an advantage, but to many it is confusing.

For a multiprime team, all contracts must be compatible and clearly designate which firm has the primary project management responsibility. The project manager's role is probably more difficult because coercive and reward power have been stripped. It is the client who is forced to resolve disputes.

Under all types of project teams, the importance of the relationships between team members has not received sufficient attention in the past. The trend for the future will be to better understand the subtleties of team relationships and to select team members who actively work toward the achievement of project objectives. There will be less room for ego and self-interest.

The best projects are produced by compatible teams where members have trust, are cognizant of each other's vulnerabilities, and can anticipate moves by others. Project managers need to carefully select team members and develop these kind of relationships. Obviously, teams that have had good past relationships have an advantage on a current project.

Searching deeper as to why some teams mesh better, it is necessary to explore the values of the firms and individuals. Firms that are strategically positioned (Coxe et al., 1987, pp. 24, 47) close together should be able to develop good team relationships more easily. This will tend to result in similar priorities and methods of operation.

Planning

Before a project can be done effectively, there must be a plan. The formality of the plan is a function of the size and complexity of the project. The plan or proposal used to land the project often lacks sufficient detail to serve as a guide for the project. Developing the plan helps to define objectives and responsibilities. It also provides a base line against which changes of scope can be measured. It is surprising how often planning and design professionals plan everything except how they are going to do their own work.

The plan should include the following sections:

1. General description of the project.

2. Project objectives. This includes both the client's and the design team's objectives.

3. Project organization.

4. Staffing. This has a large impact on the ability to meet schedule commitments. See Chap. 19.

5. Schedule and control methods.

6. Budget and control methods.

7. Quality control methods.

8. Administrative procedures.

The plan should break the project down into tasks or activities required to complete the project. Then determine who will do each task, how much it will cost, how long it will take, and in what sequence it must be done.

To organize this information and communicate it to team members, a format needs to be developed. Since design professionals think graphically, charts are frequently utilized (also see Chap. 19). This might be a bar chart or Gantt chart which shows the start, stop, and duration of each task. Or it might be a flow diagram, a PERT or CPM chart which also identifies the interrelationships of tasks. The chart will be used during the project for monitoring schedules, just as the budget will be used to monitor costs.

Implementing

Once the project starts, it is the project manager's job to initiate the start-up of each work group at the proper time. He or she then must shepherd the flow of information and control the process so that all objectives are met. The project manager must manage both the team and the client.

Excellent communications are required. A breakdown in communications not only means objectives may not be met but can lead to professional liability suits. Studies by the major professional liability insurers show that suits are frequently filed against design professionals when clients believe their expectations are not being met. Every project has some low points, and it is up to the project manager to guide the team and client through these difficult periods.

If the project team has not worked together before, members will go through a stage of testing each other before reaching a comfort level of trust. In a project with a short schedule, there can be insufficient time for this to happen.

In the hierarchy of communications, a face-to-face meeting has the best chance of being effective, because verbal and nonverbal channels can be used. The most important or most difficult communications should be done in this manner.

The next best method is to use the telephone. Factual information and simple questions can be communicated effectively by this means. People who know and trust each other can deal with more complex transactions by telephone.

The least effective method is written communications. Frequently, important conversations resolve issues; then written letters, minutes, or reports are used to make a permanent record of the issues. Busy members of the project team tend to not read written communications except when there is a major dispute.

Since many design professionals have not developed good listen-

Tips on Meetings

1. The objective of business meetings is to reach a unanimous assent in the minimum time. The leader may not get agreement from all present but at least should get acknowledgment that those with opposing views accept the decision that has been made.
2. The leader needs to be clear on the purpose of the meeting and invite only those people who need to attend.
3. The leader begins the meeting by stating the purpose, reviewing the agenda, and defining the estimated length.
4. At the end of each item, the leader summarizes what has been agreed to and ensures that the proposed action is defined.
5. To end the meeting, the leader restates the purpose, notes the planned time to end, and acknowledges what has been accomplished.
6. Minutes should be distributed after the meeting summarizing decisions made and identifying what action by when needs to be taken. A summary of information or discussions can be included if it seems worth recording.
7. Meetings should have a businesslike tempo with a sense of direction and a feeling of progress. Despite periodic differences of opinion, attendees should maintain a spirit of cooperativeness. It is up to the leader to set the mood of the meeting.

Figure 14.5 Tips on meetings. (*From Scott (1984).*)

ing skills, the project manager has to be especially tuned into communications during a project. By periodically testing what people think they heard and understood, the project manager can evaluate the success of communications.

One way face-to-face communication takes place is at meetings. Much has been written about how to conduct effective meetings. Project managers need to learn these techniques so that team members do not get frustrated sitting through endless meetings. See Fig. 14.5 for some tips to better meetings. Before calling a meeting, the project manager should evaluate whether this meeting is even necessary or whether some other method would be sufficient.

Team members need to be encouraged to identify potential problems and bring them forward as early as possible. The project manager then must have an appropriate procedure for resolving problems before they develop into conflict. A project manager also needs conflict-resolution skills. Conflict should be considered an expected part of the process.

All members of the team must be trained to bring problems forward. Solutions and recommendations should be proposed where possible. Sometimes recommendations can be made only after sharing interdisciplinary information.

Control

All the efforts picking the right project manager, staffing with a qualified team, and planning the project may be wasted if there is no control system. What is needed is an early warning process that triggers an appropriate response when the project is wandering off track.

Effective project control has four components:

- A set of yardsticks by which progress will be measured; these are offered in the work plan and in the owner-architect agreement.
- A reporting system that tells where the project stands.
- A way of comparing progress to yardsticks to establish any deviations.
- A willingness to take corrective action to keep the project on track.*

Cost reporting software is readily available to simplify the tracking of project costs. With this software, monthly or weekly reports can swiftly tell where the project is. For maximum benefit, this information needs to go to the people who have direct control over the time being spent on the project.

This information on project costs is feedback to detect deviation from the yardstick. It should not be used in a punitive way. The goal is successful projects, not catching the guilty.

Scheduling monitoring is similar to cost monitoring. Both generally require some simple way of quantifying what percentage complete the current work is. Averaging the percentage complete of all drawings on the last day of each month is an example of one method. The percentage complete is then compared against hours or dollars expended or against elapsed time. These quick comparisons pinpoint deviations. When deviations occur, the project manager must decide what course corrections are necessary.

Overruns do not necessarily mean inefficient work on the project. Other possible meanings are insufficient fee or work outside the contracted scope of work. Before appropriate corrections can be made, it is necessary to accurately interpret the information.

Quality must also be controlled under the direction of the project manager. The yardstick for this includes the contract, the firm's standards, industry standards, and regulations. Checklists, standard details, and checking procedures are tools used in the process of quality control but are effective only when quality is a state of mind.

Building codes are increasingly important regulations in the work of design professionals. The enforcement of codes is aggressively conducted in many municipalities. Therefore, code review for each project by all disciplines should be standard procedure. At the rate that code revisions are now occurring, keeping up to date in publications and knowledge takes constant attention.

Quality control of specifications requires a planned approach. As materials, methods, and reference standards change, master specifications must be updated. In addition to keeping office master specifications current, their careful adaptation for each project is vitally important. The language of specifications should be readable instead of traditional lingo from the past.

Peer reviews are an emerging technique for improving quality.† The methods are still being fine-tuned and the experience database small, but growing. The concept is to provide a focused review conducted by a knowledgeable, independent peer.

---

*From Haviland, 1984.

†See *Quality in the Constructed Project,* 1988, chap. 13.

The purpose of the review is signaled by who initiates it. Frequently, design firms will request a peer review for the purpose of identifying weaknesses so that self-improvement efforts can be focused on key issues. In this type of review, the report will be made to the design firm only and all reviewed documents will be returned to them. Frequently, the report will be oral only and regardless of the form will be strictly confidential.

Sometimes peer reviews are initiated by an authority having jurisdiction over the design firm, therefore signaling a different purpose. Examples are as follows:

1. An owner wanting a higher level of confidence that a design solution is appropriate and properly executed

2. A regulatory agency that by law is required to initiate an independent structural review to ensure public safety on essential facilities or buildings over a specified size

3. The corporate office of a national design firm requesting a peer review of one of their branch offices or departments

The types of peer review currently in use are organizational, technical, and project. The organizational peer review looks at policies, procedures, and practices. The technical peer review looks at design standards, calculations, drawings, specifications, and shop drawing procedures. The project peer review looks at one project only, reviewing the project management process or the project design technical work or both.

The procedure for conducting peer reviews involves defining the purpose, the scope of what is included, the method, indicating the size of the samples examined, the schedule, who will perform the review, and what type of report will be provided.

Detailed procedures for organizational peer reviews have been developed by ASFE, ACEC, and the Chicago chapter of the AIA. Procedures for technical peer reviews have been developed by the Coalition of American Structural Engineers (CASE), a subgroup of ACEC. Project peer review procedures have been jointly developed by ASCE and ACEC. All these organizations have publications describing the recommended procedures.

Bibliography

Burstein, David, and Frank Stasiowski, *Project Management for the Design Professional*, Whitney Library of Design, New York, 1982.

Coxe, Weld, et al., *Success Strategies for Design Professionals*, McGraw-Hill, New York, 1987.

Greenleaf, Robert K., *Servant Leadership*, Paulist Press, Mahwah, N.J., 1977.

Haviland, David, *Office Project Management from Architect's Handbook of Professional Practice*, The American Institute of Architects, Washington, 1984.

Kerzner, Harold, *Project Management, A Systems Approach to Planning, Scheduling and Controlling*, Van Nostrand Reinhold Company, New York, 1979.

Quality in the Constructed Project, American Society of Civil Engineers, New York, 1988.

Ruskin, Arnold M., and W. Eugene Estes, *What Every Engineer Should Know about Project Management*, Marcel Dekker, New York, 1982.

Scott, Bill, *Communication for Professional Engineers*, Thomas Telford, Ltd., London, 1984, pp. 115–184.

15

Project Programming

Bryce Hastings

Programming is the dialogue between designer and client that defines the functional, technical, and aesthetic expectations for a building project. This dialogue is an integral part of the process by which facilities are designed. Programming is the problem-seeking phase that designers frequently identify as a portion of predesign services.

In addition to defining the goals and expectations for a building project, the programming process includes the collection and organization of facts, the development and testing of program alternatives, the prioritizing of alternatives to determine real need, and the clear statement of the problem. While the problem-seeking process remains basically the same, exciting opportunities exist for dramatic improvement in the techniques for programming during the next decade.

To be successful, programming must have a clear beginning and ending. The ending should coincide with the delivery of a work product or deliverable that will complete the service. Programming is part of predesign services. It normally follows needs assessment and survey of existing facilities and precedes site analysis, master planning, and design concepts.

Programming, cost controlling, and scheduling are separate but interwoven service offerings. Either the budget has been established by the client and will drive the programming effort, or it has *not* been established and will be driven by the program.

Contents of the work product are described in AIA Document B-162 and may include but are not limited to:

Spatial organization diagrams

Site space program

Building space program

Staffing analysis

Furnishings and equipment list

Growth patterns of components

Comparison with existing facilities

Technical requirements sheets for each building space

Blocking diagrams of major building components to scale

Governing codes

Planning standards

Appendix
- Workshop, interview, and survey notes and tabulations
- Photos and narrative from other facilities visited
- Compilation of applicable codes, standards, and planning references

Stacking diagrams, circulation studies, and orientation of components are reserved for site analysis, master planning, and design concept phases of work. See Fig. 15.1.

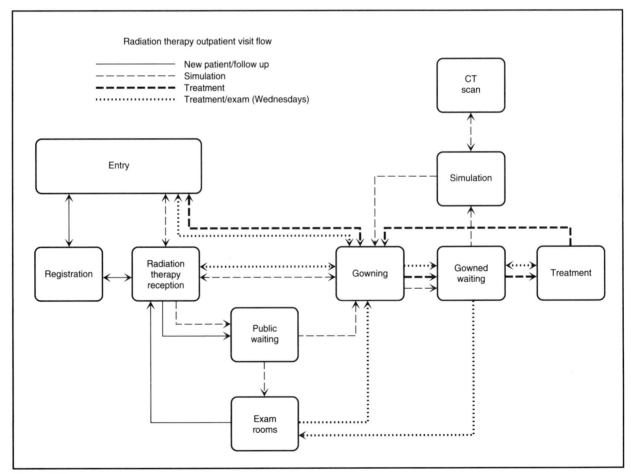

Figure 15.1

Programming has become a participatory process involving client, user, designer, special expert, and interested parties. Most frequently this process takes place away from the designer's office—in the city hall, the health care institution, the corporate headquarters, or the school campus. The designer and the client carefully plan and orchestrate the process to maintain orderly progress. The reality is a dynamic situation that frequently produces unexpected break-throughs and thoughtful insight into the problem.

Top client decision makers are involved frequently. Indeed, this may be their only involvement in the design process prior to the rib-bon-cutting ceremony. It behooves the design team to listen carefully to their priorities and expectations for the project. "Methods of inter-action with clients and users vary according to client culture, back-ground and decision making capability," notes David A. Chassin, from Hellmuth, Obata & Kassabaum of St. Louis. "The consummate business executive trained and experienced in decision making may move rapidly through the programming process in a one-on-one rela-tionship with the designer. Some clients with their respective political constituencies may favor an extensive participatory process to develop programming decisions."

"The client representatives who are responsible for the operations of specialized institutional facilities are usually the advocates for involuntary users such as detainees or patients," says Michael A. Griebel, associate at HOK. "The operating personnel seek to keep their charges safe, comfortable and happy to minimize stress on staff and to forestall unnecessary problems." These building types often contain highly detailed spaces, such as cells or patient rooms, which are repeated throughout the complex. They also are microcosms of the world beyond their boundaries and contain all the functions required for living. Functional and technical mistakes in their design result in risks to life, safety, civil rights, and well-being. In some cases the programming team may consider building a standardized model of a critical unit to create a physical setting to stimulate client reaction and response.

Speed is an important element in the participatory process. The length of meetings, their frequency and number, and the span of time beyond which interest lags frequently require major programming efforts be accomplished in 10 to 12 weeks. The time between meetings available for the design team to produce a work product may be short.

Other benefits to client, designer, and project accrue from the par-ticipatory process. The process can be sold by the designer as a unique portion of an additional predesign service offering. HOK con-venes a panel of experts who are not designers (educational, finan-cial, gerontological, laboratory specialists, sociological, etc.) to contribute to the process in a timely and meaningful way. Their inter-action with the group will clarify important issues and priorities. If the proposed project is budget-driven, the client may wish to include financial experts, leasing agents, and operations people interested in first cost, timing of building occupancy, operating cost-effectiveness, and staffing and user satisfactions.

The process can promote a project and build constituencies and consensus for proceeding with the project. Public forums may help publicize the project. If properly organized in advance, the programming process can be effective in getting the project off to a fast start. Long time delays for the review process are eliminated since review is instantaneous.

Survey and Interview Techniques

Programming sets the framework for the design services that are to follow. Surveys and interviews are two means of gathering and organizing data relating to the project. For example, programming a corporate office headquarters may involve gathering information from hundreds of people. Surveys have long been used for this purpose. The designer also may want to personally interview corporate officers, vice presidents, and other officers (Fig. 15.2).

Other techniques have been proved in evaluating, comparing, and tabulating survey results. Consultants specializing in the field can be very cost-effective in preparing the survey questions and processing the results. Carefully constructed telephone interviews and surveys are a fast and effective way to gather information for the program. Interviewers do not have to be designers. They can use prepared scripts and enter user responses directly into a computer for instant tabulation. Special comments by the interviewee can be recorded as well.

"Getting the client to visualize a five- to ten-year planning horizon to establish future growth patterns is one of the most difficult aspects of programming," says Merlin Lickhalter, managing partner of Stone Marraccini & Patterson's St. Louis office. "It takes the design firm's very best people to get the user to think about work load projections, staffing patterns and office procedures that may change dramatically in a new environment."

Stone Marraccini & Patterson custom designs the programming procedure for each client. Survey forms are developed with client administrators who determine with whom in the organization the interviews will be conducted. The firm uses lap-top computers to gather and process information obtained in the field. "Algorithms relating projected work load and/or staffing to quantity of net space required are kept in the computer, along with grossing factors for various functional areas/department," according to Lickhalter. "We have developed our own planning standards after finding published standards were inadequate, outdated and not representative of current practices."

Database

Touring recently completed, existing, and comparable facilities, attending facilities planning conferences, and researching current publications are techniques used by both designers and clients alike to learn about specific facility types. In addition to extensive 35-mm slides of related projects maintained by most firms, videotape libraries of special facilities are now being developed. Photographic and video

POPKIN, STERN LAW OFFICES
CLAYTON POINT TOWER

Space Programming Questionnaire

Name of Individual: _____

Title: _____

Right or Left Handed: _____

Department:
Attorney _____
Paralegal _____
General Administration _____
Word Processing _____
Accounting _____
Data Processing _____
Filing and Storage _____
Secretarial _____
Library _____

Critical Area:
Litigation _____
Corporate Law _____
Taxation and Probation _____
Real Estate _____
Labor _____
Bonds _____
Other _____

Names of Individuals
with whom you work
on a *daily* basis:
_____
_____
_____
_____
_____

Names of Individuals
with whom you work
on a *weekly* basis:
_____
_____
_____
_____
_____

Please indicate departments
with which you have personal
contact on a daily basis:
Attorney _____
Paralegal _____
General Administration _____
Word Processing _____
Accounting _____
Data Processing _____
Filing and Storage _____
Secretarial _____
Library _____

Figure 15.2

(Continued)

Work Surface

Which of the following items do you have on your work surface or desk?	Dictaphone	_____
	Stapler	_____
	Intercom	_____
	Directory	_____
	Telephone	_____
	CRT	_____
	Calculator	_____
	Other	_____

During an average work day, how many copies will you make on a photocopier? _____

Do you keep files at your workstation? _____

If the answer to the above is yes, how many standard file drawers?_____

How many lateral file drawers? _____

How adequate is the amount of filing space you currently use?

_____

Conferences

During an average work week, how many conferences or meetings will you participate in?	None	_____
	1–3	_____
	4–6	_____
	7–10	_____
	More than 10	_____
Where are your conferences most frequently held?	Own work space	_____
	Private conference room	_____
	Other work space	_____
Not including yourself, how many other persons will usually participate in conferences?	1	_____
	2–3	_____
	4–5	_____
	More than 5	_____
What is the most frequent duration of conferences?	1–10 minutes	_____
	10–30 minutes	_____
	30 minutes–1 hour	_____
	1–3 hours	_____
	Over 3 hours	_____

Storage

For reference materials, how many linear feet of shelving do you require in your work area? _____

What do you consider the best feature of your current work space?

_____

What do you consider the worst feature of your current work space?

_____

Figure 15.2 *(Continued)*

presentations to client and user groups are effective in educating these parties. They are also an excellent method to portray alternatives for setting priorities.

The lack of meaningful up-to-date planning standards, the rapid changes in the marketing of certain facilities, and the continued increases in user expectations make it necessary for design firms to develop and maintain their own databases for planning and programming. Codes, standards, and regulations that impact programming are changing constantly and designers continually struggle to keep up to date.

Data Collection and Organization

Development and maintenance of a database on the built environment is the responsibility of the design firm's programming specialist. Principals or design directors in small- or medium-sized firms will have this responsibility. Large firms may have a research librarian to maintain hard copy or computer-based data.

Planning-oriented normative data were developed in the late 1960s and early 1970s. Efforts are on the national scale to develop normative data and standards information. Many design firms are contributing to this effort through national and state organizations such as International Facilities Management Association (IFMA) and Building Owners and Managers Association (BOMA) in the corporate office field. The amount of data and the speed with which the data are input to the design team during the participatory, survey, or interview process can be overwhelming. Tape recorders, flip charts, digitizer boards, and note taking are techniques in use to handle client input. The computer is an ideal tool for recording, organizing, processing, formatting, and editing data.

Unorganized, randomly received data can be coded efficiently and recorded in a prearranged database for future use. While no two assignments are alike, an experienced programmer knows what categories of information are required to define the problem. Technical data, spatial relationships, growth rates, and occupancy loads are but a few of the categories to be coded into the database. "Image exercising is a technique used to help determine client likes and dislikes," said Mary Jane Whitaker at HOK. "Not only are we looking for visual reactions but also for audio, olfactory sense and tactile response as well." Stimuli may include tours of existing facilities and viewing of images to check reaction to such items as density, color, odors, and lighting.

Data Processing

For example, client input may call for an aerobics and dance room to accommodate a class of forty. The design firm's database calculates the room size and critical dimensions and identifies the lighting and air change requirements, the finishes, equipment, and furniture, special surfaces, storage requirements, adjacencies, alternate functions, and so forth (Fig. 15.3).

MARY WASHINGTON COLLEGE
CONVOCATION CENTER
TECHNICAL DATA SHEET

PROGRAM DESIGNATION	N40
ROOM NO	
ROOM NAME	Natatorium (deck area)
NUMBER REQUIRED	1
NUMBER OF OCCUPANTS	N/A
NET AREA	13,000 SF
CEILING HEIGHT	26'-6" minimum over diving area
HOURS OF USE	112 hours/week
CONSTRUCTION	Concrete and masonry unit construction with finished surfaces. 1" × 1" ceramic tile deck. Exposed ceiling structure. Acoustical roof deck. Deck dim. should be: 20' at ends, 16.5' at locker rm side, and 15' at opposite side.
HVAC	Heating and ventilation. Dehumidification.
PLUMBING	Cold water supply to 2 drinking fountains and drain. Several drinking fountains required. Water supply and drains for pool tanks.
ELECTRICAL/LIGHTING	High intensity discharge lighting for good quality color rendition for video and TV telecast. Conduit for timing system. Conduit for scoreboard and clocks. Provide enough light to eliminate glare.
COMMUNICATIONS/AV	Sound system. Conduit for video and timing system.
FIXED EQUIPMENT	Pool equipment. Colorado timing system (4 score lines and 10 read-outs). 20 event record board. (2) three meter boards and (2) one meter boards. Elevated platform for TV crew and video taping.
MOVABLE EQUIPMENT	Pull out bleachers, starting blocks, touch pads, lane lines for both length and width.
SPECIAL FEATURES	Deck level gutter with surge capability. Need access for motorized lift.
RELATIONSHIP TO OTHER SPACES	Adjacent to shower and locker rooms. Adjacent to pool equipment room and pool storage area. Direct access to main circulation and pool office. No need for outdoor deck.
ACTIVITY/FUNCTION	Competitive varsity swimming, P.E. swim, recreational and competitive diving, scuba training, student and staff socialization and recreation.

Figure 15.3

The designer's database also contains net to gross area relationship for several facility types, parking ratios, floor area ratios, staffing requirements, workloads, and procedure loads as related to quantity of space. This database requires continued updating as new information becomes available. While prioritizing diverse needs and wants is basically a client activity, the designer's responsibility is to furnish the information and the procedures to facilitate these decisions. "Processing collected data by comparison with normative standards is a means of broadening the access to information beyond client's associational, prejudicial and familiar thinking," Chassin said. "Our firm customized the programming process to meet their client's specific needs to the point of selecting design team members to match or contrast with client team members." (See Fig. 15.4.)

Presentation

The material input from the client, which is organized, tested, and processed by the designer, prioritized, and reduced to real need, ultimately must be presented to the client as a clear statement of the problem. The client and user need evidence that the design team has listened to and is acting on their input. The designer must be prepared to present the material in the media most familiar to the client. A corporate client may be more comfortable with business graphics, charts, and tables presented on an overhead projector. Overhead projectors are compact and powerful, exhibits are made easily on 8½- by 11-inch transparencies, and every board room has a screen. Covering the walls in the board room may not be well received if it means removing portraits of board members and taping displays on hand-rubbed Karelian burl walnut paneling.

Electronic copy boards that record and reproduce client input as fast as the designer can write are replacing the flip chart in the participatory process. These digitizers can reproduce full-sized copies for instant use in the room or can reproduce 8½- by 11-inch copies for inclusion in the final report.

Lap-top or personal computers are becoming the designer's companion in the programming workshop. Many meeting facilities have overhead projectors with liquid crystal display equipment to project the computer image onto a large screen where interested parties can study the impact of program alternatives in a spreadsheet format (Figs. 15.5 and 15.6). Hard copy from the computer by way of a laser printer can also be included directly in the final report.

Interim and final presentations still are being made in color on 30- by 42-inch foam core boards. Strong graphic presentation capability is a necessary part of the programming phase. Complex programming concepts must be presented to the client and user group with concise verbal and written skills backed up with clear graphics. Color photocopy reductions or photographically reduced, four-color printed reproductions of the presentation boards usually are included in the final report. Hand-drawn bubble diagrams still play an important role in the programming phase. Clients may consider computer-generated

BUILDING SPACE PROGRAM / PRELIMINARY COST ESTIMATE
MARY WASHINGTON CONVOCATION CENTER

PROJECT NO: 2310.00
PROJECT NAME: MARY WASHINGTON
PRINCIPAL IN CHARGE: _____
PROJECT MANAGER: _____
PROJECT DESIGNER: _____

ACTIVITY AREAS		PROGRAM AREA	ACTUAL AREA	UNIT COST	TOTAL COST
A10	Events Arena/Gymnasium	38,368 SF	43,855 SF		
A20	Seating for 3000 persons (area also included above)	6,000 SF	4,060 SF		
A30	Racquetball courts	6,400 SF	6,400 SF		
A30	Squash courts	1,184 SF	1,184 SF		
A35	Racquetball Observation	3,200 SF	5,862 SF		
A40	Gym Storage	2,000 SF	3,068 SF		
A50	Gym Mechanical	3,000 SF	1,080 SF		
A60	Gym Gallery	1,500 SF	1,560 SF		

NATATORIUM

N10	Pool Tank	12,300 SF	12,900 SF		
N20	Bulkheads, Movable (Included in Pool Tank)	SF	SF		
N25	Underwater Pool Obsevation	880 SF	880 SF		
N30	Handicapped Ramp	260 SF	260 SF		
N40	Natatorium (Deck Area)	13,000 SF	12,230 SF		
N50	Natatorium Observation	4,200 SF	3,245 SF		
N60	Pool Storage	600 SF	840 SF		
N70	Pool Office	150 SF	110 SF		
N75	Swim Team Coach's Office	150 SF	162 SF		
N80	Filtration Equipment Rooms	800 SF	1,869 SF		
N90	Chlorine Room (Included above)	48 SF	SF		
N100	Pool Mechanical	1,500 SF	1,600 SF		

USER SUPPORT

U10	Training Room	1,200 SF	2,100 SF		
U11	Training Room Office	200 SF	187 SF		
U12	Training Room Rehabilitation Area	300 SF	456 SF		
U13	Training Room Wet Area	200 SF	294 SF		
U14	Training Exam Room	200 SF	176 SF		
U20	Weight Training	10,000 SF	10,284 SF		
U21	Training Classroom/Video Office	600 SF	775 SF		
U25	Weight Training Office	200 SF	192 SF		
U30	Athletic Eqip. (Uniform) Storage Area	2,500 SF	3,426 SF		
U40	Men's Locker Room	2,500 SF	2,740 SF		
U50	Women's Locker Room	2,500 SF	2,520 SF		
U80	Men's Faculty/Coaches Locker Room	1,250 SF	1,500 SF		
U90	Women's Faculty Locker Room	750 SF	600 SF		
U100	Visiting Team Locker Room	1,750 SF	1,792 SF		
U120	Laundry	300 SF	252 SF		

PUBLIC AREAS

P10	Vestibule	1,280 SF	1,040 SF		
P20	Lobby	9,000 SF	7,000 SF		
P25	Trophy Display Cases	8			
P30	Control Station	400 SF	360 SF		
P31	Storage	100 SF	56 SF		
P32	Ticket	150 SF	132 SF		
P50	Facilities Manager	150 SF	192 SF		
P60	General Office Area	450 SF	720 SF		
P70	Work Room	200 SF	240 SF		
P80	Offices	450 SF	960 SF		
P90	Conference Room	1,000 SF	1,550 SF		
P100	Men's Public Toilets	1,000 SF	1,112 SF		
P105	Women's Public Toilets	1,000 SF	992 SF		
P110	Lounge	7,000 SF	6,700 SF		
P120	Concession	200 SF	238 SF		
P121	Concession Storage	120 SF	112 SF		
P122	Concession Prep.	150 SF	140 SF		
P125	Vending (Included in Lounge)	225 SF			
P130	Elevator	2 EA			
P140	ElevatorMachine Room	150 SF	152 SF		

BUILDING SUPPORT

B10	Receiving Area	500 SF	630 SF		
B20	Mechanical Room	4,000 SF	4,700 SF		
B30	General Storage Rooms	4,310 SF	2,805 SF		
B50	Electrical	250 SF	250 SF		
B60	Sound	320 SF	320 SF		
B70	T.V./Play-by play	320 SF	320 SF		
B80	T.V. Platforms	1,000 SF	1,044 SF		

SUB-TOTAL	153,725 SF	160,224 SF		
14% CIRCULATION/WALLS	21,162 SF	25,578 SF		
TOTAL	174,887 SF	185,802 SF		

Figure 15.4

Figure 15.5 *(Courtesy of 3M Visual Systems.)*

diagrams with their high degree of precision to be design concepts far more developed than intended by the design team.

Some design firms are using computer-generated diagrams to graphically portray relative sizes of building components and their adjacencies. Plotting these graphics in color makes a powerful presentation tool. Composing and editing the final report is done most efficiently on the computer desktop publishing software, drawing on the spreadsheets and database developed during the process.

Summary

Historically, the client furnished the designer a facility program, a site, and a budget at the start of the project. Today, the opportunities and challenges in a building project are beyond the scope of all but the most sophisticated clients. Many design firms are offering predesign services (often as a separate fee) including needs assessment, existing facilities evaluation, programming, site analysis, master planning, design concepts, cost and schedule control, financing alternatives, and project promotion.

The programming phase is an established process for problem seeking, a clear statement of the client's problem as related to a specific project. The techniques for handling the process are changing

Figure 15.6 *(Courtesy of 3M Visual Systems.)*

rapidly. These techniques fall directly into the category of information management and involve the processing of thoughts and ideas most easily handled by computer.

Personal contact between the client and the designer is critical during the programming phase. The client must have constant assurance that the designer is listening. The designer must educate the client to the breadth of opportunities available for the project.

The most important part of the programming phase is the process itself with its dynamics and interaction between client, user, specialist, and designer. A work product, however, must be produced along the way to indicate that the client is being heard and that the designer is processing the desired input.

Powerful graphics that can be clearly understood by large groups of interested parties are essential. Concise narrative supported by graphics and data is essential for a final report. All the presentation material required can and should be produced with a computer.

The final work product delivered to the client will usually be a published report suitable for board approval, project funding, or project promotion. Frequently client representatives expect to review drafts of their report, and they may want to include data generated by themselves or others. The design team should develop a standardized format for reports that is well organized and easily revised. Tabs for major sections, a thorough table of contents, a concise executive summary, a succinct easily followed narrative, powerful graphs and charts, and a large appendix of supporting data are the basic components of a successful programming work product.

While the final report is tangible evidence of the completion of the programming phase, most clients and designers agree that the process itself is more important than the product in this phase of service delivery.

Bibliography

Allan, Robert Class, and Robert Koehler, (Editor). *Current Techniques in Architectural Practice*. chap. 11, "Programming." New York: McGraw-Hill, 1976.

"Developing Client Expectations—The Pre-design Process." *American Institute of Architects Newsletter*. February 1990. Washington D.C., The American Institute of Architects, 1990.

Driver, J. Wade, Jr., and E. Davis Chauviere. *Training Area/Programming*. Washington, D.C.: NCARB, October 1989.

Evers, Benjamin H., and C. Herbert Wheeler, Jr. *Emerging Techniques 2: Architectural Programming*. Washington, D.C.: The American Institute of Architects, 1969.

Gordon, Douglas E., and M. Stephanie Stubbs. "Programming." *Architecture*. May 1988. New York, The American Institute of Architects, 1988.

Haviland, David (Editor). "Facilities Planning and Programming" (sec. 2.3 "Pre-design Services"). American Institute of Architect's *Handbook of Professional Practice*. Washington, D.C., 1987.

Pena, William M, Kevin A. Kelly, and Steven A. Parshall. *Problem Seeking*. Washington, D.C., AIA Press (3d ed., 1987, copyright by CRSS, Inc., Houston, Tex.).

Stubbs, M. Stephanie. "Attention to Its Users—Successful Programming of H.E. Butt Headquarters in San Antonio." *Architecture*. December 1989. Published by BPI Communications, Inc., a subsidiary of Affiliated Publications, Inc.

16

Computerizing Your Practice

Steven S. Ross

Computerization is not just computer-aided design (CAD). The American Institute of Architects (AIA) lists more than 100 billable items in a project, but fewer than a half dozen are actually drawings. Computer functions can be categorized this way in an architectural or engineering practice:

CAD functions

Drafting
Presentations
3D (three-dimensional) modeling
Database

Office management

Word processing
Marketing
Scheduling
Billing
Accounting

Drafting is the first consideration. If you can't draw with a CAD system or can draw only with difficulty, you won't use it for all of a project. If you don't use it for all of a project, you risk an incomplete underlying database. You need good line control, good tools, fast redraw on the screen, file compatibility, and the ability to handle tolerances so that architects, civil engineers, and HVAC people can talk to one another.

In this regard, 2D drafting is still what most packages, even complicated packages capable of more than 2D drafting, are used for. Nevertheless, about 60 percent of users make use of 3D design-modeling capability. Now 3D modeling is becoming more common, at least for client presentations (see Fig. 16.1). Also, when dealing with complex matters, showing interferences makes life easier.

Less spectacular, but perhaps even more important in the long run, are uses that treat the drawing as only one part of a project's database. From the drawing database you can pull a bill of materials, client billing, scheduling, and resource allocation data. You also can perform parametric design functions, such as automatically fitting parking stalls into a garage, HVAC ducts into an office, or cabinets into a kitchen.

With many programs you can also fit supplier specifications into a drawing. You can tailor the level of detail you want. For example, in some software an "attributes" window asks the designer to fill in details requested by the estimator. The designer can fill in all the blanks or some of the blanks or can simply sign off on the details with only CAD dimensions filled in.

The advent of the optical CD-ROM disk with its huge data-handling capabilities has been great for architects and engineers. The CD-ROM

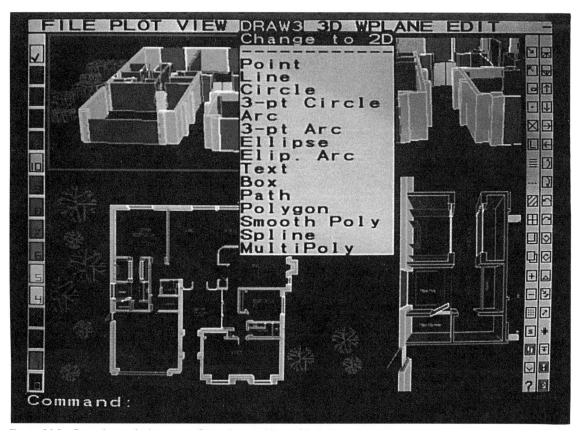

Figure 16.1 Four views of a house—a floor plan and three 3D shots—all on-screen at the same time with FastCAD 3D. The pull-down menus can be customized by users. (*Steven S. Ross photo.*)

can hold 540 megabytes of information. CAP (Grand Rapids, Mich.) has furniture and equipment catalogs on CD-ROM. The U.S. government has construction specifications. Large map files may ride the ROM, too, to add planners in a given district.

More than Equipment

John Sviokla of the Harvard Business School says design professionals are facing the same challenge the computer has brought to other professions, such as law, medicine, and even stockbrokerage. "The computer is not like other, older tools," he says. "The computer embodies some design ability. It is not like the telephone or the parallel rule." Organizations will evolve to accommodate computing, he says.

CAD technology has moved faster into engineering offices than into architectural practices because engineering functions are generally easier to computerize. Now, the technology is suitable, at a reasonable price, for all design practices (see Figs. 16.2 and 16.3).

Architect-educator Fred Stitt of San Francisco says one of the most exciting products of computerization may very well be what he called the "demystification" of architecture. "People without any architectural training can design a building" with the computer. "The next step is to teach them what *good* is."

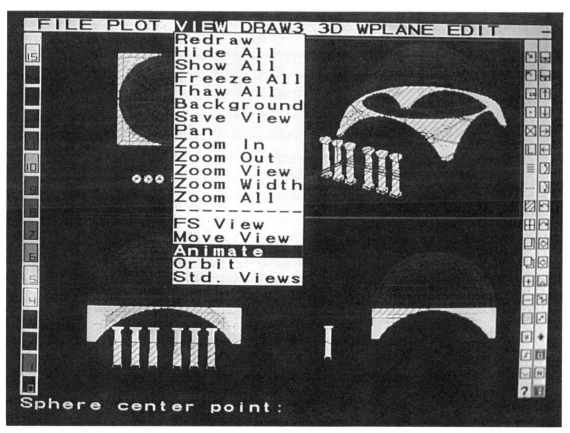

Figure 16.2 Modern 3D programs such as FastCAD (shown) and AutoCAD allow editing as well as viewing while in 3D mode. Earlier programs allowed editing in 2D, and only viewing in 3D. Here, the drawing is about to be used to create an animated "walkthrough." (*Steven S. Ross photo.*)

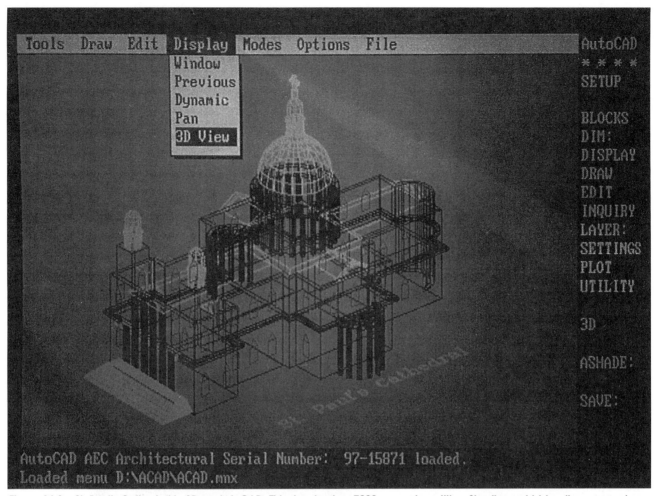

Figure 16.3   St. Paul's Cathedral in 3D on AutoCAD. This drawing has 7000 separate entities. Shading or hidden-line removal can take 10 to 30 minutes on a fast personal computer without extra graphics processing hardware. With the hardware, the task might take 30 seconds. (*Steven S. Ross photo.*)

Jay Pace, computer manager at Taliesin West, puts it another way: "If the architect does not grasp the technology fast, there's going to be a machine down at the building supply store to do all this. Architecture has to lead, to set standards." Already, some building supply firms have computer terminals to help customers design their own decks and window treatments.

Organizational Difficulties

Unfortunately, the computer is not being used to the fullest extent possible by design professionals, even by most professionals who use them. Nor are the current uses tuned to maximize economic benefits to design firms. The practice followed by many firms—doing designs roughly, then handing them over to drafters to enter them into a CAD system—impedes productivity. Firms must bring computers right to the designers' seats.

In the words of Frank Lloyd Wright, "The machine can be nowhere creator except as it may be a good tool in the creative artist's toolbox. It is only when you try to make a living thing of the machine itself that you begin to betray your human birthright. The machine can do great work—yes—but only when in the hand of one who does not overestimate its resources, one who knows how to put it to suitable work for the human being."

The machine's ability to help do great work has not been entirely realized. This has occurred for several reasons:

1. Because of the separation between designer and machine, the computer is often used only as a drawing tool rather than as a receptacle for all the information about a project.

2. Designers are denied the opportunity to fiddle with the design and see immediately, on-screen, the effects of the change.

3. Documentation may not be optimally arranged or complete enough for the firm to easily handle postconstruction facilities management.

4. Internal quality control can be compromised. A computer can enhance the operation of a well-run office. But it can quickly expose and worsen a sloppy operation. One tendency when using the computer is to overdetail. But just because the computer can draw it doesn't mean the construction workers will use it.

Mac, IBM, or Proprietary?

There are many routes to computerization. Here are the plusses and minuses of the main ones:

Equipment

Microcomputers
- Lower first cost (although the gap is narrowing)
- Less expensive upgrades and add-ons
- Less expensive software
- Wider user base

Mainframes
- Faster
- Shared files for big projects
- More flexibility for exchanging files with other disciplines

Operating Systems

MS-DOS, PC-DOS
- Office compatibility
- Generally more reliable
- Huge disk drives available at low prices
- Better screens
- Can be made more powerful than Macintosh equipment

There are so many possible ways to equip a DOS computer that you often have to call in an expert to combine everything into a working whole. One of the biggest problems in the past was memory management. DOS normally gives direct access to 640 kilobytes of RAM (random-access memory). Everything else has to be managed in one of two ways: "expanded" or "extended" memory. The new class of 80386 and 80486 DOS computers, however, provides easier access to extended memory. When equipped with Microsoft Windows, the access is automatic, just like a Macintosh.

Macintosh
- Fewer add-ons needed for basic system
- Basic units generally more expensive than basic DOS
- Works out of the box faster
- Easier memory management (but Windows software on a DOS machine is about as good)

The consistency of the Apple Macintosh interface—most programs share many common commands—helps promote casual use of Macintosh software by all professionals in the office. Apple's own studies suggest designers actually spend only 10 to 20 percent of their time doing design work. But newer CAD software for the Mac has so many new features that some of the consistency has disappeared recently. And, the Mac is slower than IBM-compatible equipment of similar price. New add-on equipment, moreover, is bringing complexity to Macintosh hardware and software integration. As with PC-DOS and MS-DOS equipment and software, Mac users now must often wade through setup menus to make sure everything works together (see Fig. 16.4).

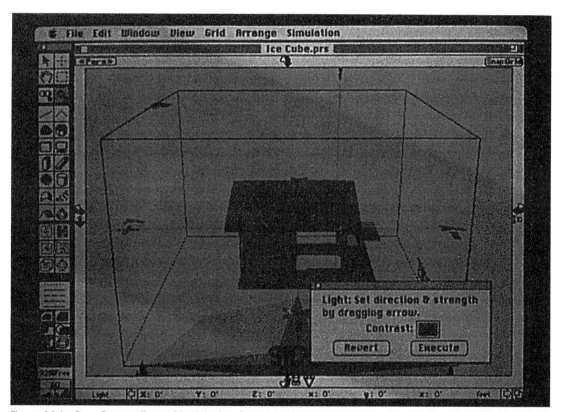

Figure 16.4 DynaPerspective, a Macintosh software package, allows easy visualization of a finished project. The original drawing is usually done inside a CAD package and then transferred to DynaPerspective for viewing. (*Steven S. Ross photo.*)

Redraws on the screen, as you edit a drawing, are generally slower than with an equivalent-priced DOS computer. This is because, on a Macintosh, the calculations needed to put things on the screen all must go through the computer's central processing unit. This preserves the consistent on-screen Macintosh "look." DOS computers can be equipped with special graphics accelerator boards that handle graphics calculations automatically.

One Macintosh trap: To keep speed up, some Mac software uses 2-byte integer math instead of floating-point. This reduces precision to about 6 significant figures—plenty for small objects, but dicey when you are working with structural steel in 40-foot lengths.

UNIX
- Needs faster computer than DOS requires
- Needs bigger disk capacity
- Needs more memory

Memory and fixed disks are getting ever cheaper, and UNIX is getting ever easier to use. There are several competing UNIX "standards," but they are being sorted out (see Figs. 16.5 and 16.6). For the future, the clear front-runner for a new operating system is UNIX. Until early 1991, OS/2 was touted by Microsoft and by IBM as a worthy substitute for UNIX. But only a handful of new products are using

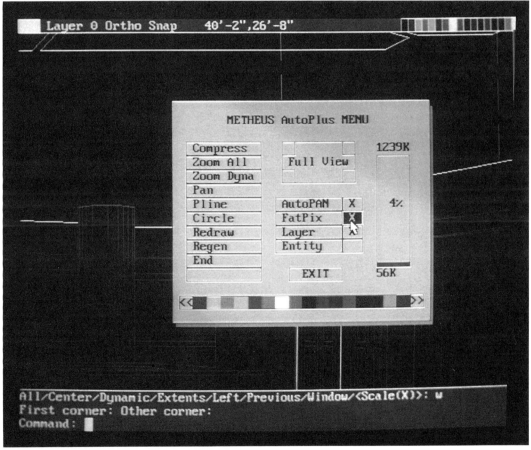

Figure 16.5   This is a typical pop-up menu for an AutoCAD add-on. This add-on, from Metheus, allows fast redraws of complex AutoCAD drawings on-screen. AutoCAD has a particularly large number of third-party add-ons available. Thus it can be customized to suit almost any needs. (*Steven S. Ross photo.*)

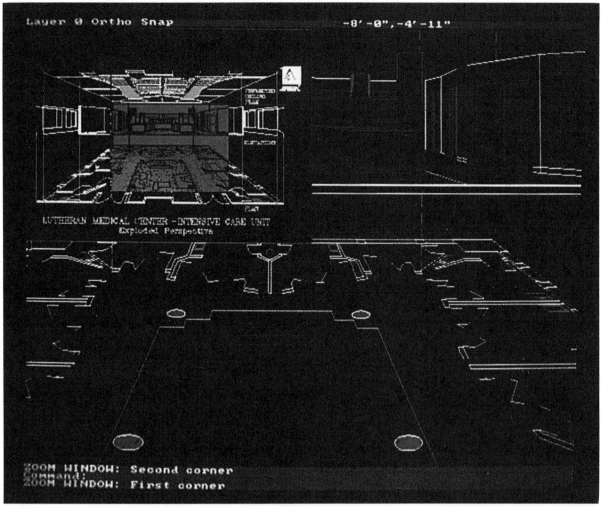

Figure 16.6 Another fast redraw add-on for AutoCAD, from GT Express. The add-on generates the bird's-eye view drawing in the upper left corner, while the specific part of the drawing being worked on covers the larger screen (and the gray area on the smaller bird's-eye view). (*Steven S. Ross photo.*)

OS/2, and Microsoft has backed away from all-out support. It seems that OS/2 is coming so late that software developers have had to overcome the relative lack of UNIX graphics standards instead. The result: Design offices will see a merging (around UNIX) of mainframe, mini, workstation, and personal computer operating systems in the next few years. That will make choices easier and investments in new equipment more secure.

Paying for All This

Equipment—amortize in 3 years

Software—2 to 5 years before total upgrade

Training—a current expense; don't capitalize (turnover hurts us now)

One way to justify computerization is to look for a lot of little hits. Ten minutes a day saved, at a $25 per hour rate, is worth $1084 a year, assuming you can still bill the client. Start small, with slower computers and no networking, if you cannot cost-justify a big system.

Michael Fox of Rebus Technology, a consulting firm in Cambridge, Mass., says the advantages of 3D modeling for client visualization cannot be overestimated. One of his clients used DynaPerspective, a Macintosh program, to create realistic views for a Digital Equipment Corp. project.

Another firm used Macintoshes equipped with Timbuctu Remote software to simultaneously display views of a project drawn with Architrion in the firm's three offices—New York, Texas, and Virginia. The project, a large department store interior, had to be completed within a year so that the store could open on time.

Crowder Land Company has computerized 3D design work at its ambitious "new town" of Santa Teresa, on the Mexican border west of El Paso. The community is expected to grow from almost nothing to well over 10,000 by 1995. Part of the computerization will help in the design of inexpensive housing. Crowder hopes to provide solid 1000-square-foot houses for $6000 to $10,000 each, using tilt-up construction. The designs are much easier to visualize in 3D than with conventional 2D drafting.

Asa Herring uses the computer to help design store interiors. Working out of Arizona, he can design to codes nationwide. "The computer also allows clients to help with brainstorming ideas, side by side," he says. "Clients can come in and stretch or change designs in 3D. The client in a sense buys into the project, so there are fewer changes later."

Designing in 3D also allows quick, easy installation, because surprises are minimized (Fig. 16.7). "We can install an interior from bare walls in four days," Herring says. He started using the computer only after failing to design a particularly complex detail by hand.

Computerized Renderings— A Glimpse of the Future

Once design is done in 3D, other possibilities present themselves. Already, software and hardware that allow near photo-realistic renderings are on the market. As of 1991 the available systems are marginal economically. But prices are falling fast. At Harvard's Graduate School of Design, students are required to take a one-semester course that acquaints them with rendering-like drawing techniques, collection and use of data, and a bit of Pascal and Hypercard programming, as well as computer-assisted drafting.

Harvard is a working advertisement for open, rather than proprietary, computer systems. Open systems reduce the risk of being tied to a computer vendor or software supplier who may go out of business. Harvard has managed to hook an eclectic collection of equipment to its Sun NFS UNIX network. There's a preponderance of Macintoshes, plenty of Sun 386i machines, some IBM RTs, and even some old IBM XTs. Most of the computers use software loaded into them "locally"—at the machine itself—and rely on the network only for retrieving and storing data, and for creating output. The result is that students can use the system for almost anything they want to do, all at the same time. That's just the way designers at noncomputerized firms would use drafting tables.

Renderings take far more computer power than merely drafting with a computer. Much of the computing power of GSD's 75-machine network is devoted to image storage and manipulation, rather than the production of working drawings. "Students can model an idea and present it in a way that a client and public bodies can understand it," says William Mitchell of GSD. Students can, for instance, use the computer to create a rendered drawing of a building, and then place the drawing into an actual photograph of the site, complete with surrounding structures.

Until now, the computer has been used mainly to make existing tasks more efficient, said Douglas Stoker, president of AESi, a Chicago-area firm. Stoker, who helped develop computer systems at Skidmore, Owings & Merrill, said this involves making the computer do what a camera, model, or drawing does.

For example, the computer now can be used to render a drawing of light and shadow, given lighting sources the architect specifies. Harvard students have used computers to produce magnificent, almost photographic-like renderings from CAD drawings.

Why not simply tell the computer where you want the light, and let the computer make suggestions? At 1991 computing speeds, the number of calculations needed would tie up the computer too long. Faster computers are available, but at too high a price.

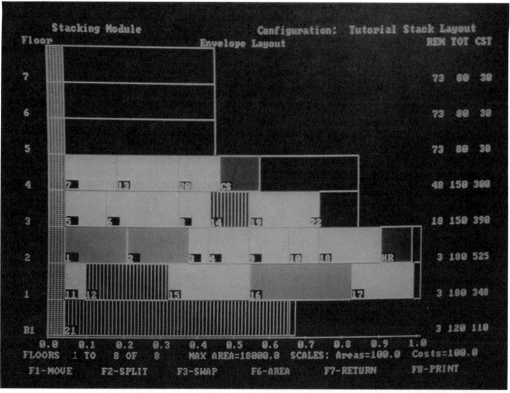

Figure 16.7 Space can be blocked out floor-by-floor or (in this case) building-by-building with computer-based space planning packages. This one, The SPACE Program, is meant to be used with AutoCAD but can accept plans from other packages as well. (*Steven S. Ross photo.*)

SOM has, block by block, built up a large database of most buildings in Chicago, their profiles and where they cast shadows, because the firm does so many projects there. The data—computerized files of the buildings as they exist now—can now be sold in its own right, to aid in planning. The data are not perfect (new buildings are always being built, and old buildings come down), but they do not have to be. SOM uses the computer to "communicate rather than to document" the context in which the new structures would sit.

Tasks that are too expensive or too cumbersome for widespread handling on the computer today will become commonplace as computing power continues to get cheaper and easier to use. The least powerful computer Sun was selling in 1991 was rated at 12 million instructions per second (MIPS). The fastest 80386- and 80486-based computers ran at about 5 MIPS. By 1994 or so computers of about the same price—about $15,000 per seat—will handle 100 MIPS.

The new equipment will be needed if large projects are to be totally computerized. There are 300 megabytes of information in a typical building. Personal-computer CAD programs do not yet easily deal with that amount of information.

Will the computer reduce some of the "art" in architecture and engineering, making the output too mechanistic? Not likely. New CAD software even features lettering fonts that appear hand-printed.

Computers can also take us to places we've never been. Stephen Ervin, assistant professor of landscape architecture at GSD, and Carl Steinitz, professor of landscape architecture and planning, have studied the Massachusetts Turnpike to make it safer and more pleasant to drive. One design study, for a structure in the median that would distract drivers from looking at the ugly roadside, uses computer-generated motion pictures to visualize how the structure would look the way drivers will see it—as they move at about 60 miles per hour rather than standing still.

Facilities Management

Dyer/Brown & Associates, a Boston-based firm, does design and restoration work in England and in the United States. One bread-and-butter service it offers is space planning, for tenants brought to the firm by developers it deals with. Thanks to automation, it can offer quick turnaround at an attractive price.

Some of the work is seemingly mundane (Fig. 16.8). Dyer/Brown must guard against concentrating on the easy, steady flow of simple jobs, thus failing to attract the larger clients who will pay for creativity. But high-end clients include Olympia & York. Dyer/Brown has been one of five firms handling space planning for the O&Y Canary Wharf development in London.

A CAD-Buying Checklist

What system to buy? The approach often taken is simply to look at what the office down the block is doing, and then copy it. But the

Figure 16.8   Your 3D drawing can be turned into a 3D shape with the Roland Digital CAMM-3. This milling machine cuts the shape out of blocks of wax, available in different colors.

office down the block might have a practice significantly different from yours. I review CAD software, in part, by observing how real-world practices use it. The nuances in needs have stimulated dozens of core systems from such firms as Autodesk and Intergraph. More importantly, each core system has stimulated scores of add-on products. And, needs differ from practice to practice.

Before you make the rounds of suppliers, therefore, it would be wise to determine what your needs really are (Figs. 16.9 and 16.10). Vendors, after all, will tell you that the computer can do it all, with little human intervention. Not true. The annotated checklist below is designed to help you navigate through all the questions you should ask yourself. The answers, typed up neatly, can be handed to prospective suppliers—usually dealers—in advance of your first appointments.

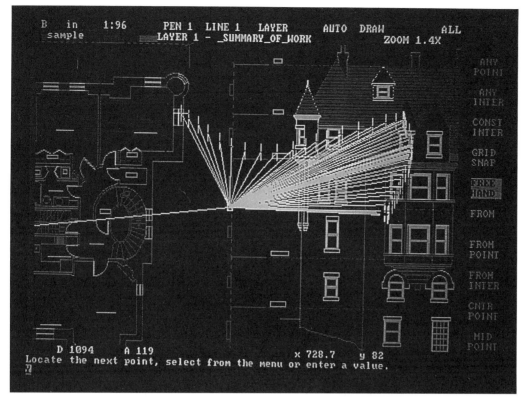

Figure 16.9 Incompatibilities between the software and an early-issue EGA card caused these white streaks. Such problems are becoming rare because the computer industry is becoming more standardized. But they still often require dealer intervention. (*Steven S. Ross photo.*)

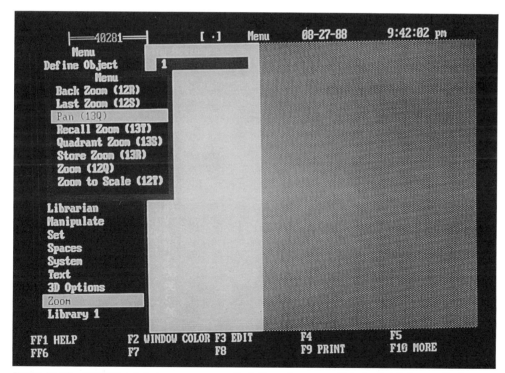

Figure 16.10 Using the drawing as one manifestation of an overall project database will give you the greatest payback from CAD. This menu (from Drawbase) gives access to various views of the project, and also to underlying data on such things as the amount of wallboard or the number and cost of a specific door model used in various places in the structure. (*Steven S. Ross photo.*)

Your Links to the Outside

For each supplier or client (HVAC, structural engineering, rebar detailing, architect, or whatever), you should ask the following questions:

- What software, if any, does the supplier or client use for drafting or design?

It helps if the package you buy is compatible with the supplier's system. There is flexibility, however. Systems do not have to be identical to exchange files.

- If the supplier has not installed a system yet, is any planned? By what date?

You may be able to get together and hammer out a better discount with a dealer for equipment, software, and training. Likewise, if you are looking for a faster turnaround time with suppliers, you may want to help them computerize when you do.

- Does the supplier use drafting software that controls a database for handling specifications or schedules? Or only for producing drawings as end products?

If you must share the database with a supplier, make sure that the supplier system and your system can produce database files in a common format (Lotus 1-2-3, dBase, comma-separated variables, or whatever).

- What file formats (DXF, IGES, and so forth) and disk formats (typically 3.5-inch DOS or Macintosh, 5.25-inch, or modem transfer) can be handled by your reproduction service bureau?

Service bureaus are usually quite flexible. But rude surprises can happen. For instance, you may have to modify your phone system to allow use of a modem if the system uses a digital PBX (switchboard).

- Likewise, during a typical project, how often do you exchange, update, or otherwise modify information sent to or returned from the supplier? If the exchange is usually one-time or one-way, it may be cost-effective and time-effective to endure a file translation step. Otherwise, you may want to use identical, or totally compatible, software. Let's say, for instance, that you design and draft a project in AutoCAD, then hand the files in AutoCAD DXF format to a mechanical engineer to design the HVAC. The engineer uses VersaCAD, which can handle DXF files, and returns drawings to you, on paper, for review and markup.

Once changes are made, the supplier produces final drawings. Simple enough. But what if the nature of the project, or of your practice, is such that you must incorporate computer files with HVAC back into the overall project files? What if changes are made to the space after HVAC design is done, requiring another trip to the supplier? With care (confining all HVAC data to one or two layers in the drawing files, for example), you can indeed go back and forth. But coordinate approaches with your supplier before investing in a system that may be difficult for you to use together.

- Does a much-used materials vendor (a window or office-equipment manufacturer, for instance) offer computerized specification files that only work with certain CAD systems?

Most who have computerized their catalogs start with AutoCAD DWG or DXF files, but vendors are always widening their reach. It may pay to give them a call to discuss their plans if a less widely used CAD system is particularly attractive to you for other reasons. They may be on the verge of supporting it.

Specific Client Wants and Needs

The desires of specific, large clients are often cited as the driving force behind computerization of a practice. Usually, however, you do not have to use the same software a client demands. It is not uncommon for larger firms, for instance, to use a mainframe or minicomputer system in-house, and then transfer files to another format with a personal computer for a client to archive or to use for facilities management.

Nevertheless, you have to specify client needs and wants (they are not necessarily the same thing, but it is up to you to tell the client!) to prospective system vendors.

- Are any current or prospective clients demanding that you submit files in a specific computerized format (IGES, AutoCAD DXF or DWG, for instance)?

Obviously, you will have to supply the file format. Some CAD systems may use the format the client wants, or have a translator built-in. Other systems may require add-on software, at extra cost.

- For promotional purposes or for client presentations, have you sensed any demand for computerized "walkthroughs" of CAD—generated designs, color output, on-screen "slide shows," and so forth?

These items tend to be high on clients' wish lists. Walkthroughs and slide shows can be astoundingly expensive, however, because they can take many days to create. Realistic renderings also require more processing time, more disk space to store images, and more care in placing lighting sources and eye points. They may require fancier color monitors and graphics cards, too. A client may balk once the true cost is discussed. Talk it over with clients before you invest!

On the other hand, even crude graphics (four- or eight-color with semirealistic shading) can be more understandable to some clients than construction drawings. They have, in fact, been a boon to interior designers of office, residential, and retail space. Interactive, though crude, 3D graphics are a boon to designers of retail space; an interactive session with a client can help the client "sign on" to your solutions.

For outdoor lighting, the computerized, standard IES file format is a boon for showing local planning boards where light will fall on neighbors' properties. IES files are compatible with many CAD packages, but not all.

- Has a client asked for automation of specifications or material schedules?

If the answer is yes, you might consider a package that handles such matters. But if the client need was stated as a vague "quality assurance" issue, your software does not have to be as sophisticated as it would be if the client expects to go back and forth during the design phase, looking for permutations of your design.

- Is your turnaround time an issue?

CAD is not an automatic solution to slow turnaround times. You must match your system to your way of doing business. To do that, you must find what activities slow things up. Using CAD to speed drafters' output does not help the client if the hangups are in the design phase. If you are producing many draft drawings for client review, you may want a fast electrostatic or thermal plotter, rather than one or two pen plotters.

If you have repetitive detailing tasks—HVAC ducts, ceiling lights, parking-lot striping, etc.—tell prospective dealers. Specific software packages may have add-ons to automate such jobs.

Determine carefully whether people often work late or on weekends. If their work habits are bad, they will delay even longer getting down to business if they know the computer will handle it.

General In-House Matters

You should install a system that fits the way you and your practice work, and that enhances your firm's reputation. Some packages are particularly good at customizing output so that it looks almost hand-drawn, for instance. On the other hand, some architects *want* their CAD drawings to look machine-plotted, to advertise the fact that the practice has access to the latest technology.

- Do principals create rough sketches for young associates and drafters to flesh out?

If so, designers might not want to use CAD equipment themselves, either. Giving all CAD tasks to drafters—or even to low-level associates along with drafters—is less efficient than doing a project top to bottom with CAD. But one way or another, you should think out the work flow to help prospective vendors design a system for your practice.

- How many people work on a project at the same time? And how is the typical project divided?

If only one person works on a project at a time, you obviously do not need a networked system. Nor do you need a network if many people work on the same project but on different aspects (either different floors or sites in a project, or different tasks such as exterior finishes and interior lighting or HVAC). In such cases, you may have to move files from computer to computer on disk, but that is a small inconvenience.

Consider networking when you have to coordinate different design tasks in the same spaces—wiring, structural, plumbing, HVAC, lighting, and furnishings in a space with flexible partitioning schemes, for example. Many firms say networking is a must when files become larger than about 1 megabyte and must be moved from computer to computer on multiple disks. But larger files can be easily moved with plug-in Bernoulli or cartridge-type fixed disks, or on backup tapes.

■ How often must you replace or add employees?

If turnover is high, a CAD system with an easy-to-use interface—Claris CAD or PowerDraw on the Macintosh, for example, or FastCAD or Drafix Windows, or even the PS/2 version of AutoCAD for IBM-compatibles—might be better than systems like Intergraph MicroStation or AutoCAD/386, which require much training and experience to use at their productive limits. On the other hand, the local labor market might be such that there are plenty of drafters or architects available who have familiarity with complex software and systems, and who have never worked on a Macintosh or a computer that uses MS-DOS Windows.

■ Do items get lost? Do they *stay* lost?

Automation will not make a disorderly practice more orderly. If anything, it will make things worse. Fix the disorder, then automate. But dealers may have specific solutions that can help—large-capacity optical storage disks, for instance, and add-on file managers.

■ Are there any existing functions at the practice, such as word processing or marketing, that are already computerized?

If so, compatible equipment for CAD makes some sense. A laser printer, for example, can be used to print letters, or (with proper add-on software) quick-plot CAD drawings. Commonality of equipment can also simplify training and maintenance.

■ Have any current members of the firm become familiar with CAD or other computerized functions at earlier employers or in college?

Choosing a similar system can simplify the startup process for your practice.

■ What is the firm spending now on outside reproduction services? If outside suppliers are used now, can they handle computerized files? At what cost, and in what file formats?

More than absolute dollar amounts are at stake. It may seem tempting to compare the annual costs of maintaining your own plotter, for instance, with the charges of a service bureau. But, depending on the circumstance, you may be able to bill external costs and not fully recover internal overheads. Likewise, your external cost cycle may be episodic, high one month and low the next. Your internal costs would be more constant, even if client billings aren't.

■ Is your firm multidisciplinary? That is, do you have architects and engineers working on the same projects?

If so, you may need a system that handles differences in such matters as tolerancing. A statement about a "9 by 12" room means one thing to an engineer and another to an architect. But computers rarely can tell the difference.

- Do you expect to finance automation internally or externally? At what level of spending *must* you seek external financing? Do you have an absolute ceiling on expenses or are you able to spend more to get more functionality?

Dealers expect you to finance a new system; they usually have worked out lease or lease-purchase arrangements with financial institutions. You may do better at your own bank, of course. Either way, though, most dealers expect you to be prepared to discuss financing at the outset.

You may want to hire a consultant to help you answer all the questions. Or, you may find that you and members of the other professional practices you deal with can answer everything yourselves. Some dealers offer consulting services, too, either for a specific fee or as a cost buried in their quotes for hardware, software, and training. No matter how you do it, though, the questions must be answered before you settle on a system.

The Future

What does the future hold? Dazzling new products. New in 1990 was software to sense handwritten commands on a digitizing tablet. Already piloted are laser holographic screens for true 3D on-screen representations and gloves and special eyeglass cameras equipped with sensors that an architect or client can "wear" to walk through a design.

There's no sense waiting for the future to invest, however. You have to start learning by doing *now*. Get comfortable with the technology before it is too late to catch up.

Bibliography

The literature in this field has begun to grow exponentially. The books listed here are of particular lasting value.

Foster, Caxton C. *Computer Architecture.* Van Nostrand Reinhold, New York, 1976.

Frank, Judith M. *Managing Business Microcomputer Systems.* Brady Books, 1987.

Gerlach, Gary M. *Transition to CADD: A Practical Guide for Architects, Engineers, and Designers.* McGraw-Hill, New York, 1991.

Hales, H. Lee. *Computer-Aided Facilities Planning.* Marcel Dekker, New York, 1984.

Head, George O., and Jan Doster Head. Ventana Press, 1989.

Head, George O., Charles A. Pietra, and Kenneth J. L. Segal. *The AutoCAD 3D Book.* Ventana Press, 1989.

Lange, Jerome C. *Design Dimensioning with Computer Graphics Applications.* Marcel Dekker, New York, 1984.

Leigh, Ronald W. *AutoCAD: A Concise Guide to Commands and Features,* 2d ed. Ventana Press, 1991.

Port, Stanley. *The Management of CAD for Construction.* Van Nostrand Reinhold, New York, 1989.

Raker, Daniel, and Harbert Rice. *Inside AutoCAD.* New Riders Publishing, 1985.

Reynolds, R. A. *Computing for Architects.* Butterworths, London, 1987.

Ryan, Daniel L. *Computer-Aided Architectural Graphics.* Marcel Dekker, New York, 1983.

Ryan, Daniel L. *Principles of Automated Drafting.* Marcel Dekker, New York, 1984.

Schmitt, Gerhard. *Microcomputer Aided Design for Architects and Designers.* John Wiley & Sons, New York, 1988.

17

Managing CADD Use

Gene L. Montgomery and Howard G. Birnberg

No tool used by designers holds more promise for great productivity increases than the computer. Despite the inflated claims of many hardware and software vendors, the computer can be a significant timesaver. It can provide the option of examining far more alternatives than would otherwise be possible. In many cases, the failure to achieve productivity gains is a result of your staff's inability to use the equipment and programs to their fullest potential.

In their rush to sell, many hardware manufacturers, software vendors, and seminar sponsors are claiming that design firms using computer-aided design and drafting (CADD) systems are more productive and profitable than nonusing firms. The few surveys conducted on this subject have usually been sponsored by firms with a vested interest in showing a better performance on the part of CADD users.

Before accepting this sweeping generalization, design firm managers should evaluate several points.

1. The type of work that a firm does will significantly affect the benefits of a CADD system. For example, firms with projects of a similar nature, where some repetition of details and layout is possible, will reap far greater benefits than will a firm whose client base is composed of varied and complex projects.

2. Profitability and productivity depend far more on management skill and organization than on the use of a CADD system. A well-managed firm without CADD capability will be far more productive and profitable than a poorly managed firm with CADD. Well managed is not synonymous with using CADD.

3. CADD is a tool that will be used by a large percentage of design

firms. Do not be panicked into making a large investment in CADD simply because self-serving individuals make dramatic claims. Think for yourself and evaluate how your firm can use CADD and how it will impact your staff and organization. Also, carefully evaluate the merits of seeking projects where the client demands that interested firms have a CADD capability. In some situations, clients demand or urge use of CADD without a willingness to fairly compensate a firm for its use.

4. For many firms, the interim period of establishing a CADD system will be a time of lower profits and productivity. Hardware must be purchased, software obtained or written, staff trained and reorganized, and management processes developed. Unfortunately, this period may last several years until all the proper components are in place.

5. By now, most architects and engineers have discovered that productivity gains promised by vendors are overstated. If their estimates apply at all, they apply only to certain limited activities. Talk to peers, vendors, and consultants to determine which activities offer the greatest possibility of gain.

6. Learn how to properly bill for CADD use. Failure to determine and negotiate proper charging methods will result in lower profitability if the alternative use of labor could have been billed at a greater rate or in greater quantities. Some clients expect that any savings made by the firm in using CADD should be passed along to them and not kept by the firm who considers this savings a reward for doing the work more efficiently.

How CADD Systems Change Firm Work Methods

The time required to do a particular task and the most efficient sequence for drawing on the computer is substantially different from drawing manually. This would not be much of a problem if a design office's major operation were drawing, but this is not the case. While staff may spend a lot of time working at a drawingboard, much of that time is not spent actually drawing. A staff member may spend an hour researching a problem, talking on the telephone, or checking a shop drawing.

Staff cannot work in the same way when they use a graphics terminal. Because the cost of ownership is high, the equipment must be kept running as many hours a day as possible. Not everyone with a drawingboard can be provided a graphics terminal. Time on the terminal must be scheduled. This requires greater organization of each user's time.

This organization leads to a different way of doing work. Tasks must be more clearly defined before work is started on the terminal. Once terminal work begins, full attention must be concentrated on keeping up with or waiting for the machine. Drawing tasks are more clearly separated from design analysis.

Since not all staff in an office can be provided with a terminal, not everyone can be drawing at the same time. This demands a change in the way design offices work. Because nearly every staff member has a drawingboard in a conventional office, everyone can draw to meet a deadline. In the computerized office, it is not possible to put more people on a job in order to finish it on time. Once the office becomes dependent on the machine, the computer controls the schedule.

It is not easy to browse through drawings stored in a computer file. Many people in a design office need only to browse quickly through the drawings. Managers, for example, may only need to rapidly scan the drawings to judge progress. The designer may only be interested in checking that a certain wall is finished in brick. The specifier is only looking to see what materials are being used.

For these people, the use of conventional hard-copy drawings is easier than using a CRT. Unfortunately, the biggest obstacle in computer graphics equipment is the process that converts digital files to hard copy. It may take 30 minutes to plot a drawing with a pen plotter. To plot a 50-drawing set may take a couple of days of plotting each time a checkset is ordered. Electrostatic plotters are faster, but more expensive.

Imposing a computer graphics system on a conventional office without planning for a drastic change in the way work is done is doomed to failure. As a result of the new system, changes in office practice are inevitable.

Utilization Strategies

Because of the organization required and the natural separation of drawing tasks from other activities, many design firms have set up separate computer graphics departments whose primary task is to run the machines. In some cases, CADD operators may not be design professionals and may not have had previous drawing experience. The department is geared to produce drawings based on design and analysis decisions made by others. Recent graduates may be required to spend a specific time as graphics terminal operators.

At the other extreme is an office that expects all its staff to know how to operate the equipment and use CADD whenever it is in the best interests of the project. There are many variations of these two opposing strategies. It is important to consider the implications of each strategy before devising a policy for an office.

The first strategy uses the professional drafter approach to office organization. Since there is a great deal to learn and master in the mechanics of computer graphics operation, it is believed more efficient to have the work done by computer graphics professionals. The department can be organized with its own hierarchy. Equipment operators may have only the type of training required to run the equipment. The department's role is to produce drawings.

This organization can lead to serious personnel problems. Since all work filters through them, operators may act like prima donnas. In addition, the department may become divorced from the project with motivations separate from the best interests of the job. In addition, full-time operation of graphics terminals may lead to operator fatigue and burnout. Professionals-in-training, frustrated with the lack of project involvement, may look for ways to escape the computer graphics department.

The most serious problem with this organization is its tendency to inhibit more productive use of the computer. If the operator's only purpose is to convert instructions to drawings, he or she does not have the opportunity or motivation to take advantage of the more sophisticated uses of the computer. If a computer graphics department is a separate profit center, the motivation is to produce drawings as efficiently as possible, not to complete the project in the most satisfactory manner. Professionals not directly involved with the computer do not learn the computer's capabilities. Operation of the terminals, delegated to a subprofessional department, tends to devalue the desirability of operating or using the computer.

The second strategy of teaching all professionals to use the system also has limitations. It takes time to learn and a certain amount of regular operation to develop and maintain proficiency on the machine. It is naive to assume that all professionals can and will learn to use the system effectively. Also, if everyone is expected to use the system as much as possible, it is likely that time conflict will occur. Some types of graphics operations are very simple and repetitive. It is a waste of a professional's time to do them when a subprofessional can do them just as well.

On the other hand, great economies can be achieved when the decision maker actually prepares the drawings. For an engineer to make a sketch, send it to an operator to enter into the computer, obtain a hard copy for checking, make corrections, send it back to the operator, and then go through the process all over again is both time-consuming and expensive. This is especially true if the engineer could have taken a little extra time and completed the operation at the same time the initial sketch was made. Even greater economies are possible if the engineer can combine graphics operations with analytical operations.

Most firms devise a strategy somewhere between these two extremes. Their goal is to gain the advantages of using the system without the disadvantages.

Bibliography

Crosley, Mark Lauden, *The Architects Guide to Computer Aided Design,* Wiley, New York, 1988.

Gerlach, Gary M., *Transition to CADD,* McGraw-Hill, New York, 1987.

Hamer, Jeffrey M., *Facility Management Systems,* Van Nostrand Reinhold, New York, 1988.

Jordani, David, "Growing Pains," *Architectural & Engineering Systems,* March 1987, pp. 51, 54.

Kennedy, E. Lee, *CAD Drawing Design and Data Management,* Whitney Library of Design, New York, 1986.

Kvan, Thomas, "Management Case Study: Controlling CAD," *Progressive Architecture,* November 1990, p. 43.

Mitchell, William J., *Computer Aided Architectural Design,* Petrocelli Charter, New York, 1977.

Radford, A. and G. Stevens, *CADD Made Easy,* McGraw-Hill, New York, 1987.

Sanders, Margaret, "Making the Move to CADD," *The Construction Specifier,* June 1990, pp. 41–42.

Schilling, Terrence G., and Patricia M. Schilling, *Intelligent Drawings,* McGraw-Hill, New York, 1987.

Task Force on CAD Layer Guides, *CAD Layer Guidelines,* AIA Press, Washington, D.C., 1990.

18

Noncomputerized Production Systems and Tools

Thomas W. Berg

The drafting room has come a long way from the days when people sat at tall oak tables, all in a row, producing meticulously rendered drawings. Today's studio might house an array of specialists sitting at sleek modular furniture, preparing small segments of a finished drawing, ready for a reprographic shop to assemble into final form. The tools of the trade have changed from 2H drafting pencils on linen to numerous pens, appliqués, photographs, and machinery, each used to produce a unique part of the work. Truly, the methods to produce contract documents that were used for generations have all but completely changed.

The Concept

For years artists have employed tools and methods of production that have enabled them to reproduce their work photographically. For example, animation artists create a background over which the animation scene is produced on overlaying layers. These layers are then photographed in sequence over the background to produce a composite image that moves.

Graphic artists use transfer letters, film patterns, and textures to obtain crisp, clear images. These images can be reproduced photographically with "like original" clarity.

These ideas and more can be used by architects and engineers to help them produce a better drawing package for less overall cost. First, however, the concept hinges on the acceptance of the camera as an effective and economical graphic tool. Second, the production of camera-ready artwork must be done in a clear, systematic, and consistent manner.

The main elements of such a systematic process include:

1. Standard drawing module

2. Reusable elements

3. Appliqués

4. Layering

5. Drawing assembly

6. Tools

7. Reproduction

Standard Drawing Module

The first element of systematic production is the standard drawing module. The most popular drawing sheet size is the metric E size, 30 by 42 inches. This sheet can be subdivided into 7¼-inch wide by 4½-inch high modules, producing the standard format illustrated in Fig. 18.1.

Two basic modules fit on an 8½- by 11-inch page which can be used for book form publication of drawings as well as a handy way to store standard details (Fig. 18.2). This page also should contain vital title block information such as office name, job name and number, and date.

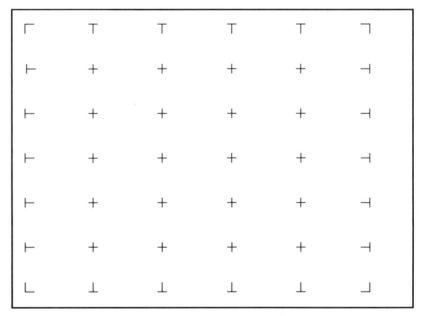

Figure 18.1   Standard 7¼ by 4½ drawing module arrayed on a 30 by 42 drawing sheet.

Every drawing, schedule, and general note should be composed to fit this standard layout. By doing so, you will always have a place to put things, and things will always fit the space you have. Figure 18.3 shows a plan, finish schedule, and details all arranged to fit the standard module.

Reusable Elements

Anything that repeats itself can qualify as a reusable element. Some examples include the format used for a door or finish schedule, an abbreviations list, graphic symbols, fixture schedule, and repeat details. Even floor plans can be considered reusable elements when used as backgrounds for mechanical and electrical work or when reduced in scale as composite plans.

Separate information into that portion which repeats itself, i.e., a blank schedule form, and the information that is unique to a specific use, i.e., the data on a schedule form.

Figure 18.2   Standard 7¼ by 4½ drawing modules on an 8½ by 11 drawing sheet.

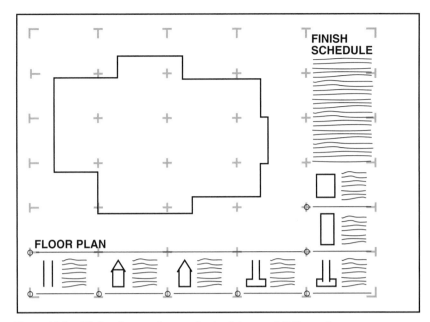

Figure 18.3 All drawings, notes, and schedules must fit the pattern.

Once these elements are separated, the repeat items can be standardized and mass-produced for future use. For example, take any common schedule. Design the form to fit the standard drawing module (7¼ by 4½ inches). Many schedules could fit into two such modules, such as an electric panel schedule. This would then fit the standard 8½- by 11-inch page. These are then easy to store and use for future work. See Fig. 18.4.

Details that are reused from job to job, i.e., concrete curb details, sprinkler pipe brace details, or hollow metal frame details, are good examples of reusable elements. These details can be collected and stored for future use. The filing system used should be "subject" related as shown in Fig. 18.5. It is important to use a system that provides you with quick retrieval of the desired element.

These small reusable elements can be produced like any drawing, using ink on mylar film with press-on letters or machine-produced letters for headings. Masters (originals) should be stored in a safe place, away from copies, to avoid their being inadvertently used. Consider your quality assurance manager's office.

Reproduction processes for general use can take many forms. These will be discussed later in this chapter.

Layering

Ten years ago, an electrical lighting plan for a school building would have been drawn entirely by the electrical engineering office. This would include the architectural backgrounds.

Today, information is separated into layers, with each discipline drawing only that portion of the work for which it is responsible. The architect draws the plan background on one layer. On a unique layer are added the notes, dimensions, references, etc. The original base layer is copied by a diazo process onto silver slick film and is sent to consulting engineers to be used as their base sheet. The engineers then draw their unique overlay containing lighting, power, diffusers, etc. The process is completed by recombining the drawing on a flatbed vacuum frame and diazo printer, or through a photographic process.

Storage and identification of layered drawings is much more complicated than single-sheet drawings. First, a hanging vertical file is essential. See Fig. 18.6. Drawings are suspended by a mylar tape containing a series of holes gauged to fit the special vertical holder. Drawings can then be hung in a cabinet, on pegboards attached to walls, or on office partitions.

Since the title appears on only one layer of a drawing, each composite layer must be individually identified. This is done on the binding edge by using a coded matrix. See Fig. 18.7. The matrix may be preprinted with the office standard title and border or applied as a reverse-reading sticky-back.

The code that identifies each layer is determined from a list like the one in Fig. 18.8.

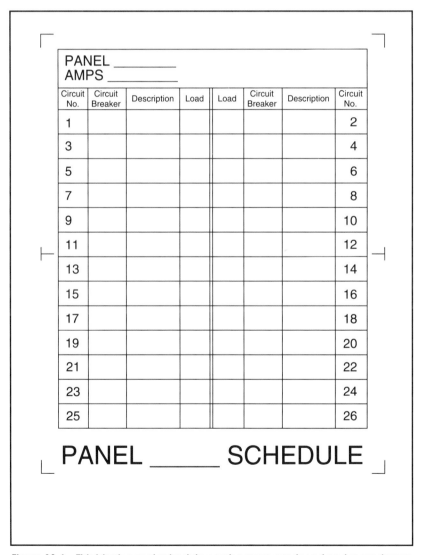

Figure 18.4 This blank panel schedule can be mass-produced and reused many times.

The following is a complete listing of detail book chapters and subheadings.

MASTER DETAIL INDEX

0   GENERAL
0–1   General Architectural Drawing Index
0–1S   General Structural Drawing Index
0–1M   General Mechanical Drawing Index
0–1E   General Electrical Drawing Index
0–2   General Notes
0–3   Graphic Standards
0–4   Abbreviations
0–5   Legal Descriptions
0–6   Project Identification
0–7   Temporary Facilities

1   SITEWORK
1–1   Site Drainage (CB, YD)
1–2   Pavement and Walks
1–3   Site Furniture and Improvements
1–4   Landscaping

2   EXTERIOR CONDITIONS
2–1   Concrete (CIP, Precast)
2–2   Masonry (CMU, Brick, Stone)
2–3   Misc. Metal Louver Schedules (see also category 6)
2–4   Wood, Stucco, Plastic
2–5   EQJ/Exterior
2–6   Prefab Panel Systems (GFRC, Brick)

3   MOISTURE PROTECTION
3–1   Membrane Roofing
3–2   Roof Accessories (Hatches)
3–3   EQJ/Roof
3–4   Membranes (Sheet, Fluid)
3–5   Shingles (Wood, Tile, Composition)
3–6   Metal Roofing

4   WINDOWS
4–0   Schedules
4–1   Metal Sash
4–2   Storefront, Curtain Wall
4–3   Wood Sash
4–4   Miscellaneous (Atrium)

5   DOORS, RELITES, AND OTHER OPENINGS
5–0   Schedules
5–1   Hollow Metal
5–2   Wood
5–3   Specialties (Roll-up, Overhead)

6   STAIRS AND RAILINGS
6–0   Schedules
6–1   Concrete Stairs
6–2   Metal Stairs
6–3   Wood Stairs
6–4   Ladders, Catwalks
6–5   Railings

7   INTERIOR CONDITIONS
7–0   Schedules
7–1   Floor and Base
7–2   Walls, Partitions, Furring
7–3   Ceiling, Soffits
7–4   EQJ/Interior

Figure 18.5   System-driven detail file index system.

(Continued)

8 SPECIALTIES
8–1   Toilet Partitions and Accessories
8–2   Conveying Systems (Elevators)
8–3   Operable Walls, Folding Doors
8–4   Misc. Specialties
       Curtain Tracks
       Drapery Tracks
       IV Tracks
       Chalk and Tack Boards
       Dock Facilities
       Chutes
       Access Panels

9 CASEWORK AND MILLWORK
9–0   Schedules
9–1   PLAM Casework
9–2   Metal Casework
9–3   Hardwood Casework
9–4   Demountable Casework
9–5   Millwork

10 EQUIPMENT
10–0   Schedules
10–1   Fixed Equipment

When the details are organized under this system, a Table of Contents is included in Chapter 0. This table lists every drawing in the detail book. It also lists any chapters or subcategories which are not used, by title, followed by the note: "not used."

Figure 18.5 *(Continued)*

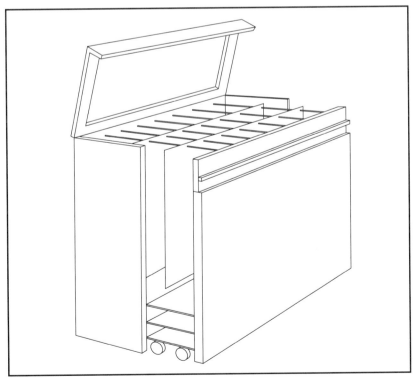

Figure 18.6 An example of a vertical hanging file for large-format drawings available from Teledyne Post.

MATCH BOX		BASE	OVERLAY	OVERLAY	OVERLAY	OVERLAY	OVERLAY
	SCREEN						
	DRAWING LAYER						
	THIS LAYER						

Figure 18.7 This coded matrix appears on the base drawing layer with entries made on each drawing overlay.

A drawing is produced by placing base information common to all subsequent layers on a mylar sheet containing preprinted title and border. Layers for notes, etc., are drawn on blank mylar sheets. (Never use preprinted title and border for overlays.) Layers are aligned by using a metal pin bar. This device is a thin metal strip with seven brass pins that mate into prepunched holes at the top of each mylar sheet.

Site Plan Layer Codes	
SB	Site Base Plan
SS	Site Survey
SX	Site Demolition
SP	Site Paving
SG	Site Grading
SD	Site Drainage
SL	Site Landscaping
EC	Erosion Control
IR	Irrigation
SE	Site Electrical
SS	Site Signage
SM	Site Mechanical

Floor Plan Layer Codes	
B	Architectural Base Plan
G	Building Grid Plan
A	Architectural Plan Notes
R	Reflected Ceiling Plan
M	Mechanical (HVAC) Plan
P	Plumbing Plan
E	Electrical (Power) Plan
L	Lighting Plan
S	Signal and Communications Plan
AR	Agency Review Plans
X	Demolition Plan
Q	Equipment Plan
FP	Fire Protection Plan
FS	Food Service Plan
GR	Graphics and Signage
CM	Color and Materials Plan
TI	Tenant Improvements

Miscellaneous Codes	
AS	Architectural Notes and Schedules
AD	Architectural Details

Figure 18.8 Drawing layer coding chart.

The key to drawing assembly is the master matrix. See Fig. 18.9. When properly filled out, the master matrix serves three functions:

1. As a list of all project drawings and their associated layers and negatives

2. As a print order, for compositing check prints at any time during the project

3. As a print order for final project compositing

In the left column is entered the project drawing list. This list should include all drawings, whether a composite of individual layers or not.

The layers by code (from Fig. 18.9) and general description that make up each drawing are entered on the top row. The first space should be marked "no layers this sheet" for single-sheet drawings. Each subsequent space should list in order the individual layers that make up the drawings listed in the left column.

Some drawings are a combination of full-sized artwork and previ-

PRINT ORDER MATRIX	Drawing Layers / Code	No Layers This Sheet	SITE SURVEY	SITE BASE	LEVEL – 1 BASE PLAN	LEVEL – 1 PLAN NOTES	LEVEL – 2 BASE PLAN	LEVEL – 2 PLAN NOTES	ROOF BASE PLAN	ROOM PLAN NOTES	LEVEL – 1 PLUMBING	LEVEL – 2 PLUMBING	LEVEL – 1 HVAC	LEVEL – 2 HVAC	ROOF HVAC		FINISH SCHEDULE MASTER	OPENING SCHEDULE MASTER	STD TITLE & BORDER
Project / Job No / Date / Page / Of			SS	SB	B–1	A–1	B–2	A–2	B–3	A–3	P–1	P–2	M–1	M–2	M–3		NEG–3	NEG–2	NEG–1
Sheet / Drawing Title																			
A1	SITE PLAN																		
A2	LEVEL 1 PLAN																		
A3	LEVEL 2 PLAN																		
A4	ROOF PLAN																		
A5	BUILDING ELEVATIONS																		
A6	BUILDING SECTIONS																		
A7	WALL SECTIONS																		
A8	EXTERIOR DETAILS																		
A9	WINDOW DETAILS																		
A10	STAIRS & ELEVATORS																		
A11	SCHEDULES																		
A12	INTERIOR DETAILS																		
M1	LEVEL 1 PLUMBING PLAN																		
M2	LEVEL 2 PLUMBING PLAN																		
M3	LEVEL 1 HVAC PLAN																		
M4	LEVEL 2 HVAC PLAN																		
M5	ROOF HVAC PLAN																		

Figure 18.9 Drawing overlay master matrix with drawing index and layer lists complete.

ously filed negatives of specific reusable elements, i.e., standard title and border and large-sheet schedule formats. List these negatives in the last few column headings so the reprographics shop can tell how many you are going to be supplying. See Fig. 18.10.

The field of the matrix is completed to show which layers are composited to form a finished drawing.

1. Enter any mark: period, star, or check to designate an overlay.

2. Enter a 1, 2, 3, etc., to denote which layer is closest to the print medium, with 1 being closest. This is important when making contact paper sepias on the office light table.

3. Enter the screen percent for the layers to be screened. Thirty percent of original is an acceptable value.

The completed matrix is used each time a drawing or group of drawings is printed. See Fig. 18.11. The master matrix also serves as a list of all items used to form the final printed documents. Remember, until a drawing is composited from its many parts, there is no single original. Once a drawing has been composited, the resulting reproducible becomes the original-of-record for that date.

Figure 18.10 Drawing overlay master matrix with negatives of existing work indicated.

Many graphic elements are easier to read and faster to place if they are machine-made rather than hand-drawn. Examples include graphic tape patterns like dots and dashes that can be used to designate fire-rated partitions on a floor plan. Another appliqué is the sheet pattern and texture. These come in many forms including dots, grids, shades, and textures. They can be used to differentiate new work from existing work as in Fig. 18.12. When using dot patterns, choose a size and spacing that can be drawn over, i.e., 20 percent 55 dots per inch. Never use solid-color film to obtain shade. The camera will see it as all black or not at all.

Another form of appliqué is the dry transfer or rub-on letter. These are often used for drawing titles because they lead the reader's eyes to their locations on a sheet of drawings. Rub-on letters are also used in artwork for presentation, project manual covers, and anywhere perfect lettering is needed. Another form of manufactured letter is the Kroy or Merlin system. An image is set on transparent tape, which is then applied to the drawing. If the drawing is treated roughly, the let-

PRINT ORDER MATRIX

Project _____
Job No _____ Date _____
Page _____ Of _____

Sheet	Drawing Title	Code	No Layers This Sheet	SITE SURVEY SS	SITE BASE SB	LEVEL – 1 BASE PLAN B-1	LEVEL – 1 PLAN NOTES A-1	LEVEL – 2 BASE PLAN B-2	LEVEL – 2 PLAN NOTES A-2	ROOF BASE PLAN B-3	ROOF PLAN NOTES A-3	ARCHITECTURAL SCHEDULES AS-1	LEVEL – 1 PLUMBING P-1	LEVEL – 2 PLUMBING P-2	LEVEL – 1 HVAC M-1	LEVEL – 2 HVAC M-2	ROOF HVAC M-3	FINISH SCHEDULE MASTER NEG-3	OPENING SCHEDULE MASTER NEG-2	STD TITLE & BORDER NEG-1
A1	SITE PLAN			50%	✓															100%
A2	LEVEL 1 PLAN					100%	✓													100%
A3	LEVEL 2 PLAN							100%	✓											100%
A4	ROOF PLAN									100%	✓									100%
A5	BUILDING ELEVATIONS		✓																	
A6	BUILDING SECTIONS		✓																	
A7	WALL SECTIONS		✓																	
A8	EXTERIOR DETAILS		✓																	
A9	WINDOW DETAILS		✓																	
A10	STAIRS & ELEVATORS		✓																	
A11	SCHEDULES											✓						50%	50%	100%
A12	INTERIOR DETAILS		✓																	
M1	LEVEL 1 PLUMBING PLAN					30%							✓							
M2	LEVEL 2 PLUMBING PLAN							30%						✓						
M3	LEVEL 1 HVAC PLAN					30%									✓					
M4	LEVEL 2 HVAC PLAN							30%								✓				
M5	ROOF HVAC PLAN									30%							✓			

Figure 18.11 Example of completed master matrix used as for final compositing. Notice the screen values when architectural base layers are used with other discipline overlays.

ter image can flake off. It is a good idea to cover the Kroy tape with another layer of clear tape. This product does not leave a ghost on final prints.

Graphic decals are often used to affix the professional seal to a drawing original. They can be preprinted and reverse-reading so they are placed on the back side of the original.

The sticky-back is another form of appliqué. It can be made in-house on the office copier. Any artwork can be used. Frequently used examples include typical details, schedule forms, key plans, professional seals, and title blocks.

An item intended for use as a sticky-back must first be copied on clear acetate using the office copier. This copy is then used to obtain a reverse-reading sticky-back for application to the back side of the drawing sheet. Your copier may not burn on an image. If so, you will have to fix the image with standard artist's spray fixative. Sticky-backs made in this way do not make good permanent originals. The image is often brittle and can therefore flake off. When a more permanent sticky-back is desired, have the image offset printed or photographically processed.

Tools

The first part of this chapter deals with a systematic production process geared toward photographic reproduction. Camera-ready artwork of the highest quality is required for the photographic reproduction process. Graphite line work on vellum will not do. Ink on mylar is the medium of choice.

Mylar drawing sheets come in many combinations of thickness and finish. Select a sample that is finished on one side only. This allows

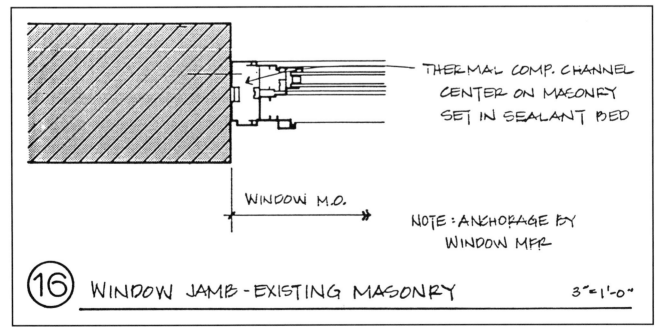

Figure 18.12 Use of shading film denoting existing construction.

you to place appliqués on the reverse side and to take them off again. Select a thickness that has the durability needed for the length of time spent on a drawing. Consider a 4-mil product for average drawing life. Last, select a finish that will last through repeated erasures without eating up your pen points.

Pen and ink are used to achieve line work of uniform thickness and density. The technical pen is produced in a range of price and performance characteristics from the expensive jewel tip to the inexpensive tungsten tip. For work on mylar, the jewel tip is recommended. The mylar face will quickly destroy any other tip.

Drawing ink has improved over the last 10 years. There is now a product that offers a longer cap-off time without clogging the point. This good news, however, comes with some bad news too. To keep the ink from clogging, the manufacturers have removed some of the solids. The result is a line of less density. This translates into poor-quality prints and sepias when made on the office copy machine. This will be most noticeable when compositing check prints. The camera, however, can correct for ink density and produce good copies.

For best results, do not mix the two ink types (old and new) on the same drawing. Also, don't use graphite of half-n-half drawing lead on ink drawings. The camera cannot see mixed media with equal clarity. The print shop technician then must adjust the camera for best overall quality. This will often result in less than desirable reproductions. Soft plastic lead can be used for hand-lettered notes on ink drawings. This medium is almost as dense as ink and can be seen well by the camera.

The largest and by far most expensive tools are the reproduction machines. For small-sized drawings, specifications, and letters, the electrostatic dry copier has been the office workhorse. Quality of reproduction has improved steadily until today's copiers produce an image that rivals offset printing. With this improved quality of image and scale variability, drawings can be reproduced for a variety of end products. Here are just a few:

1. Reproducing a book of details on 8½- by 11-inch bond rather than on large-sheet diazo

2. Copying details to trace (100 percent scalability)

3. Making sticky-back images of details

4. Making clear film images for cut and paste to slick carrier sheet

5. Making clear film copies for overhead projection

6. Reducing and enlarging images to any desired value, limited only by paper size

For large-format copying, there has been only one affordable form, diazo imaging. Recently, however, the large-format xerographic imaging machine has become both affordable and competitive with diazo imaging. Each machine will reproduce drawings up to 36 inches wide by any length, but that's where the similarity ends.

Diazo imaging requires a transparent to translucent drawing

Figure 18.13 Tabletop diazo copy machine. *(Courtesy of Diazit.)*

medium to allow light to pass through to the print medium. Drawings are therefore typically produced on vellum and mylar.

Diazo machines come in tabletop models (see Fig. 18.13) for convenience copying, to large floor models (see Fig. 18.14) capable of mass-producing sets of drawings.

Diazo copiers are used to make blue-line, black-line, and sepia-line copies as well as unscalable sepia reproducibles on vellum and mylar. When used in conjunction with the flatbed vacuum frame (see Fig. 18.15), the diazo machine acts as a processor to "develop" the exposed image on sepia mylar and diazo slick. Copy medium has improved in quality and speed, allowing the machine to produce better copies in less time.

The main objection to diazo copying is the ammonia smell that accompanies a new set of prints. Various forms of scavenging and ventilation make the copier location tolerable most of the time, but it is almost impossible to remove all the ammonia gas from copies. When scavenging systems need changing, or if the ventilation system malfunctions, the copier location quickly becomes unbearable. This

Figure 18.14 Floor-model diazo copy machine. *(Courtesy of Diazit.)*

shortcoming, when combined with the requirement to run translucent originals, has led to the popularity of large-format xerographic imaging.

Xerographic copiers can produce black-line copies with the same clarity as the office electrostatic dry copier, from any original, even old blueprints. The resulting copy can be produced on paper, mylar, slick, or other medium. Some machines can be set to "half size" or "double" originals. There is no ammonia smell and it's affordable. The one thing it will not do is composite drawing overlays. This still must be done by diazo imaging or sent to the local reproduction shop for compositing photographically.

Conclusion

The production of architectural and engineering contract documents has changed a great deal over the past few decades. Tall oak tables are all but gone, as are drawing linen and ruling pens. Today's tools are geared toward automation and production efficiency. Tomorrow's tools will likely further improve the ability to produce and reproduce contract documents with greater accuracy and in less time.

Figure 18.15 **A vacuum frame light table with programmable exposure settings.** *(Courtesy of Design Mates, Inc.)*

Bibliography

Berg, Thomas W., *Architectural Contract Document Production,* McGraw-Hill, New York, 1991.

"Drawing from Logic," *Architecture,* December 1990.

Giummo, Vince, *Overlay Drafting Techniques,* Marketing Education Specialist, Drafting and Reproduction Technology, Eastman Kodak Co.

Giummo, Vince, *Photoreproduction as a Drafting Tool,* Marketing Education Specialist, Drafting and Reproduction Technology, Eastman Kodak Co.

Guidelines Newsletter, Orinda, Calif. (P.O. Box 456, 94563-0456).

Guzey, Onkal K., and James N. Freehof, *ConDoc: The New System for Formatting and Integrating Construction Documentation,* A Professional Development Program, The American Institute of Architects.

Recommended Standards (POP Manual), Northern California Chapter, American Institute of Architects (latest edition).

Vendor catalogs. One of the best sources of information is vendor literature. Every manufacturer of drafting and reprographic supplies and equipment offers a plethora of information, and all of it is available by telephoning your local vendor. Some companies, like Eastman Kodak, offer seminars or will come to your office to provide in-house training.

19

Project and Staff Scheduling

Robert E. Olden

Projecting and scheduling project and firm staffing needs is an integral part of your overall planning efforts. It is vital to a successful firm regardless of size, discipline mix, age, or specialty service. In most instances, it is an easy process. With even a minimum level of experience, you can predetermine the required skills and necessary time to provide a project's professional design services. The biggest variable is the "redo" time—and it is inevitably in inverse proportion to the time spent in task planning (Fig. 19.1).

Scheduling is one part of the three-way equilibrium that must be maintained in balance by a successful project manager (Fig. 19.2). These are services quality, services schedule maintenance, and design and production budget maintenance. Balancing all three without favoritism or omission is the true test for those who aspire to success in project management. It is relatively easy to keep any combination of two in balance while ignoring the third.

For example, it takes a minimum of management effort to maintain a tight schedule and equally tight in-house design and production budget and let the quality of the documentation drift as may be convenient. Likewise, it will not challenge project managers to maintain both the project's in-house budget and an inappropriately high level of documentation by continually postponing the scheduled completion date.

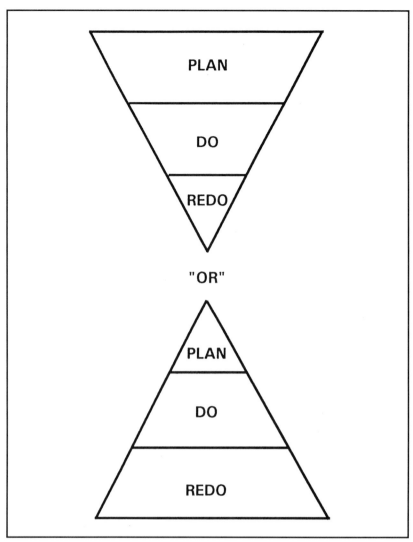

Figure 19.1 The design professionals' choice. (*From The Construction Specifier, December 1989.*)

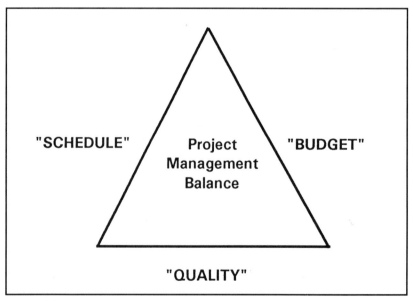

Figure 19.2 Project management balance. (*Courtesy of Olden/Associates.*)

The only other variable in the successful firm's planning process is the scheduling method chosen from the myriad available—bar charts, wall schedules, CPM or PERT, milestone (or events), and the like. All have particular, appropriate, and unique characteristics justifying their use within a given management environment or with a particular project. In making your choice, the method that is simplest to prepare, to use, and equally important, to update is the superior device.

Large projects and large project teams can and do require detailed, even complex, scheduling methods. Small projects and small project teams most often do not.

Bar Charts

Bar charts (Fig. 19.3) are particularly appropriate for designers' use due to the inherent graphic representation of tasks and time frames on these charts. While bar charts can be complex, they are most often effective when kept simple in format and execution. Complex horizontal bar charts, when enlarged and mounted on the wall of a

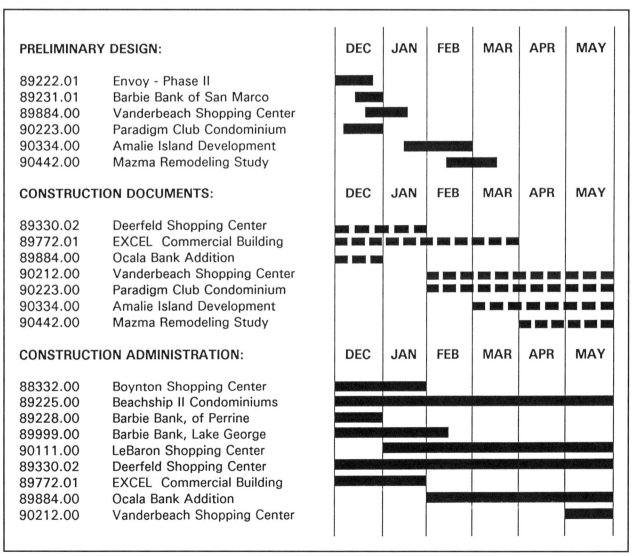

Figure 19.3 Master project schedule. (*Courtesy of Olden/Associates.*)

design and/or production team's studio, can be "colored in," representing the percentage of each scheduled task's completion, as the work progresses. Adding a calendar grid across the top of the chart emphasizes the participation in schedule achievement or underachievement.

Wall Schedules

Wall schedules evolved many years ago as a method of maintaining a flexible, interactive, "living" schedule. While this is accomplished, its drawback lies in its immobility. As its name implies, a wall schedule is assembled on a wall, generally in the team's studio or conference area. Usually a matrix is created or drawn on one or more walls with time in columns of days, weeks, or months plotted horizontally. Activities are then listed in horizontal rows, and usually on 3- by 5-inch or larger cards pinned to the wall. The major disadvantage of this method is that the users of a wall schedule must physically assemble in the location of the schedule for its use.

On the plus side, this system is extremely flexible and interactive. The entire design team, including your client, can participate in preparation and revisions while maintaining a constant overview of the entire schedule.

CPM and PERT

The critical path method (CPM) identifies and focuses on the most time-consuming individual task among a group of tasks, all of which must be accomplished during a given period of time. A CPM schedule need not be complex. However, it often is made so in preparation because of its ease of computerization.

The key to CPM is the determination of the task or tasks which are perceived to take longest to perform within a given overall time frame. Accomplishing these tasks then comprises the "critical path" to timely completion of that portion of the project schedule.

PERT was developed in the 1950s by the United States Navy along principles similar to CPM, but PERT is neither as well-known nor as widely used in the planning for professional design firm projects. The primary difference between CPM and PERT is PERT's use of three time estimates for each task: the most optimistic, the most pessimistic, and the most likely.

Key Date Schedule (KDS) Milestones

For the majority of professional design firm offices and projects, the most effective method of scheduling project team efforts is the milestone chart. These are often maintained on a microcomputer or word processor. Milestones are defined as points in time when certain key activities must be accomplished to measure, monitor, and react to progress or lack of progress against the adopted schedule (Fig. 19.4).

Milestones are key dates for the transfer of information from one design and/or production team member to one or more others on the team—hence the acronym KDS (key date schedule or scheduling). A key date then becomes the point in time when information which has been developed or assembled is transmitted by the initiating party or discipline to others whose work progress is dependent upon receipt of this same information. The premise is that these tasks and their fruition dates can be predicted and scheduled. If the team is then meeting the incremental dates, they will in all likelihood meet the end date. The process works well for any size of project and for as finitely

PROJECT NAME:			PM:	
PROJECT NO:			DATE:	

DATE DUE	DATE COMPL		SCHEDULED FR	TO
____	____	1 Project Budget	A	CSME
____	____	2 Structural info for wall sects	S	A
____	____	3 M&E equip spc confirmed	ME	A
____	____	4 Floor plans w/ fire protn shwn	A	CSME
____	____	5 Wall sections	A	SME
____	____	6 Finish schedule	A	SME
____	____	7 Owner-provided equip layouts	A	SME
____	____	8 Exposed mech & elec equip	ME	A
____	____	9 Site plans	C	ASME
____	____	10 Framing plans	S	AME
____	____	11 Exterior lighting	E	AC
____	____	12 Reflected clgs	A	ME
____	____	13 Spec drafts	CSME	A
____	____	14 Technical Review	ACSME	QA

Code: A = Arch, S = Struct, C = Civil, M = Mech, E = Electrical, & QA = Quality Assurance

Figure 19.4   Key date schedule format. (*Courtesy of Olden/Associates.*)

a detailed breakdown as its author desires. The key to the successful application of this method lies in its combination of ease in customization and in updating.

Preparation

Preparation of a key date schedule is best begun with a standard format such as Fig. 19.4, adapted for your office. The actual schedule for a given project may be created on a computerized spreadsheet, on word processing equipment, or for a very small project and/or unautomated office, it is easily prepared and updated manually. Following your office's procedures, a KDS can be prepared and updated at the project manager or operations manager levels. It is usually quite effective to have the schedules initiated by the project's manager, distributed in draft form to all in-house and outside consultant team members, and revised as appropriate before formal issuance or adoption.

This initial draft distribution is for review, input, and comment of team members. This procedure, asking for input at the draft level, is often most productive in expediting schedule adoption. Expecting team members to react, either positively or negatively, to tentative schedule decisions and proposed deadlines in relationship to their remaining work load is easier for them than their independently generating coordinated deadlines from scratch. The generation of schedule milestones is a function of project management; the acceptance of such dates by various team members and/or disciplines, even passively, is the quickest route to general acceptance.

What to Schedule

Including key dates in any schedule is simple. List only items that transfer information from the discipline or team member who generates or acquires the data required to complete the input of another team member. These inclusions are only intrateam transactions, and only team members involved directly in a project's design, production, or construction observation receive the key date schedules. These documents should be considered an in-house design and production aid. Often they contain shorthand, coded descriptions of typical and repetitive information transaction activities. To avoid misunderstandings, a KDS should never be distributed to a client.

When to Schedule

Two date columns are provided on each schedule: the first for the anticipated date of the data distribution and the second for the actual distribution date. If the incremental dates are met or exceeded, the consequent end date will be met or exceeded.

Chronological Sorting

For ease of planning, monitoring, and updating, always list information transmittal dates in chronological order. This provides a handy, timely checklist of upcoming items. It is often useful to closely monitor activities of the 2-week period which includes the current and upcoming weeks.

Need to Know

In addition to the project manager, the involved team members, and the professional design firm's operations management, many others in the office will find it extremely helpful to be on the distribution list for project schedules. Normally, this includes those who must work with several or all of the firm's active projects, such as the managers responsible for quality assurance document review, specifications preparation, and construction administration.

Monitoring the Project Schedules

Many managers use the active schedules, filed in project-numerical order in a three-ring binder, as an agenda for a weekly project management operations coordination and progress meeting. The schedules can be discussed and marked up as necessary. They can be immediately updated and distributed to all involved team members. This can be either in hard copy or on your office's local area network (LAN). Following this procedure on a weekly basis is adequate to monitor most project schedules distributed in hard copy. With microcomputers and the LAN, however, the opportunity exists for instant update, monitoring access, and schedule conflict identification and resolution.

Projecting Project Personnel Requirements

Another primary use of the professional design firm's project scheduling product(s) is in the projection of the needed design, production, construction observation personnel, and overall firmwide personnel requirements. Such projections, while sometimes attempted as automated derivations of project budgets, are best determined subjectively, as derivations of project schedules.

Budget vs. "O-Basing"

Using scheduling rather than budgeting for the foundation of personnel need projections allows more flexibility to accommodate the ever-changing project schedules. This is because, while many offices are disciplined to prepare budgets at each project's initiation, few are able to maintain them current enough to accommodate the constant changes involving additional services and fees. Therefore, depending only upon the apparent need projections derived from mathematical computations rooted in the original budget can be grossly misleading. Schedules are relatively easy to update weekly, and projecting personnel needs concurrently is accomplished with relative ease.

The dollar side of projecting project personnel needs for design, production, and construction observation is also important. But, while many project budgets are prepared on time, very few are consistently updated with the actual ebb and flow of project activities.

For this reason, attempts to objectively use project budgets as a continuing source for derivation of project personnel requirements inevitably fail. Concurrently projecting billings with personnel need projection can provide the regular, timely feedback on operations profitability. This procedure is sometimes referred to as "O-base" or bottom-up projecting since the project manager will need to start with the imminent work load as suggested by the project schedule rather than only backing out needs from budget availability.

Project Personnel and Billings Projection Preparation

A good, simple approach to summarizing a firm's project personnel needs for each 1-month period is illustrated by Fig. 19.5. While this approach only addresses project personnel, knowing and using your firm's utilization or chargeable ratio (project and total firm time) the firmwide personnel needs are also easily estimated for any given point in time. Most firms, except those who are very large or whose project(s) are very large, will find it counterproductive to make these projections for periods longer than 90 days in advance. Most smaller firms find that the work load inevitably tapers off after about 3 months, and some even find it depressing to see this declining work-load curve constantly approach zero when projecting the backlog of scheduled project operations out to 6 and 12 months and beyond.

For this reason, and to achieve easy distribution and hard copy filing, the illustrated format(s) limits the overall schedule's physical size for 3 to 6 months' projections, which will fit on an 8½- by 11-inch piece of paper. If these schedules are maintained and distributed via computer, it is a good procedure to limit the format's overall size to that of the available computer or terminal screen.

Single vs. Multidiscipline Formats

Either single-discipline and -department (Fig. 19.5) or multiple-discipline and -department (Fig. 19.6) firms can project personnel needs in this simple, spreadsheet format and in the contracted and negotiated fee categories illustrated or others equally appropriate. In most instances, even a single-discipline firm will, however, find it helpful to consider the construction administration phase as a separate department due to the differing impact of the schedules of these personnel when distributed more thinly over a longer period of time than are those of design and/or production's scheduled needs.

The contracted and negotiated fee categories illustrated represent those projects that should receive regular, ideally weekly, personnel needs projection. These categories are typically active projects currently under contract, active projects still under fee negotiation, and inactive but imminently active projects still under fee negotiations. Some firms have, by policy, only projected and hired personnel based upon the work which they have under written contract, but this is unrealistic. It only leads to staff use of overt, or more often covert, contingencies.

AVAIL STAFF:	GROSS AVAIL:	% CHBLE		AVAIL NET:
Garris	1.00 X	92%	=	0.92
Gransome	1.00 X	92%	=	0.92
Handel	1.00 X	50%	=	0.50
Tillmer	1.00 X	65%	=	0.65
Desmond	1.00 X	92%	=	0.92
Specmar	1.00 X	92%	=	0.92
Doughty	0.50 X	50%	=	0.25
Parker	1.00 X	65%	=	0.65
				5.73
				X173 HR/MO

AVAILABLE FIRMWIDE PROJECT MH/MO THIS DATE =   **991 MH**

PROJECT NUMBERS:	PROJECT NAMES:	MO: JAN $ NET BILLG	EST HRS
A. PROJECTS UNDER CONTRACT:			
89018.00	BAKERHOUSE BLDG BN/CA	$15,000	300
88002.00	USAA SITE/ROOF SURVEY	$1,000	25
88030.00	GUNTHER HS ADDN		
90032.00	SHOPPERS OUTLET - MYERS	$12,000	250
90034.00	DALE EDWARDS OFFICE	$3,000	60
	MH & $ NET SUBTOTALS	$34,000	715
B. PROJECTS UNDER NEGO/WORKING ON:			
90193.00	B M H MOTERS MP	$5,000	280
90036.00	MULTIFAMILY, PRADO ST	$0	0
MH & $ NET SUBTOTALS		$5,000	280
	NET ACTIVE PROJECT TOTALS	$39,000	995
C. PROJECTS UNDER NEGO ONLY:			
89023.02	EAGLE DEVELOPMENT	$5,000	100
90321.01	BANK OF OKALOOSA	$1,500	30
	MH & $ NET SUBTOTALS	$6,500	130
	TOT NET PROJECTED BILLINGS & MH	$45,500	1125
	LESS AVAILABLE MANHOURS		991
	MH OVER (UNDER)		-134

AVAIL TOTAL PROJECT STAFF OVER (UNDER) =   **-1**

BILLING RATE PROJECTED /MH =   **$40**

Figure 19.5 Staff needs and billings projection format. (*Courtesy of Olden/Associates.*)

AVAIL STAFF:	GROSS AVAIL:	% CHBLE:	AVAIL NET:	AVAIL MH/MO:
ARCH DEPT:				
Garris	1.00 X	60%	= 0.60	
Gransome	1.00 X	92%	= 0.92	
Handel	1.00 X	92%	= 0.92	
Tillmer	1.00 X	92%	= 0.92	
SUBTOTAL			= 3.36 X 173 HR/MO =	**581 ARCH MH**
STRUCT DEPT:				
Desmond	0.50 X	63%	= 0.32	
Specmar	0.50 X	92%	= 0.46	
SUBTOTAL			= 0.78 X 173 HR/MO =	**134 STR MH**
CA DEPT:				
Doughty	1.00 X	63%	= 0.63	
Parker	1.00 X	92%	= 0.92	
SUBTOTAL			= 1.55 X 173 HR/MO =	**268 CA MH**

PROJECT NUMBERS:	PROJECT NAMES:	MO: JAN $ NET BILLG	ARCH HRS	ST ENG HRS	CA HRS
A. PROJECTS UNDER A/E CONTRACT:					
89018.00	BAKERHOUSE BLDG BN/CA	$15,000	100	50	40
88013.00	USAA 153/375/714	0	0	0	20
88002.00	USAA SITE/ROOF SURVEY	$1,000	20	5	0
89030.00	GUNTHER HS ADDN	$0	0	8	0
90032.00	SHOPPERS OUTLET - MYERS	$12,000	20	55	0
90034.00	DALE EDWARDS OFFICE BLDG	$3000	0	6	0
	MH & $ NET SUBTOTALS	$31,000	140	124	60
B. PROJECTS UNDER NEGO/WORKING ON:					
90193.00	B M H MOTORS MP	$5,000	240	40	0
90036.00	MULTIFAMILY, PRADO ST	$0	80	0	0
	MH & $ NET SUBTOTALS	$5,000	320	40	0
	NET ACTIVE PROJECT TOTALS	$36,000	460	164	60
C. PROJECTS UNDER NEGO ONLY:					
89023.02	EAGLE DEVELOPMENT	$0	0	0	0
90321.01	BANK OF OKALOOSA	$0	0	0	0
	MH & $ NET SUBTOTALS	$0	0	0	0
	TOT NET PROJECTED BILLINGS & MH	$36,000	460	164	60
	LESS AVAILABLE MANHOURS		581	134	268
	M H OVER (UNDER)		121	-30	208

AVAIL TOTAL PROJECT STAFF OVER (UNDER) = **1.87**

BILLING RATE PROJECTED PER MH = **$53.**

Figure 19.6   Staff needs and billings projection format. (*Courtesy of Olden/Associates.*)

Projecting work required by contracts currently under fee negotiation assumes that the client is only holding fee and services discussions with your firm. If this is not the case, and other firms are under consideration for the contract by the client, then you are not negotiating, you are still marketing. Other types of contingent projects should be projected similarly as contracted work under negotiation.

The upper portion of the page (screen) in both formats sets forth the full-time equivalent (FTE) personnel available to the department(s) or discipline(s). Totaling the available hours of each individual from the multiple of their office availability (full-time, part-time) times their project time availability (expressed as a percentage-utilization or chargeable ratio) produces the FTE subtotals and totals available during the average 173-hour work month.

Next, the individual project personnel hour needs are projected, along with the billings these efforts are expected to produce over a 3- to 6-month planning period. These projections are then subtotaled and totaled for each involved discipline.

The available FTE totals are next subtracted from the project personnel projections, and the over- or understaffing is thus determined in hours. Dividing this total by 173×89 percent (allowing 11 percent for vacation, sick leave, holidays, etc., and assuming no other nonchargeable time occurs) will produce an estimate of the actual project personnel required for the involved period(s). The exact number developed through this process is not as important as the consistent application of the methodology. A firm may find that they operate very comfortably when this number is slightly negative combined with a reliance on inevitable project schedule slippage and occasional overtime assignment of staff.

The final closing of the projection loop is represented by the computed average dollars per hour that results from dividing the total billings projection dollars by the total projected project personnel hours. Project by project, this unit projection may or may not be able to meet or exceed the unit price required for firm profitability but this bottom-line summary must or reevaluation of the projections is in order. As with the project schedules, it is well to update your projections regularly. This is done by way of receiving weekly project managers' input. Monthly distributions of summaries are normally adequate for others in the firm.

Bibliography

Birnberg, Howard. *Project Management for Small Design Firms*. Chicago, Ill.: Birnberg and Associates, 1992.

Burstein, David, and Frank Stasiowski. *Project Management for the Design Professional*. New York: Watson Guptill, 1982.

Coxe, Weld. *Managing Architectural and Engineering Practice*. New York: John Wiley & Sons, 1980.

Foote, Rosslynn. *Project Scheduling*. University Park, Pennsylvania: Pennsylvania State University Press, 1986.

Haviland, David. *Managing Architectural Projects: The Process*. Washington, D.C.: The American Institute of Architects, 1981.

Haviland, David. *Managing Architectural Projects: The Effective Project Manager*. Washington, D.C.: The American Institute of Architects, 1981.

O'Brien, James J. *CPM in Construction Management*. New York: McGraw-Hill, 1984.

Olden, Robert E. *Manpower and Billings Projections Spreadsheet Templates.* Tampa, Fla: Olden/Associates, 1990.

Olden, Robert E. *New Firms and New Principals Business Initiation/Continuance.* Tampa, Fla: Olden/Associates, 1990, 1991.

Olden, Robert E. *Organization For Project Management Manual.* Tampa, Fla: Olden/Associates, 1990.

Olden, Robert E. *Project by Project Spreadsheet Template and Graphs.* Tampa, Fla: Olden/Associates, 1990.

Olden, Robert E. *Prototype Professional Design Firm Policies and Procedures Handbook.* Tampa, Fla: Olden/Associates, 1990, 1991.

Stitt, Fred A. *Design Office Management Handbook.* Santa Monica: Arts & Architecture Press, 1986.

20

Construction Cost Control

Brian Bowen

Controlling costs during design and construction is an intrinsic part of the architectural and engineering process. It is a creative denominator of good building design. The design professions are often criticized for failing to control costs. This chapter examines recent advances in cost control and project scheduling.

These newer methods and tools include:

- Using UNIFORMAT as a sensible cost control framework during design
- Using better methods for analyzing and establishing budgets at early project stages
- Establishing cost plans and adopting a design-to-cost approach
- Using published cost information creatively and building in-house cost data files
- Using computers for effective estimation and cost control
- Better methods of defining value and using value engineering creatively

UNIFORMAT

An essential component of any cost control system is a standard framework that acts as a continuous thread running through each stage of project development. In some respects, the most logical choice for such a framework would be the ubiquitous 16-division Construction Specifications Institute (CSI) MASTERFORMAT, which is widely used as a data communication medium in the construction industry. Unfortunately this classification system does not provide a sound basis for design cost control. It is heavily product- and material-oriented and is best suited for final specifications and design. In response to this inadequacy, the American Institute of Architects (AIA) and the General Services Administration (GSA) during the early 1970s began to develop an alternative descriptive framework to act as a more powerful design cost control tool. It was named UNIFORMAT. Levels 1, 2, and 3 of the UNIFORMAT appear in Figure 20.1*a, b,* and *c* and, as can been seen, effectively translate costs into the language of design. So, for example, if one wishes to establish the costs of an interior door, these will be gathered together as a subheading under 061 Partitions, rather than scattered through as many as five different divisions of the MASTERFORMAT.

The CSI recently has endorsed the use of UNIFORMAT for the development of outline specifications at early project stages. The UNIFORMAT continues to gain adherents as its logic and power is demonstrated on actual projects.

The UNIFORMAT is a complete system for cost control from inception and budget development through design and construction, with eventual feedback of completed project cost histories for reuse. One of the obvious challenges in using UNIFORMAT is how it can be made to relate to MASTERFORMAT and whether designers can afford the luxury of operating under dual control frameworks with all the attendant potential for confusion that this might create. In the past, this was a problem as no transition mechanisms were readily available. Today, with cheap and flexible computing power at our disposal, it is perfectly reasonable to work in both frameworks, allowing the computer to sort and present reports as desired.

The connection between UNIFORMAT and MASTERFORMAT can be made at any level. An example is the schedule of values that appears as Fig. 20.2 which is structured first by 16 divisions and then breaks down to correlate with level 3 of the UNIFORMAT. Contractors often tend to resist the provision of cost breakdowns in this way. Experience has shown that not only do they get used to it, but they actually like it as it gives them better control over their subcontractors.

Budget Analysis

At the risk of oversimplification, two situations face the architect or engineer at the initiation of design:

1. The owner may specify program requirements *and* state a budget limit.

2. The owner may state program requirements, leaving a budget to be established after some further design analysis has been performed.

In either case, a budget that is accepted by all parties is the single most important figure in the life of the project. Everyone remembers this first figure, and it is therefore vital to both owner and designer that it is accurate. Owners are increasingly insisting on commitments

UNIFORMAT	LEVELS 1 & 2

Level 1	Level 2
A. CONSTRUCTION	01 Foundations 02 Substructure 03 Superstructure 04 Exterior Closure 05 Roofing 06 Interior Construction 07 Conveying Systems 08 Mechanical 09 Electrical 10 General Conditions & Profit 11 Equipment 12 Sitework
B. FURNITURE & EQUIPMENT	01 Furniture & Furnishings 02 Administration Equipment 03 Production Equipment
C. DESIGN & MANAGEMENT	01 Architecture & Engineering 02 Special Consultants 03 Construction & Project Management 04 Testing & Inspection 05 Market Studies 06 Owner`s Administration Expenses
D. SITE ACQUISITION	01 Land Costs 02 Legal Fees 03 Surveys 04 Appraisal Fees
E. LEASING/OCCUPANCY	01 Moving Expenses 02 Leasing Commissions 03 Tenant Inducements 04 Taxes During Construction
F. FINANCING	01 Interim Financing 02 Permanent Financing
G. CONTINGENCIES*	01 Escalation Contingencies 02 Design Contingencies 03 Construction Contingencies 04 General Contingencies

* Alternatively contingencies may be distributed separately to individual Level 1 accounts.

Figure 20.1a

Group Element - Level 2	Element - Level 3
01 FOUNDATIONS	011 Standard foundations 012 Special foundations
02 SUBSTRUCTURE	021 Slab on grade 022 Basement excavation 023 Basement walls
03 SUPERSTRUCTURE	031 Floor construction 032 Roof construction 033 Stair construction
04 EXTERIOR CLOSURE	041 Exterior walls 042 Exterior doors & windows
05 ROOFING	
06 INTERIOR CONSTRUCTION	061 Partitions 062 Interior finishes 063 Specialties
07 CONVEYING SYSTEMS	
08 MECHANICAL	081 Plumbing 082 HVAC 083 Fire protection 084 Special mechanical systems
09 ELECTRICAL	091 Distribution 092 Lighting & power 093 Special electrical systems
10 GENERAL CONDITIONS & PROFIT	
11 EQUIPMENT	111 Fixed & movable equipment 112 Furnishings 113 Special construction
12 SITE WORK	121 Site preparation 122 Site improvements 123 Site utilities 124 Off-site work

Figure 20.1*b*

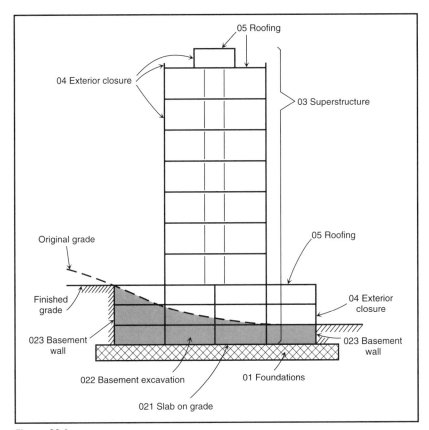

05 Roofing

04 Exterior closure

03 Superstructure

05 Roofing

Original grade

Finished grade

04 Exterior closure

023 Basement wall

023 Basement wall

022 Basement excavation

01 Foundations

021 Slab on grade

Figure 20.1c

by designers to recognize (or even guarantee) budget limits. They are requiring redraw clauses in the contract under which the architect or engineer may have to redesign the project at no cost to the owner to bring it within budget, if an overrun is encountered.

Dealing with the problem of establishing reliable budget figures is never easy when minimal information about the proposed project is available. Here are some suggestions on how to cope with the situation:

1. Never accept a design commission where the owner insists on controlling cost, scope, and quality. This leaves the designer with little freedom of action if cost problems develop. If cost is fixed, the other two components must be left free to be adjusted.

2. Designers should attempt to delay the final confirmation of the budget until some form of design analysis has been done to test the client's program. As a first task in the design process, conduct a program-budget compatibility study to balance program requirements with cost. Do not move into schematic design until this task is finished and resolved with the client.

3. When you are presented with a maximum budget limit by the owner, find out how it was determined. Often, this reveals that it may have been set arbitrarily, was out of date, or does not fully relate to the program.

SCHEDULE OF VALUES

Project :
Owner :

Architect :
Contractor :

Project No.:
Date :

Item description	UF Code	Item Amount	Item description	UF Code	Item Amount
1. GENERAL REQUIREMENTS			**6. WOOD & PLASTICS**		
a. Mobilization & initial expenses	10		a. Rough carpentry(framing & decking)	03	
b. Site overheads & fee	10		b. Rough carpentry(exterior wall)	041	
			c. Rough carpentry(partitions)	061	
			d. Rough carpentry(roofing)	05	
2. SITE WORK			e. Heavy timber & prefab. struct. wood	03	
a. Clearing & demolition	121		f. Exterior wood siding & trim	041	
b. Grading & earthwork(site)	121		g. Fin. carpentry,mill- & cabinet-work	063	
c. Excavation & backfill(foundations)	011		h. Wood paneling	062	
d. Excavation & backfill(basement)	022		i. Wood stairs	03	
e. Fill below grade slab	021		j. Plastic fabrications	063	
f. Rock excavation	012				
g. Pile foundations & caissons	012				
h. Shoring	022		**7. THERMAL & MOISTURE PROTECT.**		
i. Underpinning	012		a. Water & dampproofing(slab)	021	
j. Site drainage & utilities	123		b. Water & dampproofing(basement)	023	
k. Foundations & underslab drainage	021		c. Water & dampproofing(ext. walls)	041	
l. Dewatering	012		d. Thermal insulation(foundations)	021	
m. Paving,landscaping & site improvements	122		e. Thermal insulation(exterior walls)	041	
n. Off-site work	124		f. Thermal insulation(roof)	05	
o. Railroad,marine work & tunnels	124		g. Roofing shingles & tiles	05	
			h. Shingles on exterior walls	041	
			i. Preformed siding & panels	041	
3. CONCRETE			j. Preformed roofing	05	
a. Conc.,forms & reinf.(foundations)	011		k. Membrane roofing,traffic topping	05	
b. Conc.,forms & reinf.(slab on grade)	021		l. Sheet metal & roof accessories	05	
c. Conc.,forms & reinf.(basement walls)	023		m. Sealants & calking	041	
d. Conc.,forms & reinf.(superstructure)	03				
e. Conc.,forms & reinf.(exterior walls)	041				
f. Conc.,forms & reinf.(site work)	062		**8. DOORS & WINDOWS**		
g. Concrete finishes(exterior walls)	122		a. Exterior doors & frames	042	
h. Concrete finishes(interiors)	062		b. Exterior windows & curtain walls	042	
i. Concrete finishes(site work)	122		c. Interior doors & frames	061	
j. Precast concrete(exterior wall panels)	041		d. Exterior glass & glazing	042	
k. Precast concrete(structural component	03		e. Interior glass & glazing	061	
l. Precast concrete(site work component	122		f. Hardware & specialties(exterior)	042	
m. Cementitious decks	03		g. Hardware & specialties(interior)	061	
4. MASONRY			**9. FINISHES**		
a. Masonry foundations	011		a. Lath & plaster(exterior)	041	
b. Masonry basement walls	023		b. Lath & plaster(interior)	062	
c. Masonry exterior walls	041		c. Gypsum wallboard	062	
d. Masonry interior partitions	061		d. Tile & terrazzo(interior)	062	
e. Interior paving & finish	062		e. Tile & terrazzo(exterior)	041	
f. Exterior paving & masonry(site work)	122		f. Acoustical ceilings & treatment	062	
			g. Wood flooring	062	
			h. Resilient flooring	062	
5. METALS			i. Carpeting	062	
a. Structural steel in foundations	012		j. Exterior coating	041	
b. Structural steel framing	03		k. Interior special flooring & coatings	062	
c. Metal joists & decking	03		l. Exterior painting	041	
d. Metal stairs	03		m. Interior painting & wall covering	062	
e. Misc. & ornamental metal(building)	063				
f. Misc. & ornamental metal(site work)	122				

Figure 20.2a Schedule of values. (*Courtesy of American Institute of Architects.*)

Item description	UF Code	Item Amount	Item description	UF Code	Item Amount
10. SPECIALTIES			15. MECHANICAL		
a. Chalkboards & tackboards	063		a. Exterior mechanical (to 5ft)	123	
b. Compartments & cubicles	061		b. Water supply & treatment	081	
c. Signs & graphics	063		c. Waste water disposal & treatment	081	
e. Partitions	061		d. Plumbing fixtures	081	
f. Lockers	112		e. Fire protection systems & equipment	083	
g. Toilet, bath, wardrobe accessories	063		f. Heat generation equipment	082	
h. Sun control devices	041		g. Refrigeration	082	
i. Access flooring	063		h. HVAC pipe, ductwk & terminal units	082	
j. Miscellaneous specialties	063		i. Controls & instrumentation	082	
k. Flagpoles	122		j. Insulation (plumbing)	081	
			k. Insulation (HVAC)	082	
			l. Special mechanical systems	084	
11. FIXED & MOVABLE EQUIPMENT	111				
			16. ELECTRICAL		
			a. Utilities & service entrance (to 5ft)	123	
12 FURNISHINGS	112		b. Substations & transformers	091	
			c. Distribution & panel boards	091	
			d. Lighting fixtures	092	
			e. Branch wiring & devices	092	
			f. Special electrical systems	093	
			g. Communications	093	
13.SPECIAL CONSTRUCTION	113		h. Electric heating	093	
14. CONVEYING SYSTEMS			TOTAL	S	
a. Elevators, dumbwaiters & lifts	07				
b. Moving stairs & walks	07				
c. Conveyors, hoists, etc.	07				
d. Pneumatic tube systems	07				

NOTES :

1. This Schedule of Values is to be completed by the Contractor within the time period specified in the bidding documents. When approved by the Architect, who may require supporting evidence as to its correctness, the schedule shall be used as a basis for certificates of payment.

2. Any item listed may be separated for convenience of distinguishing sub-trades and additional items added in the spaces provided under the appropriate division.

3. The code numbers appearing under "UF Code" refer to the UNIFORMAT system, a copy of which may be obtained from the Architect.

4. On approval of this Schedule, items with values entered against them, should be transfered to AIA Documents G702 and 702A " Application and Certificate for Payment".

Figure 20.2*b*

4. A good budget should:
   - Reflect the anticipated project scope, include everything required for a complete project, and state clearly what is excluded.
   - Adequately reflect the owner's quality and performance expectations. This is one of the most difficult things to determine and quantify, especially with lay owners not accustomed to specifying their needs in clear technical terms. In these cases, comparisons of quality and performance levels with existing completed projects can be helpful.
   - Reflect the owner's value objectives, i.e., the hierarchy of objectives: first cost, long-term life cycle cost, maintainability, reliability, aesthetics and image, flexibility for change, etc. It is always worth discussing with an owner at the outset of a project what the objectives are to help him or her evaluate priorities.
   - Be achievable and be acceptable to all parties. Everyone involved must feel that the budget is fair and balances program needs against cost.
   - Be defensible. If challenged there must be a rationale as to how it was established.
   - Be based on the best techniques and data available.
   - Contain adequate reserves against unforeseen events that are almost certain to be encountered during design and construction.
   - Adequately reflect the anticipated implementation time frame and allow suitable inflation provisions.

In preparing budgets, do not fall into the trap of either basing them on socially acceptable estimates or playing it safe. The socially acceptable estimate tells people what they want to hear or misuses commonly accepted estimating standards in the wrong set of circumstances. Playing it safe generally involves including contingency upon contingency and can be equally damaging in the long run.

Budgeting Techniques

Traditional budgeting has been based on single unit rate methods tied to parameters, such as gross building floor area, number of accommodation units (e.g., hospital beds, parking garage stalls), or equal parameters, such as length of a road or the capacity in gallons per day for a waste water treatment plant. This approach, while commonly used and well understood, can be hazardous. The unit rates selected are derived from the cost of completed projects, which vary widely due to a complex set of influencing factors. It is not unusual for the unit rates of a building classified as an office building to vary as much as 100 percent from low to high, even after weeding out extremes. This is because, for example, office buildings vary in character, size, height, content, architecture and engineering, location, and time frame. As many designers have discovered to their embarrassment, even if prototypes are used, there cannot be a guarantee that identical unit costs will be experienced from project to project.

Faced with this problem, cost engineers have developed budgeting techniques that identify the key factors which drive the cost of construction projects. In the case of buildings, this approach recognizes the effect which configuration, height, and functional use have on each individual key construction component. Configuration, for example, dictates the quantity of exterior wall; building height, the quantity of roof; functional use, the character and intensity of the interiors. Each of these elements displays cost characteristics that are determined by required quality performance levels.

The UNIFORMAT system of estimation and cost analysis grew out of the need for a better budgeting and cost control framework during the design of building projects. UNIFORMAT is used in budgeting by preparing mini-estimates for each of the components, usually at level 2 or 3, and then aggregating each estimate to a whole. The quantities for each UNIFORMAT category are calculated from a real or simulated design. For example, if you know the client's required net floor area, which can be converted to a gross floor area based on historical ratios, and assume a number of floors, which is often dictated by zoning or other considerations, you can easily simulate a probable area for the roof. The next step is to assign a unit cost to include the coverings, insulation, skylights, and openings. Cost data to support such estimating is now available from published sources or can be developed from a cost analysis of your own completed projects.

Cost Planning

Having established a reliable project budget, the next step is to ensure that the emerging design respects the agreed limits. The traditional approach is to develop a conceptual design within the context of the project scope. When this is complete, a cost estimate is prepared and the bottom line compared with the budget. If the estimate exceeds the budget, some formal or informal value engineering occurs and necessary redesign is performed.

The cost planning approach replaces this sequence of events. It first establishes a cost plan, which translates the budget into a series of cost targets for each UNIFORMAT category (to level 2 or 3). This acts as a guide for the designers *before* any serious design is undertaken. Thus in the example in Fig. 20.3, an allowance of $814,000 has been established for the exterior closure element, which also includes a target area for the closure of 60,000 square feet. As can be seen, this results in a target price of $13.57 per square foot for this element and immediately conveys to the designer the limitations on wall and window selections and also provides a quantitative design target area. This means that the designer can approach the development of the design on a design-to-cost basis and help to ensure that the result will respect the overall budget limit.

Once a schematic design has been developed and the cost plan verified and perhaps modified, cost control continues during design with frequent cost checks as appropriate. These usually are carried out at

UNIFORMAT ELEMENT	Amount $	Total Cost	Rate $/SF Floor Area	%	ELEMENTAL COST			ADJUSTED	
					Quantity	Unit	Unit Rate	Total Cost	$/SF
A	B	C	D	E	F	G	H	I	J	K

Project: HOTEL *Phase:* COST PLAN *Date:* 4 Feb. 1987 ☒ **New Const.**
Location: Suburban Washington, D.C. *GSF:* 156,000 SF *Sheet No:* ☐ **R & I**

UNIFORMAT ELEMENT (A)	Amount $ (B)	Total Cost (C)	Rate $/SF Floor Area (D/E)	% (F)	Quantity (G)	Unit (H)	Unit Rate (I)	Total Cost (J)	$/SF (K)
01 Foundations		201,000	1.29	2.2	33,366	SF	6.02		
011 Standard Foundations	201,000		1.29						
012 Special Foundation Conditions	–0–		–0–						
02 Substructure		115,000	0.74	1.2	33,366	SF	3.45		
021 Slab on Grade	115,000		0.74						
022 Basement Excavation	–0–		–0–						
022 Basement Walls	–0–		–0–						
03 Superstructure		1,183,000	7.58	12.7	156,000	SF	7.58		
031 Floor Construction	875,300		5.61						
032 Roof Construction	225,200		1.44						
033 Stair Construction	82,500		0.53						
04 Exterior Closure		814,000	5.22	8.8	60,000	SF	13.57		
041 Exterior Walls	468,000		3.00						
042 Exterior Doors & Windows	346,000		2.22						
05 Roofing		439,000	2.81	4.7	33,366	SF	13.16		
06 Interior Construction		1,933,000	12.39	20.8					
061 Common Areas	432,000		2.77		30,600	SF	14.12		
062 Suites	1,501,000		9.62		223	RMS	6,731		
07 Conveying Systems		249,000	1.60	2.7	21	STOPS	11,857		
08 Mechanical		1,764,000	11.31	10.0					
061 Common Areas	694,000		4.45		30,600	SF	22.68		
062 Suites	1,070,000		6.86		223	RMS	4,798		

Escalation Rate:

Figure 20.3 UNIFORMAT elemental cost summary. (*Courtesy of Hanscomb Associates, Inc., Atlanta, Ga.*)

appropriate stages to match the architects' and engineers' contractual obligations. So, for example, under the AIA contract, cost checks would be performed prior to the completion of each design stage—schematics, design development, and construction documents.

Obtaining Reliable Cost Information

Feedback obtained from the use of UNIFORMAT throughout a project can lay the foundation for the development of powerful in-house data files. After all, the information obtained from your own projects is much more valuable than published information. A project data file should include not only cost breakdowns, but also other information that will allow the correct interpretation of prices, such as key statistics on areas, measurements, capacities of key systems, descriptive information on scope, and an outline specification. Figure 20.4 illustrates a very simple data collection format used by the General Services Administration (GSA) to recycle real project costs.

One can never have too much cost data. Unfortunately, most design practices do not generate a sufficient number of projects to create a

Project: HOTEL	Phase: COST PLAN					Date: 4 Feb. 1987			☒ New Const.	
Location: Suburban Washington, D.C.	GSF: 156,000 SF					Sheet No:			☐ R & I	

| Escalation Rate: | Amount $ | Total Cost | Rate $/SF Floor Area | | % | ELEMENTAL COST | | | ADJUSTED | |
| UNIFORMAT ELEMENT | | | | | | Quantity | Unit | Unit Cost | Total Cost | $/SF |
A	B	C	D	E	F	G	H	I	J	K
09 Electrical		788,000		5.05	8.5					
091 Common Areas	480,000		3.08			30,600	SF	15.68		
092 Suites	308,000		1.97			223	RMS	1,381		
10 General Conditions & Profit		785,000		5.03	8.5					
NET BUILDING COST		8,271,000		53.02	89.2					
11 Allowances		296,000		1.90	3.2					
111 Decor	246,000		1.58							
112 Pool	50,000		0.32							
12 Site Work		280,000		1.79	3.0	165,000	SF	1.70		
121 Site Preparation	48,000		0.30							
122 Site Improvements	179,000		1.15							
123 Site Utilities	53,000		0.34							
CONSTRUCTION COST		8,847,000		56.71	95.4					
13 Contingencies Design		430,000		2.76	4.6					
		$9,277,000		$59.49	100%					

Figure 20.3 *(Continued)*

meaningful statistical base for in-house purposes. They therefore must rely on published information. Fortunately, the amount of published data has expanded in recent years. Table 20.1 is a recommended list of cost information publications that should be considered for inclusion in every designer's library. Several smaller and regional publishers also release cost data. For example, on the West Coast, the Lee Saylor products are probably more relevant to those locations.

TABLE 20.1 Cost Information Publications

R.S. Means Company   100 Construction Plaza, Kingston, Mass. 02364

Building Construction Cost Data

Square Foot Costs

Assemblies Cost Data

In addition to the above, Means publishes a variety of specialist price books in such areas as civil engineering, landscaping, and renovations.

I.S.I. Publications   6 Cielor Vista Drive, Monterey, Calif. 93942

Design Cost & Data (published 6 times per year)

Richardson Engineering Services Inc.   1742 S. Fraser Drive, Mesa, Ariz. 85214

General Construction Estimating Standards

Process Engineering Estimating Standards

Project:

Building Type:

Location:

<table>
<tr><td colspan="2">Bid date:</td></tr>
<tr><td colspan="2">Market conditions:</td></tr>
<tr><td colspan="2">Award amount:</td></tr>
</table>

Description:

Sketch:

Floor area (by level)			
Level	No.	Gross area	%
Basements		GSF	
Ground floor		GSF	
Upper floors		GSF	
Penthouse		GSF	
Totals		GSF	100%

Floor area (by type)	occupiable	%
	SF	
	SF	
	SF	
	SF	
	SF	
Total occupiable area	SF	%
Circulation	SF	
Mech. & Elec. Equip. spare	SF	
Toilets	SF	
Walls, partitions, etc.	SF	
Custodial	SF	
Total support area	SF	%

Configuration area	
Below grade	
depth	FT
volume	CF
Above grade	
height	FT
volume	CF
Exterior closure area	SF
Average perimeter	LF

Design Data

01	FOUNDATIONS	
	Soil bearing capacity	KIPS/SF
02	SUBSTRUCTURE	
	Footprint area	SF
03	SUPERSTRUCTURE	
	Bay size	
	Loads: live	PSF
	Stairs	FLIGHTS
04	EXTERIOR CLOSURE	
	Fenestration	%
05	ROOFING	
	Openings/skylites	%
06	INTERIOR CONSTRUCTION	
	Perm. partitions	LF
	Demount. partit.	LF
	Specialties	
07	CONVEYING SYSTEMS	
	Freight elev.	EA
	Passenger elev.	EA
	Escalators	LF
08	MECHANICAL	
	Heating	MBH
	Cooling	TONS
	Ventilation	CFM
	Control	ZONES
	Roof/floor drains	EA
	Plumbing fixtures	EA
	Sprinkler system	HEADS
	Standpipe system	LF
	Special systems	
09	ELECTRICAL	
	Light/power	WATTS/SF
	Transformer cap.	KVA
	Motors	HP
	Special systems	
10	GENERAL CONDITIONS	
	No. bidders	EA
11	EQUIPMENT	
12	SITEWORK	
	Site size	ACRES
	Avg. utility run	LF
	Landscaped area	SF
	Ext. parking	CARS
	Other paved areas	SF

Figure 20.4a GSA cost data. (*Courtesy of General Services Administration.*)

	ELEMENTAL CATEGORY	MATERIAL QUALITY OR SYSTEM TYPE	SYSTEM COST	PARAMETER QUANTITY	UNIT MEAS.	UNIT COST	% COST
01	FOUNDATIONS						
011	Standard foundations						
012	Special foundations conditions						
02	SUBSTRUCTURE						
021	Slab on grade						
022	Basement excavation						
023	Basement walls						
03	SUPERSTRUCTURE						
031	Floor construction						
032	Roof construction						
033	Stair construction						
04	EXTERIOR CLOSURE						
041	Exterior walls						
042	Fenestration						
05	ROOFING						
051	Roof system						
052	Opening/Skylights						
06	INTERIOR CONSTRUCTION						
061	Partitions						
062	Interior finishes						
063	Specialties						
07	CONVEYING SYSTEMS						
071	Elevators						
072	Escalators						
08	MECHANICAL						
081	Plumbing						
082	HVAC						
083	Fire protection						
084	Special mechanical systems						
09	ELECTRICAL						
091	Service and distribution						
092	Lighting and power						
093	Special electrical systems						
10	GENERAL CONDITIONS & PROFIT						
	NET BUILDING COST						
11	EQUIPMENT						
111	Fixed and movable equipment						
112	Furnishings						
113	Special construction						
	GROSS BUILDING COST				GSF		100%
12	SITE WORK						
121	Site preparation						
122	Site improvements						
123	Site utilities						
124	Off-site work						
	CONSTRUCTION COST						
	REMARKS						

Figure 20.4*b*

When relying on published information, be sure to understand exactly what the published costs represent. For example, in the Means publications:

- They generally include subcontractors' overhead and profit in the unit rates but not general contractors'.

- They are a U.S. average.

- Materials and labor are priced at the first of the year.

- Material costs do not include sales taxes.

- They apply to a $500,000 industrial and commercial project in a metropolitan area.

The *Design Cost & Data* publication is interesting. Cost analyses are published every 2 months for up to four projects and serve as useful points of reference.

Computer-Assisted Estimating

Computers and estimation were made for one another. Surprisingly, very few software products adequately address design cost control. Most vendors have tended to concentrate their efforts in developing detailed construction estimating programs, presumably because they regard the contractor market as larger and more lucrative. If looking for detailed estimating programs, consider the nationally marketed programs listed in Table 20.2.

All these products have databases that can be readily tailored to a specific location and time. They also have the ability to estimate by "assemblies" (e.g., a door complete with frame, hardware, decoration, etc.). Continuing enhancements are likely to improve their appeal to the design professions for budgeting and conceptual estimating. Stay in touch with these vendors and make your needs known to them.

In the meantime, most architects and engineers fall back on the ubiquitous spreadsheet and database programs to create their own estimating systems. The more adventurous link these to digitizer systems that help automate quantity measurements.

Cost estimating systems linked to CADD are a natural progression and are already available in a limited manner. It is also anticipated that eventually three-dimensional CADD programs will be capable of producing elemental UNIFORMAT quantities to help support good conceptual estimating. Other links to scheduling programs, manage-

TABLE 20.2   Construction Estimating Programs

Program	Vendor
Composer Gold	Building Systems Design, Inc.
	1175 Peachtree Street, Atlanta, Ga. 30309
	1-800-875-0047
G2 Estimator	G2 Inc.
	P.O. Box 7867, Boise, Idaho 83707
	1-800-727-5502
Precision Estimating	Timberline Software Corp.
	9405 SW Gemini, Beaverton, Oreg. 97005
	1-503-664-8155

Project _____	Item _____	
Team _____	Date ___ MARCH 7, 1989 ___	

Criteria	Weight	Raw Score
A. FIRST COST	27	18
B. O & M / ENERGY COST	8	5
C. OPERATIONAL EFFICIENCY	21	14
D. PATIENT IMAGE	10	7
E. AESTHETICS	2	1
F. QUALITY/PERFORMANCE/MAYO STANDARDS	16	11
G. FLEXIBILITY FOR CHANGE	10	1
H. SCHEDULE COMPLIANCE	—	—
I. BALANCED INVESTMENTS	6	4
	100	67

How Important:
4–Major Preference
3–Average Preference (+)
2–Average Preference (−)
1–Slight Preference
0–Equal Preference

Criteria Scoring Matrix

	B	C	D	E	F	G	H	I
A	A2	A1	A3	A3	A3	0	A4	A2
B		C1	D1	0	F2	G1	B2	B3
C			C2	C3	0	C2	C3	C3
D				0	F1	D1	D2	D2
E					F2	G1	E1	I2
F						F2	F3	F1
G							G3	G2
H								I2

Figure 20.5   Criteria weighting process. (*Courtesy of Hanscomb Associates, Inc., Atlanta, Ga.*)

ment information systems, and the like will soon begin to integrate estimating with other activities in a sensible way. In addition, we will soon see the creative use of cost modeling and statistical analysis to help produce better estimates.

Finally, a few range estimating programs are on the market. These essentially say there is no such thing as a fixed price for construction—it is a moving target subject to a wide range of variables over which the estimator has no control. The programs use statistical methods to predict a likely range within given levels of confidence.

Value Engineering

The last 15 years have seen an expanded use of value engineering (VE) during the design of construction projects. The reputation it has gained among the design professions has generally been negative. This is largely because VE has been used as a crude cost cutting tool by most of the entities that use it. In the Department of Defense, for example, most of the agencies that operate VE programs justify its use by keeping score of the capital cost savings achieved and the number of proposals accepted. This emphasizes cutting first costs, sometimes to the detriment of long-term economics and other considerations.

The concept of value engineering is very powerful. Architects and engineers should recognize it as a tool for optimizing value. It can satisfy clients that the best balance between multiple design options has been selected on their projects. The key is defining at the outset what "value" represents to the owner on his or her project. It is not unusual for the owner to identify several objectives. A determination must be made of the relative weightings between these objectives. Figure 20.5 illustrates such a resolution.

Value engineering is characterized by a formal explicit set of procedures that are designed to identify a wide range of options and then resolve which ones are worth consideration. These are evaluated against the value definition agreed to with the owner.

Given that value for money is what every owner wants, then VE can be the tool to provide proof that this has been achieved. It provides the basis to identify the options and then evaluates them against owner-determined objectives where cost and quality issues, first vs. life cycle, vs. flexibility, vs. image, vs. reliability, and so on, can be determined and decisions forced. Instead of fighting value engineering, design architects and engineers should use it creatively to help themselves and the owners resolve the trade-offs involved in every design.

Bibliography

Cost Estimating and Cost Control

Ahuja, H.N., and M.A. Walsh. *Successful Methods in Cost Engineering*. New York: John Wiley & Sons, 1983.

Bowen, B. "Design and Construction Cost Management." Chapter B-5 in *Architect's Handbook of Professional Practice*. Washington, D.C.: American Institute of Architects, 1984.

Collier, K. *Estimating Construction Costs; A Conceptual Approach*. Reston, Va.: Reston Publishing, 1984.

Cox, B.J., and F.W. Horsley. *Square Foot Estimating*. Kingston, Mass.: R. S. Means Company, Inc., 1983.

Heery, G.T. *Time, Cost and Architecture*. New York: McGraw-Hill, 1975.

Hunt, W.D., Jr. (ed.). *Creative Control of Building Costs*. New York: McGraw-Hill, 1967. (Currently out of print, but available in some libraries.)

Swineburne, H. *Design Cost Analysis for Architects and Engineers*. New York: McGraw-Hill, 1980.

Wolfe, L. *Cost Control for Architects: An Essay on Professional Judgment*. University Park, Pa.: The Pennsylvania State University, 1986.

Value Engineering and Life Cycle Costing

Dell'Isola, A.J. *Value Engineering in the Construction Industry*. New York: Van Nostrand Reinhold Company, 3d ed., 1982.

Dell'Isola, A.J., and S.J. Kirk. *Life Cycle Costing for Design Professionals*. New York: McGraw-Hill, 1981.

Haviland, D. *Life Cycle Cost Analysis, A Guide for Architects*. Washington, D.C.: American Institute of Architects, 1977.

Haviland, D. *Life Cycle Cost Analysis, Using It in Practice*. Washington, D.C.: American Institute of Architects, 1978.

Index

---

*An *f.* after a page number refers to a figure.